THE NEW NATURALIST

A SURVEY OF BRITISH NATURAL HISTORY

THE NATURAL HISTORY OF SHETLAND

The aim of this series is to interest the general reader in the wild life of Britain by recapturing the inquiring spirit of the old naturalists. The Editors believe that the natural pride of the British public in the native fauna and flora, to which must be added concern for their conservation, is best fostered by maintaining a high standard of accuracy combined with clarity of exposition in presenting the results of modern scientific research.

THE NEW NATURALIST

The Natural History of
SHETLAND

R. J. BERRY, D.Sc.

and

J. L. JOHNSTON, B.Sc.

With 29 colour photographs
44 photographs in black and white
and 47 line drawings

COLLINS
GRAFTON STREET, LONDON

The former county of Shetland is a group of more than a hundred islands, islets and skerries, forming the northernmost Scottish administrative unit whose capital, Lerwick, is 300 miles north by east of Edinburgh and 222 miles west of Bergen in Norway. It lies between 59°31′and 60°57′N, and from 0°43′W to 2°04′W. Extending 70 miles in length and 36 in extreme breadth, the county has a total area of 551.8 square miles (142,923 hectares) and at the 1971 Census the population was 17,329. The largest of the 19 inhabited islands are Mainland (378 square miles), Yell (83), Unst (47), Fetlar, Bressay, and Whalsay. All the islands are gathered round the Mainland except two (Foula, 14 milest west of the Mainland, and Fair Isle, halfway between Orkney and Shetland). The sounds and voes, or firths, are so numerous that no spot is more than three miles from the sea. The surface is more rugged than that of Orkney, the highest points being Ronas Hill (1,475 feet) on the Mainland and the Sneug (1,372 feet) on Foula. The soil is peaty, barely one-sixth of the total area being capable of cultivation, and there are very few trees. The climate is equable but moist. For long the county was a Norse dependency, and it is still markedly Norse in many of its characteristics. The old Norwegian language, Norn (spoken in Foula as late as 1774) has bequeathed many words to the Shetland dialect. The chief occupations are crofting, fishing and fish processing, and knitting, although large numbers of people are now employed in oil-related industry.

First published 1980
Reprinted 1986
©R. J. Berry and J. L. Johnston 1980
ISBN 0 00 219041 9
Filmset by Jolly & Barber Ltd, Rugby
Colour and black and white reproduction by Adroit Photo-Litho Ltd, Birmingham
Made and printed in Great Britain by
William Collins Sons & Co Ltd, Glasgow

CONTENTS

PLATES

Between pp 224 and 225

EDITORS' PREFACE

SINCE their inception in 1945 New Naturalist books have been written for the general reader who is interested in the wild life of Britain. This volume, aimed at the same target, describes the natural history of our northernmost archipelago. The exposed outpost of Shetland lies nearer to the west coast of Norway than to Edinburgh, and both Lerwick and Bergen lie a little beyond 60° N. Shetland has maintained its Norse connections for centuries and, like Orkney, its distinctiveness from the Scottish mainland. Modern cartographers, inconvenienced by its remoteness, usually map the archipelago as an inset off either the Moray Firth or the Outer Hebrides. This book stresses its true northerly position, its isolation, its function as a migratory staging post, the effects of its wild seas and wild winds and the limitations which these, though tempered by the North Atlantic Drift, impose on its animal and plant life.

Readers will not find that the authors complain about their rigorous fieldwork in a sometimes hostile environment. Their enjoyment and keen observation of Shetland is evident throughout their contributions and their vivid descriptions of, for example, seal behaviour, convey their enjoyment to the reader. Professor Spence is a Shetlander, Ian Robertson of Fair Isle has lived in Shetland, Professor Flinn has spent many vacations there, Laughton Johnston has both worked and taught there and Professor Berry has been researching in Shetland since 1959. Readers of Professor Berry's *Inheritance and Natural History* in this series will recall many references to his work in Shetland. His is the guiding hand in the preparation of *The Natural History of Shetland*. The book covers a wider field than Pat and Ursula Venables' *Birds and Mammals of Shetland*; it presents the 'living Shetland' and surveys its bird life at a time when oil pollution could dramatically reduce its variety and richness. Dr Syratt, resident ecologist during the completion of the Sullom Voe terminal, describes B.P's anti-pollution planning in Chapter 13. Experience of spills near Pembrokeshire's 'bird islands' suggests that human error and uncaring tanker crews clearing bilges well offshore can sometimes negate the high standards enforced in the immediate vicinity of oil terminals. It is thus pertinent to have the present status of Shetland's wild life recorded by dedicated observers before possible deterioration of this superb environment.

There was a thriving Bronze Age community at Jarlshof and since then the people of Shetland have farmed the better patches of land by the sea and, like the Viking ancestors of many of them, grazed their flocks in common on the hill land and fished the sea. Visiting naturalists, joined by local people as observers of the wild life of Shetland, are described in Chapter 12 of this book.

The many amateur naturalists who visit Shetland today will appreciate this record of the wealth and attraction of the archipelago for students of all ages. This volume should encourage both specialists and amateurs to visit and revisit a group of islands whose beautiful landscapes and seascapes are full of geological and biological interest.

AUTHORS' PREFACE

SHETLAND is probably best known among naturalists for its teeming bird life, and for many years ornithologists have flocked to the islands from all parts of the world. There have been a number of excellent accounts of Shetland birds, notably the Venables's *Birds and Mammals of Shetland* (1955) and Williamson's *Fair Isle and its Birds* (1965). For botanists, Thomas Edmonston* published a *Flora of Shetland* (1854), Druce a *Flora Zetlandica* (1922) and a check-list of flowering plants and ferns was compiled by Palmer and Scott (1969; an up-to-date revision appears on pp. 282–303 of this book). In 1974 the Nature Conservancy Council (N.C.C.) organized a meeting on the *Natural Environment of Shetland*, and the proceedings thereof (edited by Rawdon Goodier) are the nearest to a complete account of the biology and geology of the islands that has yet appeared.

We have undertaken this book in an attempt to make these works available to a more general readership and to summarize much of the other fascinating information about Shetland natural history in a more systematic way, as well as complementing more general accounts of the islands. Furthermore:

1. Much information is hidden in theses and specialized journals, and there are many scientists who have worked in Shetland but never published their results. We have tried to record the sources of these data, so that they will be accessible to future workers.

2. The Venables's book is now out of print. A short *Guide to Shetland Birds* by Tulloch & Hunter (2nd edition, 1972) gives basic information for the ornithologist and a shorter *Guide to Shetland Mammals* (1978) also by Tulloch, describes both the land and sea mammals, but these are only introductions and cannot provide the background essential for a full appreciation of Shetland biology.

3. North Sea oil is going to affect Shetland life considerably over the next few decades, and there is need for a record of the state of Shetland and how it may be affected by oil-related developments. In 1974 the Nature Conservancy Council commissioned the Institute of Terrestrial Ecology to survey some aspects of the ecology of Shetland. The objectives were to classify 'the principal biota and ecosystems of Shetland and assemble the information in a

---

* The more usual spelling is "Edmondston". We have used the spelling "Edmonston" for all members of this family.

13

flexible, readily accessible form for use in systems models and to assess the environmental impact of development'. The results of this work have only been published as a general article in the *Geographical Magazine* (Milner, 1978), but we have been granted access to the full report in the N.C.C. library through the kindness of Drs Morton Boyd and David Goode of the N.C.C.

4. Finally, Shetland has a biological significance as an isolated series of communities exposed to the stressful rigours of the North Atlantic. This outweighs any purely local importance it has as, for example, the principal British breeding site of the Great Skua or the possessor of the highest cliffs in the British Isles (on Foula). We believe that Shetland should stand alongside the Galapagos, Hawaiian and Seychelles Islands as a gigantic field laboratory giving fundamental information about the reaction and resistance of living organisms to their environments.

The book necessarily builds on and summarizes the work of very many naturalists. Three chapters have been written by people who have made special contributions to our knowledge of Shetland: Professor Derek Flinn of the Geology Department of Liverpool University (Chapter 2), Professor David Spence of the Botany Department, St Andrews University (Chapter 4), and Mr Ian Robertson, Warden of the Fair Isle Bird Observatory (Chapter 11). The effects of North Sea oil on the Shetland environment and the steps being taken to minimize any damage are summarized by Dr W. J. Syratt (Chapter 13), who acted as resident ecologist for British Petroleum in Shetland during the latter stages of building and commissioning the oil terminal at Sullom Voe. We are responsible for the rest of the text, but because our background and approach is so different (one of us is a schoolmaster who was formerly Nature Conservancy Council officer for Orkney and Shetland; the other is a professional biologist who has carried out research in Shetland), the whole text has been edited by one of us (R.J.B.) to attempt some unity of style.

We want this book to be useful to both the first-time visitor to Shetland and the specialist concerned with particular groups or habitats. To make the text more readable, we have gathered pertinent references together at the end of each chapter, with a full Bibliography on p. 353. The Bibliography does not include all reports of species records for Shetland, but we hope it is otherwise reasonably complete. We have also collected as many lists of different plant and animal groups as we could into an Appendix (pp. 265–334). Some of these lists (such as that of the birds) will, we believe, be widely used; others (such as those referring to the lower plants) will be understandable and relevant to fewer people. Notwithstanding, it has seemed right to include all the lists as a summary of available facts about Shetland natural history, and an indication of current ignorance (particularly of invertebrate groups). We are very grateful for all those who compiled or helped to compile these lists: Dr David Irvine of the Polytechnic of North London (Marine Algae); Dr David

Hawksworth of the Commonwealth Mycological Institute, Kew (together with Dr H. J. M. Bowen and Mr P. W. James) (Lichens); Dr D. A. Goode and the Nature Conservancy Council for permission to quote the lists of Bryophytes and Liverworts compiled by Dr M. O. Hill and Mrs Jean Paton for the Institute of Terrestrial Ecology Report to the N.C.C.; Messrs Richard Palmer and Walter Scott for revising their published checklist of Flowering Plants; Mr R. S. George and Professor Miriam Rothschild (Fleas); Dr Michael Bacchus of the British Museum (Natural History) (Beetles); Mr E. C. Pelham-Clinton of the Royal Scottish Museum for checking the list of Lepidoptera given by Wolff (1971); Dr Philip Ashmole of Edinburgh University (Spiders); and Mrs Nora Macmillan of the Liverpool Museum (Freshwater and Terrestrial Molluscs). The list of Fungi is from Dennis (1972). The summary of birds breeding and visiting Shetland is based on the compilation of Venables & Venables (1955), but updated from the records of the Shetland Bird Club with the help of Messrs R. J. Tulloch (Royal Society for the Protection of Birds representative in Shetland), P. Kinnear, I. Robertson, Dr B. Marshall, J. D. Okill and M. Sinclair.

We have also included an annotated list of 'Places to Visit' (pp. 335–51). We hope this will help tourist and professional alike to share the diversity and excitement that we find in the topography and natural history of Shetland. Our thanks are due to those who have helped us make this both representative and (we hope) accurate: Dr Michael Richardson (N.C.C. officer for Shetland), Mr M. Mullay (Tourist Officer for the Shetland Islands Council), and Professor Derek Flinn.

A host of friends and colleagues have helped with information or criticism. As well as those named above, we acknowledge with gratitude comments from Elizabeth Balneaves, Dr Morton Boyd (N.C.C.), Dr S. G. Browne (Leprosy Study Centre), Dr James Cadbury (R.S.P.B.), John Crothers (Field Studies Council), Professor G. M. Dunnet (Aberdeen University), Dr R. Furness (Glasgow University), Tom Henderson (formerly Curator of the Shetland County Museum), Dr A. W. Johnston (Aberdeen University), Dr H. B. D. Kettlewell (Oxford University), Dr A. D. McIntyre (Fisheries Laboratory, Aberdeen), M. A. E. Mortimer (Brathay Trust), Veronica Muir, Natural Environment Research Council Sea Mammals Unit (Dr C. F. Summers, Sheila Anderson, S. G. Brown and R. W. Vaughan), Professor D. F. Roberts (Newcastle University), Professor Alan Small (Dundee University), Dr Don Tills (British Museum (Natural History)), Alan Whitfield (formerly chief Loganair pilot in Shetland), and many Shetlanders who have assisted us directly and indirectly. Pat and Ursula Venables have encouraged us from the start of our labours, when we ascertained that they had no intention of revising their *Birds and Mammals of Shetland*. Messrs D. Coutts and R. J. Tulloch helped us find appropriate photographs, as well as providing many of their own. Mr J. Lynch drew the figures for Chapter 2; Mr A. J. Lee drew most of the rest. Dr Gillian Truslove aided us in checking the proofs, and Madeleine Loates coped heroically with producing a legible typescript.

Finally we must record our debt to the generosity of British Petroleum for a grant which has made the publication of this book possible.

There are many gaps in our knowledge about Shetland natural history. It is our hope that some may be stimulated by this book to fill them. Readers will no doubt find other blemishes and for these we must take the blame. Notwithstanding, we shall feel our labours worthwhile if the volume helps amateur and professional alike to study and profit from the fascination of these islands called Shetland that were the *ultima thule* of the ancient world, and remain the northernmost extent of the British Isles.

General modern accounts of Shetland (full citations are given in the Bibliography on p. 353

Balneaves, 1977; Cluness, 1951, 1967; Fenton, 1978; Linklater, 1965; Nicolson, 1972, 1978.

CHAPTER I

ISLAND LIFE – AND THE PLACE OF SHETLAND

The Zoology of Archipelagoes will be well worth examination
(Charles Darwin, after visiting the Galapagos Islands in 1835)

ISLANDS have a glamour – usually greater to outsiders than to those who live permanently on them. They are often pawns in political machinations, witness the Falklands (Malvinas). But supremely and perhaps surprisingly, they have played a significant part in the development of modern man.

Until the latter half of the nineteenth century, the world was assumed to be unassailably stable, regulated by rational laws, albeit afflicted with decay through human greed. All this changed with the painful and necessary revolution effected by Charles Darwin and his advocacy of evolution by natural selection. As a result, we are now conditioned to think of change and cause rather than inevitable advance; future shock has taken over from eternal stagnation; intellectual rootlessness has replaced the often fearful confidence of earlier man.

It is a far cry from the restless peace of islands to the emotional militancy of the trade unionist, urban guerilla, or sex 'liberator' but there is a direct link, because islands are biological testing-grounds for new processes, new possibilities. Many island forms are extreme parodies of their mainland relatives, and highlight the possibilities latent in more conservative fauna and flora. Indeed, islands prove the lie to dogmatic changelessness more effectively than any philosophy or history. Darwin began to realize this on his journey round the world as naturalist on the *Beagle*. He first became suspicious about current biological ideas of the origin and relationships of living things when he saw the variations of mammals in time and space in South America; he was then impressed by the tame and peculiar creatures of the Falkland Islands; but above all, he was influenced by the unique forms existing on the Galapagos. In the same period, Alfred Wallace was having his eyes opened by the unevennesses of animal distribution, particularly in the Malayan archipelago and East Indies. Naturalists who saw rather than theorized were convinced of the rapid and therefore spectacular genetical changes that can occur in isolated conditions; and as the idea of biological change was accepted, so the naive and peculiarly Victorian doctrine of progress was taken over by economists, educationalists, sociologists, industrialists, politicians, even (though they are usually loath to acknowledge their academical pedigree) by physical scientists.

However we have been slow to realize the importance of our own offshore

islands – the Channel Isles and Scillies to the south, the Hebrides and Arans to
the west, Orkney and Shetland to the north. We revel (or recoil in disgust) in
the romance and inconveniences of island life, but do not appreciate the
characteristics of their fauna and flora. This is not to belittle the achievements
of individual naturalists – geologists in Jersey, botanists in the Scillies, and
ornithologists in the north, but merely to point out the gaps in our understanding of those parts of the British Isles where isolation and environmental
pressures often mean that the pressures for adaptation are the greatest.

The group of islands known as Shetland* occupy a particular place here:
the northernmost and most isolated parts of the British Isles lying in the track
of depressions that sweep westwards across the north Atlantic yet lying in the
same latitude as the southern part of Greenland, and as far north as the
permanently snow covered South Shetland Islands in the Southern Hemisphere (Fig. 4). At the coldest part of the Ice Ages, Shetland was covered by
the main Scandinavian ice sheet from the east, so that only the tops of some of
the hills and possibly small areas in their lee remained free. When the climate
improved at the beginning of the present era, Shetland was connected to
neither continental Europe nor mainland Britain (see Chapter 2). Consequently the present animals and plants (with a few doubtful exceptions)
have colonized the islands within the past 15–20,000 years, and hence provide
information about the extent and efficiency of their transport and rate of
evolution.

ISOLATION AND ADAPTATION

One of the most remarkable biological discoveries of recent years has been the
amount of genetical variation possessed by virtually all organisms. Sexually
reproducing individuals receive sets of genes from both their parents; a
number of techniques (most important, the electrophoretic separation of
proteins) show that we get slightly different forms (*alleles*) of about one in ten
of these genes from each parent. This means that there is a tremendous
amount of inherited variation present in all populations. Now a small number
of individuals is very unlikely to carry the same alleles in the same proportions
as in the population from which they came: if a small group of individuals

---

* Never 'the Shetlands'; although the etymology of the name is disputed, the most
likely meaning is 'Hiding' or 'Retreat Land' from the Norse word *Halte*. Old maps give
the name as Hjaltland or Hjetland – hence Shetland. Other interpretations are
possible: a map published in 1558 and based on the travels of the Zeno brothers at the
end of the 14th century labels Shetland as *Estland* (*i.e.* the East Land). The Vikings
sailed across the North Sea to Shetland, and thence either north to the Faroes and
Iceland, or south to the Pentland (Pict-land) Firth and the Hebrides (Old Norse
Suthreyjar or South Isles). The official name for Shetland (Zetland) is said to have come
from writing down the pronunciation of the administrative and professional classes. It
dates at least as far back as 1733, when it was used by Thomas Gifford of Busta.

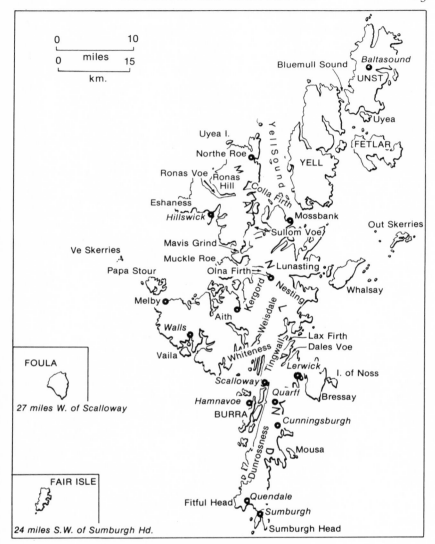

FIG I. Map of Shetland.

enters a habitat unoccupied by their species they will form the nucleus of a population which will almost inevitably differ in many ways from the ancestral population. The descendent population is likely to have a unique set of allele frequencies, and these will form the basis of the population as the colonizers reproduce to fill the available territory. Thus island forms will immediately differ from their nearest relatives, and any further immigrants will have little impact on the gene frequencies established 'by mistake' in this way. The new form will thus depend to a large extent on the chance genetical constitution of its founders; this is known as the *founder effect*.

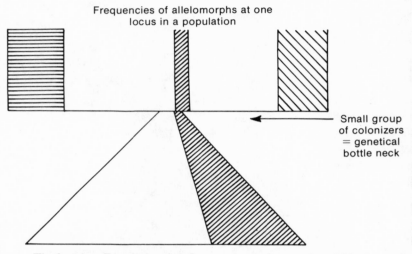

Frequencies of allelomorphs at one
locus in a population

Small group
of colonizers
= genetical
bottle neck

FIG 2. The founder effect – a drastic influence on gene frequencies, which also results in a reduction of variation.

Once a species has survived the initial establishment and dispersion phase of colonization, predators and parasites become important, and intraspecific pressures on space and fertility begin to operate. In other words, the species becomes exposed again to the checks that operated on its ancestors. However there will be differences:

1. The newly introduced form will have a paucity of genetical variation as a result of the founder effect, and possibly suffer a lack of adaptability.

2. Diseases and competitors will be less common than in a continental area.

3. The range of niches available for colonization is likely to be less than in the ancestral area.

4. Lack of gene-flow from the same species living under slightly different conditions makes local adaptation easier and more precise. For example, flightless insects and seeds with reduced dispersal potential are far commoner on oceanic islands than elsewhere.

5. The presence of few competing species provides more opportunities for

adaptation to a wider variety of environmental opportunities (the radiation of Darwin's *Geospiza* finches on the Galapagos Islands is a well-known example of this).

All these facets add up to the result that the intensities of natural selection will be strong, and not necessarily lead to convergence with the ancestral form. Almost certainly, however, the selective pressures will mean that the random changes of genetic drift will be far less common than is suggested in the literature. In time the local island races would diverge so far from their nearest relatives as to become recognizable species. This last stage has not been reached yet in Shetland (although some forms have been separated as true species by older taxonomists – such as the Shetland field mouse, *Apodemus fridariensis*), but most of the intermediate steps can be recognized and will be described in the following pages.

One last point needs to be borne in mind: the evolutionary results of a 'founder event' followed by adaptation are likely to be much more marked than the effects of simple isolation on animals and plants, leaving them as *relicts* on part of a previously continuous species range. Biogeographers tend to be overfond of invoking land-bridges to account for unusual distributions. Geologists believe the biogeographers' assertions, and suggest evidence for the existence of these hypothetical stretches of land – and in turn are believed by biologists. Let it be explicitly repeated: the living animals and plants of Shetland are post-Ice Age colonizers. The islands have a vast intrinsic interest, but they have a world-wide importance as representing in microcosm and – because of their isolation – relative simplicity, the biological pressures of the last ten thousand years. And the discovery of large quantities of oil in the North Sea will give a test of the effects of technological insults at a time when we are becoming depressingly aware of their dangers.

THE PHYSICAL CONTEXT

Tacitus records that a Roman Fleet circumnavigated Scotland, and from its northernmost foray saw the edge of the world (*Dispecta est et Thule*). From the north of the Orkneys, on a clear day it is possible to see three points of land: Fair Isle, Fitful Head at the south end of the Shetland Mainland, and the furthermost, Foula (Fig. 3). However it is probable that the Romans sailed no further; the violent currents of the 'roosts' between Orkney and Shetland and the changeable weather were unlikely to tempt early sailors towards the theological uncertainties of the *ultima thule*.

Shetland lies in the so-called 'Gulf of Winter Warmth' produced by the North Atlantic Drift. Only in very exceptional winters does any ice form on the sea. The Gulf Stream means that the mean sea temperatures are higher than the average for 60°N – there is not much difference in winter from the temperatures further south in Britain, although the northern summers are

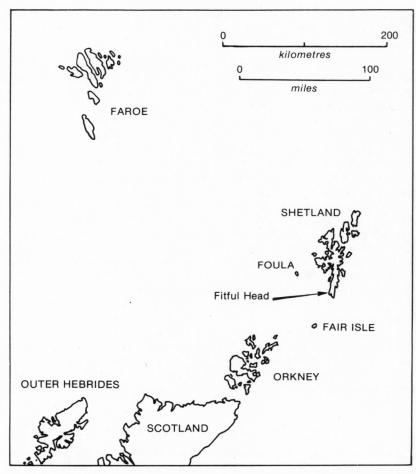

FIG 3. From the northernmost point of Orkney, it is possible on a clear day to see three points of land – Fair Isle, Fitful Head on the Mainland of Shetland, and Foula – the *ultima thule*.

much cooler (Table 1). Rainfall is not excessive (Table 2), but there is frequent 'precipitation' due to the commonness of light rain or mist. The average monthly figures for relative humidity (80–85%) are the highest in Britain. Indeed, an early writer accurately described the situation, 'the vapour of the sea tempers the air'. Sea mists are commoner in summer than winter; temperatures are often too low to disperse low-lying fog in the summer months. Snow is not often a problem even though the winter is the wettest part

TABLE 1. Long-term monthly average temperatures (°F) – mean of daily minimum and maximum

	Jan.	Feb.	March	April	May	June	July	Aug.	Sept.	Oct.	Nov.	Dec.	Annual
Lerwick 60°8'N 1°11'W	38.2	37.9	38.9	41.5	45.6	49.5	53.4	53.5	50.6	45.9	42.0	39.8	44.7
Baltasound 60°46'N 0°53'W	38.3	38.3	40.2	42.8	46.7	50.6	54.3	54.5	51.6	47.3	43.3	40.6	45.8
Hamnavoe 60°25'N 1°05'W	39.6	39.5	40.4	43.0	47.4	51.4	54.9	54.9	52.6	48.1	44.7	41.7	46.4
Kirkwall, Orkney 58°59'N 2°58'W	38.9	38.8	40.6	43.3	47.3	51.4	55.0	54.8	52.7	48.1	44.1	41.2	46.3
Torshavn, Faroe 62°02'N 6°47'W	39.2	38.6	39.8	41.2	45.0	48.4	41.8	52.2	49.7	44.7	42.1	40.6	44.5
Stornoway, Hebrides 58°12'N 6°23'W	39.8	39.9	42.3	44.5	48.8	52.9	55.8	55.9	53.1	48.8	44.5	41.8	47.3
Kew 51°28'N 00°19'W	39.6	40.3	44.0	48.9	54.4	60.7	63.7	63.2	58.8	51.9	45.7	41.7	51.0
Nanortalik, Greenland 60°10'N 45°05'W	26.2	27.7	28.9	33.3	39.2	41.9	43.7	44.6	42.4	36.9	30.2	28.0	35.2
Stanley, Falkland Islands 51°42'S 57°52'W	48.2	48.9	47.2	42.8	38.8	36.1	35.8	36.7	38.3	42.1	45.5	47.1	
Signy, South Orkney 60°43'S 45°36'W	33.2	34.0	32.7	28.7	21.0	16.3	13.3	16.7	23.6	27.8	30.1	31.6	
Deception, South Shetland 62°59'S 60°43'W	34.8	34.4	32.2	28.3	23.6	22.9	17.5	19.1	26.3	27.1	30.2	32.4	
Macquarie Island 54°31'S 158°57'E	44.1	43.9	42.9	41.2	39.6	37.9	37.6	37.9	38.3	40.0	42.7	40.4	

TABLE 2. Mean rainfall (inches)

	Jan.	Feb.	March	April	May	June	July	Aug.	Sept.	Oct.	Nov.	Dec.	Annual
Lerwick	4.52	3.31	3.09	2.71	2.20	2.11	2.53	2.76	3.75	4.44	4.63	4.44	40.49
Baltasound	4.92	3.88	3.68	2.96	2.39	2.57	2.65	2.88	4.05	4.77	5.13	5.05	44.93
Hamnavoe	4.88	3.90	3.43	2.79	2.21	2.17	2.60	2.79	3.78	4.49	4.72	4.88	42.64
Kirkwall	4.25	3.15	2.68	2.60	1.93	2.04	2.64	2.87	3.74	4.53	4.41	4.53	39.37
Torshavn	6.10	5.20	4.76	4.17	2.56	3.03	3.03	3.78	5.12	6.14	5.94	6.14	55.98
Stornoway	4.18	2.68	2.29	2.33	2.29	2.56	3.08	3.35	3.75	4.38	4.50	4.06	39.45
Kew	2.14	1.55	1.46	1.81	1.81	1.72	2.44	2.24	1.98	2.25	2.45	2.06	23.95

TABLE 3. Total sunshine (hours)

	Jan.	Feb.	March	April	May	June	July	Aug.	Sept.	Oct.	Nov.	Dec.	Annual
Lerwick	25	51	90	132	165	158	125	117	105	67	33	14	1082
Baltasound	19	44	86	128	164	156	129	122	102	61	26	10	1047
Hamnavoe	25	54	96	147	193	179	147	139	120	73	35	13	1221
Kirkwall	34	62	101	149	175	165	141	129	117	77	42	26	1218
Torshavn	14	41	78	114	148	140	117	101	85	63	24	7	932
Stornoway	35	62	108	142	195	173	128	133	111	76	45	26	1234
Kew	48	65	112	162	203	214	197	183	143	102	58	43	1529

TABLE 4. Wind

Strength (Beaufort Scale)	0	1	2	3	4	5	6	7	8	9	9+
Wind speed (knots)	0	1–3	4–6	7–10	11–16	17–21	22–27	28–33	34–40	41–47	48+
% through year — Lerwick	2.5	3.6	10.1	21.9	30.4	15.1	10.2	4.4	1.5	0.2	0.1
Kirkwall	2.8	5.7	10.8	22.6	31.3	14.1	8.5	2.8	1.0	0.2	<0.1
Stornoway	5.8	7.5	7.7	15.2	26.3	16.4	12.0	5.9	2.6	0.4	0.1

of the year: it snows on about 40 days a year, but the snow rarely lies for more than a total of about twenty days.

There is frequently low-lying cloud, which reduces the amount of sunshine (Table 3) and means that the ground is slow to dry in the spring and the crops slow to ripen in the summer. This mist may be very local – Hamnavoe on the west coast of Shetland has 13% more sunshine than Lerwick 8 miles away on the east, and only 29 days of days with frost compared with an average of 51 in Lerwick. Notwithstanding the commonness of low cloud which means still conditions in other parts, Shetland is one of the windiest places in Britain (Table 4). The mean wind speed throughout the year is 15–17 m.p.h., and gales occur on an average of 58 days a year (a gale is defined as a wind exceeding 38 m.p.h. for more than an hour). Some of the highest wind speeds in Britain have been measured at the top of Saxavord (935 feet) in Unst: in early 1979 a gust of 202 m.p.h. was recorded there before the anemometer blew away. Shetland has a mean of 236 hours of gale a year, less only than the Bell Rock (255 hours) and the Butt of Lewis (378 hours), while Kirkwall in Orkney has a mere 52 hours. Wind directions display two maxima – a wet southerly in winter due to Icelandic Low Pressure and a dry northerly in summer due to low pressure over Central Asia. High pressure over Scandinavia brings dry bright weather with winds from the east or south east.

In midsummer the noon altitude of the sun in Shetland is 53.5°; in midwinter it is 6.5°. The sun is above the horizon for 18 hours 52 minutes in midsummer (when it is possible to read a newspaper at midnight by natural light), but for only 5 hours 39 minutes in midwinter. In south west England the altitudes are 63.5° and 16.5° respectively. The extra hours of daylight in the northern summer are not very useful because the angle of the sun is low and the sun's energy is not absorbed as readily as when the sun is higher in the sky.

THE BIOLOGICAL CONTEXT

The natural history of Shetland has been moulded by the caprices of colonization and the disciplines of adaptation. The same factors apply to an even greater degree to the Faroe archipelago (61°20′N, 6°15′W to 62°24′N 7°41′W) lying to the north west of Shetland, and even more remote from continental land masses. The climate of Faroe is not strikingly different from Shetland (Tables 1–3), but the appearance of the islands is very different, consisting of unwelcoming Miocene trap and basalt, with a number of vertical cliffs of 1300 to 1600 feet. The highest sea cliffs in the world are at Enniberg on the Island of Vidøy. There is very little cultivable land, and the human economy depends heavily on fishing (the population is 33,000, almost twice that of Shetland). Fewer species exist in Faroe than Shetland: for example, Williamson (1948) lists 63 breeding birds for the former, in comparison with about 90 in Shetland; the field mouse (*Apodemus sylvaticus*) has never established itself in

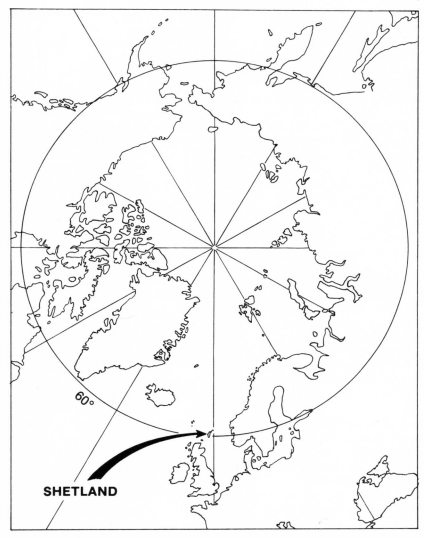

FIG 4. Shetland in relation to other parts of the Northern Hemisphere.

Faroe, despite being common in both Shetland and Iceland – its place is taken by the house mouse; rabbits survive in only two places in Faroe. Faroe has only 56 species of Lepidoptera, compared with 145 in Shetland, 282 in Orkney, and 2467 in Great Britain. Such lists could be continued for a long time. A detailed comparison between Shetland and Faroe would be of considerable interest.

In contrast, Shetland's other island neighbour, Orkney (58°42′N 3°25′W to 59°23′N 2°20′W) is both more fertile and biologically diverse. Geologically it is composed of Old Red Sandstones, which also makes the productive plain of Caithness. The landscape is more rolling and is extensively cultivated – especially for beef cattle production. Sand-dune formation is common. However the climate is very similar: Kirkwall is only slightly warmer and drier than Lerwick. The big difference between the island groups is the close proximity of Orkney to the large island of Great Britain (the Pentland Firth is only six miles across at its narrowest point). This means that Orkney shares most of its flora and fauna with the mainland, and although it's natural history has many points of interest, the extent of gene flow from the south makes it essentially an outlier of north Britain.

The influence of the Gulf Stream is most apparent when the North Atlantic islands are compared with localities outside it at the same latitude. Nanortalik on the east coast of Greenland has almost exactly the same latitude as Lerwick, yet the mean temperature in five months out of the twelve is below freezing point, and the yearly mean is 10°F lower than in Lerwick (Table 1). There is an extensive snow cover and frequent sea ice.

Even more extreme are islands in the Southern Hemisphere. In 1819, William Smith of Blyth in Northumberland was driven off course when sailing round Cape Horn, and discovered the South Shetland Islands, so named because they lie in latitude 62°s. They were, he wrote 'a land condemned to everlasting rigidity by Nature'. Their biological history has been one of seal and later of whale exploitation. The South Shetlands are mountainous and actively volcanic. Only two species of vascular plant occur in the Antarctic, *Deschampsia antarctica* and *Colobanthus crassifolius*, although mosses and lichens may grow on snow-free ground and rock. There is no soil. The only land animals are less than 100 species of invertebrates – tardigrades, mites, ticks and representatives of five insect orders. The climate in the South Orkneys (60°S) is only slightly less extreme. The British Antarctic Survey maintain a biological base on Signy Island in the South Orkneys.

The Falkland Islands are ecologically closer to Shetland than the South Shetland group, although they lie nearer to the equator (51°S – about the latitude of London in the north), and are somewhat cooler – no month is entirely frost-free. They are windy, with a mean about 17 m.p.h. like Shetland, and are treeless. This means that the climax vegetation is heath and dwarf shrub grassland. There is up to 15 feet depth of peat. Sheep-farming is the main land-use. Albatrosses replace gannets and penguins replace auks, but the general ambience of Falkland and Shetland is similar. Unfortunately Falkland natural history (with the exception of the birds: 63 breeding species, with 17 Falkland races recognized) is poorly known.

Finally Macquarie Island (58°31′S 158°57′E) can be mentioned as a truly oceanic island. It lies about halfway between Australia and the Antarctic continent, and is swept by the prevailing westerly winds at all seasons. However the most noticeable feature of its climate is its uniformity (Table 1), the coldest and warmest months having a mean temperature difference of only 6.5°F. Although it is a damp island like Shetland, the number of days with precipitation (317) is more marked than the total amount of rainfall (36 inches). Macquarie is tree-less but well grassed, and overrun with rabbits which cause severe overgrazing in parts. And like Shetland it has its own biogeographical and evolutionary successes – but only 46 bird species and 38 vascular plant species.

BIOLOGICAL SUB-DIVISIONS

The usual approach to Shetland is either by plane to Sumburgh Airport at the southern end of the Mainland or by boat to Lerwick. Both ways give an impression of a stark and dull topography, of rolling, dark, peat-covered hills bordered by a largely rocky coast. As will become apparent in the rest of the book, this apparent uniformity of the islands is very superficial, and conceals a wealth of geological and ecological variety. In their classical book on the *Birds and Mammals of Shetland*, the Venables listed nine major habitats in relation to bird life. These were: moor and hill; cultivated arable land; marshy bottoms of sedge and rough grass; plantations and gardens; sea cliffs; sandy flats; sea lochs and sheltered voes; lochs in agricultural land; lochs in moorland. Other classifications were given by contributors to a symposium on the *Natural Environment of Shetland* organized and published by the Nature Conservancy Council in Edinburgh in 1974 which has hitherto provided the most complete summary of Shetland natural history. In chapter 4 of this book Professor David Spence gives a detailed break-down of habitats in terms of their plant communities.

This is not the place to recapitulate the ways that ornithologists, botanists, geologists, pedologists and conservationists have from their varying backgrounds, recognized the complexity of the Shetland islands. However it is worth recording that Shetland was the first major attempt by the Institute of Terrestrial Ecology (I.T.E.) to quantify natural variation over a substantial area. Using aerial photographs, Ordnance Survey maps and ground surveys of biological data collected by the Institute (and by the Marine Biological Association and the Scottish Marine Biological Association) for the Nature Conservancy Council, I.T.E. ecologists employed multivariate techniques to group species and define natural communities and ecosystems. The result was an impressive bank of information which can be manipulated by computer, and added to at will. Such exercises will undoubtedly be increasingly used by planners and bureaucrats, but they reveal only broad patterns and can never substitute for dedicated observations which are the excitement and often the importance of advancing environmental science.

References for Chapter 1
(full citations are given in the Bibliography on p. 353)

Shetland general: Balneaves, 1977; Brand, 1701; Cluness, 1951, 1967; Cowie, 1871; Fenton, 1978; Goodier, 1974; Holbourn, 1938; Linklater, 1965; Nicolson, 1972; O'Dell, 1939, 1940; Sibbald, 1711; Tudor, 1883.

Names of Shetland: Angus, 1910; Fenton, 1973.

Biology and genetics of island forms: Berry, 1967, 1973, 1974, 1975, 1977, 1979; Carlquist, 1974; Lack, 1969, 1976; MacArthur & Wilson, 1967; Mayr, 1954, 1963, 1967.

Other islands:
> *Faroe:* Berry, Jakobsen & Peters, 1978; Evans & Vevers, 1938; Jensen, 1928–72; Rasmussen, 1952; Reinert, 1971; Williamson, 1948.
>
> *Orkney:* Bailey, 1971; Bullard, 1972; Goodier, 1975; Groundwater, 1974.
>
> *Falkland:* Holdgate, 1960; Moore, 1968; Strange, 1972.
>
> *South Shetland:* Holdgate & Wace, 1961; King, 1969; Wace, 1960.
>
> *Macquarie:* Costin & Moore, 1960; Gillham, 1967; Taylor, 1954.

Shetland biological diversity: Birse, 1974; Goode, 1974; Johnston, 1974; Milner, 1978; Price, 1929; Venables & Venables, 1955; West, 1912.

Weather: Irvine, 1968; Oddie, 1959.

Life in Shetland: Deyell, 1975; Edmonston & Saxby, 1889; Fenton, 1978; Howarth, 1951; Livingstone, 1947; Moffat, 1934; Nelson, 1977; Nicolson, 1978; Powell, 1938; Sandison, 1968; Shepherd, 1971; Sinclair, 1840; Thorne, 1977; Venables, 1952, 1956; Wills, 1978.

CHAPTER 2

GEOLOGICAL HISTORY

THE ROCKS

THE SHETLAND islands are a partially drowned range of hills rising above the flat continental shelf to the north of Scotland. The history of their development may be divided into two phases. During the first phase, lasting from 3,000 million to 350 million years ago, the rocks of the islands were formed in all their diverse varieties and complicated relationships. Then in the period from 350 million years ago to the present time the islands were carved by erosion from this complex mass of rocks.

The rocks of Shetland are part of the roots of an old and now deeply eroded mountain chain called the Caledonian Orogenic Belt. The deeply eroded roots of this mountain chain form most of Norway and Scotland and the northern part of Ireland, and also parts of North America and Greenland. Shetland lies on the north-west edge of the chain between Scotland and Norway and it is therefore of great geological importance as a link between these two areas.

The basement of the mountain chain

The boundary between the rocks forming the mountain chain and the older basement rocks on which the mountain chain was built, occurs in north-west Shetland. The rocks of Uyea in north-west Shetland and of the Ve Skerries to the north-west of Papa Stour have ages ranging from more than 2,900 million to 1,600 million years. The rocks are mostly metamorphic rocks; they are gneisses composed dominantly of quartz and feldspar although some horn-blendic gneisses also occur. These are probably Lewisian gneisses like those in north-west Scotland and the Outer Hebrides. They were already in existence in very much the same state as now long before the Caledonian mountains started to form. Several thousand million years ago they would have been granites intruded by small bodies of gabbro. Then they were recrystallized and deformed deep in the earth's crust and transformed into gneisses during early episodes of mountain building which in Scotland are usually called Scourian or Laxfordian.

The building of the mountain chain

The first stage in the building of the Caledonian mountain chain probably started between 600 and 1,000 million years ago. Erosion products of old

31

mountain chains composed of gneisses (such as those now seen in north-west
Shetland) began to accumulate in a continuously subsiding trough which was
later to become the new mountain chain. The accumulation continued until
four to five hundred million years ago and in that time a basin of sediments
several tens of miles thick was formed. In Shetland these rocks are collectively
called the East Mainland Succession. They form Yell, the western sides of
Unst and Fetlar, the Mainland east of Mavis Grind from Sullom Voe to Fitful

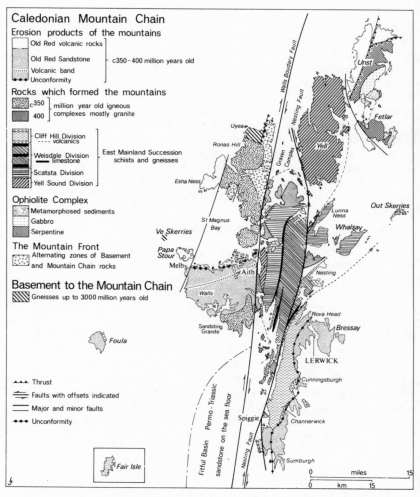

FIG 5. Geological map of Shetland.

Head (that is east of the Walls Boundary fault, Fig. 5), Burra Isle, Whalsay and the Out Skerries. The succession which can be seen in Shetland today is over 10 miles thick, but the rocks have been considerably thinned by compression and their thickness under the sea is unknown.

The oldest of these rocks can be seen in Yell. They are called the Yell Sound Division and are about 5 miles thick; they were deposited as a uniform series of feldspathic sandstones with occasional bands of quartz-sandstones and muddy sandstones. The sediments are the products of rapid erosion of granitic or gneissic areas followed by rapid deposition without much time for weathering.

Conditions changed after the deposition of the Yell Sound Division. The rocks which were being eroded to make the sediments suffered stronger weathering and the components of the erosion products were sorted before deposition. As a result the rocks forming the next division, the Scatsta Division, were deposited as quartz sands and as mudstones rich in clay. The rocks of the Scatsta Division form the west sides of Unst and Fetlar, most of Lunnasting and Whalsay, and the Mainland between Mavis Grind in the west and Voe in the east, Mossbank in the north, and Sandsound in the south (Fig. 5).

Conditions changed again when the next division, the Weisdale Division, was formed. Rapid erosion and deposition were resumed, but this time deposition was punctuated by episodes in which great thicknesses of limestone accumulated and much calcium carbonate was deposited with the sandstones. The great Weisdale, Whiteness and Laxfirth limestones belong to this division, which forms the Out Skerries, South Nesting, Laxfirth, Tingwall, Whiteness and Burra Isles (Fig. 5).

Deposition of these rocks ended with a considerable deepening of the waters in the deposition trough. At the same time there was an outburst of volcanic activity, and deposition of the Laxfirth Limestone ended when it was covered by ashes, agglomerates, and possibly lavas of rather sodium-rich basaltic rocks which became the first rocks of the Clift Hills Division. The sediments with which these volcanic rocks are interbanded and overlain are very different from any deposited before. They were mostly silts showing little sign of weathering or sorting. Those in the area north of Lerwick accumulated underwater on the edge of the trough and then periodically, perhaps triggered by earthquakes, they avalanched down to the bottom of the trough. As a result they formed layers of coarse rather muddy quartz-sands deposited from the main part of the avalanche, overlain and surrounded by thin layers of the finer muddy material which had settled more slowly from the muddy water stirred up by the avalanche. Such rocks are called turbidites.

A thickness of many thousands of feet of these rocks was laid down before conditions changed again and a layer of aluminium-iron-rich clay was deposited. Clays of this type are the result of prolonged weathering of the land area before its erosion. The clay was overlain in turn by the products of another underwater volcanic outburst. Ashes, tuffs, agglomerates and lavas derived from sodium-rich basic magma accumulated underwater on the floor of the trough in association with serpentine. At times the lava came into contact with the water and formed pillow lavas. These volcanic rocks can be seen at Cunningsburgh, Channerwick and Fitful Head.

The rocks of the Clift Hills Division form the hills between Lerwick and the Tingwall valley and extend southwards through Dunrossness to Fitful Head (Fig. 5). Any rocks which were deposited on top of these volcanic rocks are hidden beneath the Old Red Sandstones and the sea on the east side of Shetland.

The three uppermost divisions, the Scatsta Division, the Whiteness Division and the Clift Hills Division seem to be roughly equivalent to the Dalradian of Scotland, represented by the rocks forming the Scottish Highlands between the Midland Valley and the Great Glen; while the Yell Sound Division may be equivalent to the Moine, the rocks forming the Northern Highlands between the Great Glen and the Lewisian gneisses of the north-west coast. The correlation cannot yet be made in sufficient detail to allow predictions to be made about what followed the Clift Hills Division in Shetland and what was deposited before the Yell Sound Division.

As a result of continued accumulation, and also probably as a result of movements in the earth's crust, the sediments were buried to great depths and subjected to high temperatures and pressures. Under these conditions they recrystallized and even perhaps partially melted, and at the same time were deformed by flow. This metamorphism changed the sedimentary rocks into metamorphic rocks. Sandstones were changed into micaceous granulites; mudstones and clays into schists and phyllites; limestones into marbles; marly sandstones into calc-silicate granulites; quartz sandstones into quartzites; and the volcanic rocks into spilitic greenstones and hornblende schists. Depending on the composition of the original rocks and the temperatures, new minerals such as muscovite, biotite, chlorite, garnet, staurolite, kyanite, chloritoid, hornblende, epidote, diopside, microcline and others grew in the rocks. Some bands of rocks (especially in the Yell Sound Division and the Weisdale Division) were turned into gneisses during this metamorphism.

Forces operating in the crust during the metamorphism caused the rocks to flow so that they developed a schistosity due to the parallel alignment of the micaceous minerals. Many of them became very fissile. A less easily seen, but nevertheless quite common result of the flow are folds in which individual beds or layers are bent back on themselves into U-shapes. All the sediments described above were deposited as more or less horizontal layers on the sea floor. They are not only recrystallized and folded, but the individual beds which were once horizontal are now vertical or even upside down. The whole sequence has come to lie on its side, as a result of folding of the whole trough on a scale far greater than Shetland itself.

The accumulation of this great pile of sediments, and its subsequent folding and uplift to form mountains is probably the result of two continents or continental plates sliding towards one another and colliding along the general line of the mountain chain. The rocks caught between the two plates were elevated to form mountains partly by sideways pressures and partly by their own buoyancy. Along the edges of the zone of compression between the plates the crust sheared through and the compressed mass rode up onto the edges of the plates. This can be seen in north-west Shetland between Uyea and the Walls Boundary Fault. In this region several shear zones or thrusts inclined steeply to the east separate slices of the crust several miles thick. One of the slices is composed of rocks which had probably accumulated as sediments at the same time as those described above. The other slices are composed of gneisses, some as old as the gneisses of the basement to the west, but which were altered by recrystallization at the same time as the sedimentary rocks were being metamorphosed. During the collision of the plates, the mountain chain was driven westwards against the basement, and slices of the mountain chain itself and of the altered basement beneath it were dragged up onto the unaltered basement.

In Unst and Fetlar there is further evidence of thrusting of great masses of rock upwards to form the mountains. The central and eastern parts of Unst and Fetlar are composed of a great sheet of serpentine overlain by gabbro. The whole sheet is at least several miles thick. By analogy with other parts of the world it seems that this sheet was once part of the oceanic sea floor lying between the two colliding continental plates. As they collided a slice of oceanic floor rode up onto one of the plates. The surface it slid over was the surface of the earth of that time. Material eroded from this slice of sea floor as it rose above sea level, accumulated in front of it and was overridden and deformed as the slice continued to advance. Conglomerates composed of pebbles of the gabbro which forms the top of the slice can be seen on the north coast of Fetlar, deformed and recrystallized underneath the serpentine which forms the bottom of the slice. This episode probably happened not long before 400 million years ago.

Some time before this, parts of the crust beneath the mountain chain had melted and started to rise towards the surface. As a result large masses of granite and granodiorite were intruded into the metamoprhic rocks of the Shetland area about 400 million years ago. One such is the Graven Complex. It occurs in the Sullom Voe area and is about six miles in diameter. It penetrated the metamorphic rocks in a very pervasive manner so that it is full of angular fragments of metamorphic rocks up to 500 yards across. The fragments mostly retain their original positions and orientations relative to each other. Because they were heated to much higher temperatures than they had experienced before, they are rich in sillimanite.

In the region between Aith and Spiggie and under the sea to the west of Burra Isle is a large mass of coarse granite intruded at about the same time. Around its edges are associated masses of diorites of various types and of serpentine. These can be seen at Hamna Voe in Burra, between Bixter and

Aith, and at Spiggie. At about the same time that these great masses were intruded, very large numbers of thin sheets of molten rock were injected into the metamorphic rocks over most of Shetland to form sills and dykes of lamprophyre.

The erosion of the mountain chain

By the time the igneous rocks had been intruded, the buckling, folding, thrusting and metamorphism of the mountain chain had ended. Consequently the igneous rocks show little sign of deformation or recrystallization. Erosion became the dominant process. This started as soon as the rocks rose above sea level, and the higher they rose the more rapidly they were eroded. For a long time the buoyancy of the growing mountains caused them to rise as fast as the erosion cut them down. This meant that rocks came to be eroded which had once been at great depth in the crust.

The oldest known erosion products in the Caledonian mountain chain are not much more than 400 million years old. In Middle Devonian times, 350 million years ago, erosion had reached levels in the Shetland area which 50 million years before had been six or more miles deep. Moreover in the area between Shetland and Scotland the mountain chain had not only been eroded to this depth but had been buried again beneath a similar thickness of Old Red Sandstones. In other words in this area the chain had been completely breached. It is possible that this happened also between Shetland and Norway.

During this 50 million years molten granite continued to rise from the base of the crust. In places it penetrated not only the metamorphic rocks of the mountain chain but also the overlying erosion products. The Sandsting granite in the Walls area cuts the Old Red Sandstones. The Ronas Hill granite very nearly reached the surface before it crystallized. Other masses did reach the surface and formed volcanoes. Considerable amounts of volcanic ashes and lavas can be seen interbanded with the Old Red Sandstones of the Walls area. The cliffs of Esha Ness are a section through the side of a volcano. In the cliffs can be seen basaltic and andesitic lavas and great piles of rock fragments produced during eruptions. Nearby at Grind of the Navir there is a sheet of ignimbrite formed from a *nuée ardentre*, an incandescent cloud of drops of liquid rock explosively ejected by the volcano. Papa Stour may be formed of part of the same sheet.

In its time the Caledonian mountain chain was probably as impressive a feature as any modern mountain chain but by 350 million years ago it was already partially buried beneath its own erosion products, the Old Red Sandstones. The sides of the old Devonian mountains with their enveloping sandstones can be seen all along the coast of Shetland from Rova Head near Lerwick to Little Holm just west of the airport runway at Sumburgh and from Aith to Melby on the west side.

On the Devonian hillside to the south of Lerwick the Old Red Sandstones are largely composed of angular fragments which were the screes that originally covered the hillsides before their burial. To the north of Lerwick and extending eastwards into Bressay are great masses of sandstone full of large rounded boulders of granite and quartzite. These are fragments which were broken from the bed rock and then washed along steep-sided rocky canyons through the mountains to the west of Lerwick. By the time they reached the Lerwick area they had become rounded; when they came to the end of the canyon, the water carrying them spread out over the plain to the east and could no longer move them so that a great delta or alluvial cone accumulated to the north of Lerwick. At times it spread far to the south and conglomeratic bands in the sandstones can be seen in Lerwick and in the coast to the south. The sandy material washed along with the boulders was carried farther out by the stream and formed beds of sandstones which become progressively finer grained to the east.

The sandstones were deposited by braided streams and distributaries. Characteristic features of these rocks are current bedding ripple mark on bedding planes. These can be seen in the sandstones all along the east coast to Sumburgh Head. Occasionally lakes formed in which limestone was deposited and fish lived. Their fossilised remains and fossil plants can be found in several places. The plants are mostly very primitive vascular plants which lived in water. The hillsides were bare of vegetation so that the Shetland area at that time probably resembled the desert areas of south-west USA today, for example, Panamint Valley or Death Valley. There, steep-sided bare rocky mountain ranges are bounded by plains where periodic torrential floods from the mountains distribute sand and gravel over wide areas. However, the lack of vegetation in the Shetland area during Devonian times was not due to lack of water but to the fact that plants had not yet evolved which could grow there. Erosion therefore proceeded much faster than it would today.

THE CREATION OF THE ISLANDS

The story outlined above is based on the study of rocks which can be seen in Shetland today. However, from Middle Devonian times about 350 million years ago, until towards the end of the Ice Age about 50 thousand years ago, no rocks were formed in Shetland which have survived until the present day. There is, therefore, no direct evidence of what happened in the Shetland area during that period, and the next phase of history, during which the islands were carved by erosion from the remnants of the mountain chain has to be based on evidence obtained from rocks found elsewhere. Much of this evidence has been obtained as a by-product of the search for oil under the seas around Shetland.

Erosion of the Caledonian mountains continued to supply great quantities of sand to the surrounding areas long after Middle Devonian times. The metamorphic and igneous rocks of Shetland may at one time have been completely buried beneath the sandstones. In Orkney, today, a similar mass of metamorphic rocks is still buried beneath three thousand feet or more of sandstone with only its summit being visible near Stromness.

As time passed river systems flowing over longer distances were established and carried the erosion products farther away. During the Carboniferous period which followed the Devonian, these rivers built great deltas of sand from the mountain chain southwards across what is now the area occupied by Southern Scotland, England and the North Sea. Tropical forests grew on the deltas, were drowned by rising sea-level and were re-established on new deltas built out into the sea over the drowned ones. The buried forests in time became coal seams.

But in Shetland it is probable that little changed. There were still no plants which could cover the hillsides so erosion still continued as before although it was now the Devonian sandstones as much as the metamorphic and igneous rocks which were being eroded.

About the end of the Carboniferous period 280 million years ago some important changes took place. The area as a whole was no longer being eroded on the scale that it had during the Devonian period because the two colliding plates had come to a standstill. The mountains were no longer being squeezed upwards and so much erosion had already occurred that they were no longer buoyant enough to rise in response to the erosion.

During the Permo-Triassic period sandstones were once again deposited in the Shetland area. The Fitful Basin to the west and south-west of Fitful Head was deposited during this period as a layer of sandstones on land at the foot of hills which included the present islands. A similar basin may occur on the sea floor to the north-west of Yell. Thus at that time it was already possible to recognize the beginnings of Shetland as an eroded remnant rising above a level plain. The climate had become that of a tropical desert. In the North Sea area to the south, instead of seas and tropical forest, there were great ephemeral salt lakes surrounded by sand dune deserts. The buried relics of these dunes now contain the natural gas found in the southern North Sea. In Shetland the land was as bare as ever, but it was a true desert due to an arid climate instead of being a desert-like area merely for lack of plants.

During this period the crust in the Shetland area sheared along the lines of the Walls Boundary fault and the Nesting fault due to compression (Fig. 5). The crust on the west sides of these faults moved northwards relative to the crust on the east sides. On the Nesting fault the total movement was 10 miles; on the Walls Boundary fault the movement seems to have been many times greater. These faults are of the same type as the San Andreas fault in California. The displacement took place as a series of small movements each accompanied by an earthquake. The sliding movement of the two sides of the fault against each other crushed and sheared the rocks on either side. Along the Walls Boundary fault the zone of broken rock is generally more than half a

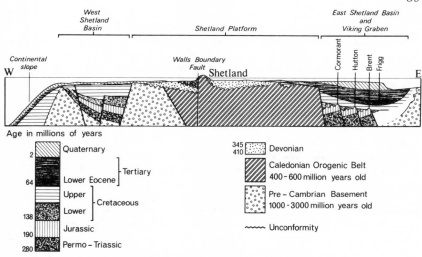

FIG 6. Diagrammatic geological profile.

mile wide. In Calback Ness in the Graven Complex the rocks are so shattered by the movement on the nearby Walls Boundary fault that the area was found to be unsuitable for underground oil storage (see Chapter 13).

The newly formed continental plate soon began to show signs of splitting to the east of Shetland in response to further tension in the crust. Two closely spaced fractures appeared and the strip of crust between them sank to form a rift valley, the beginnings of the Viking Graben. As the graben* subsided rock and sand eroded from the land on either side poured in to fill the trench. Throughout Triassic times the Viking Graben east of Shetland continued to develop and further grabens formed west of Shetland as the continental plate began to split apart. Locally eroded sands poured into the grabens on both sides of Shetland. In some places more than 5000 feet accumulated (Fig. 6).

During Jurassic and Cretaceous times from 190 to 100 million years ago the grabens continued to subside and fill with sands and muds. The sea returned to the Shetland area, periodically flooding the grabens and then retreating again. To the south of the Shetland Platform a volcano poured out large quantities of basic rock. During episodes of high sea level Shetland may have become an island for the first time. If so, due to the continued evolution of plants and the warm moist subtropical climate that prevailed then, it would

* *Graben* (German, meaning a ditch): a low-lying or depressed region between two faults, often filled-in and buried by later sediments.

probably have resembled a modern tropical island more closely than its present state.

The sediments which accumulated in the graben during this time were mostly alternating shales and sandstones. One particular layer of shale, deposited when the sea level was unusually high, was black with organic material. At a later date, after burial beneath several miles of younger sediments, the organic matter became oil. This was trapped in nearby porous sandstone layers, so making the Viking Graben a very rich oil field.

The tensions in the crust which had caused the grabens to develop to the east and west of Shetland ended in the Cretaceous period when the continental plate finally split through to the west of Shetland, and the western part forming America and Greenland started to move away to the west. In the gap between the two parts the Atlantic Ocean was formed with its newly constructed floor at a much greater depth than the surfaces of the continents on either side. New ocean floor was created by molten basic rock repeatedly rising up the fracture as it continually opened between the separating plates. The seam lies midway between the two separating continents. Very often the molten rock filling the cracks along the seam overflowed onto the seafloor as basalt lava flows. Where this happened persistently a great pile of lava flows built up to the surface to form new islands. Iceland is an example of such an island forming now. Faroe was formed in this way, beginning to grow between 50 to 60 million years ago. Basalt lavas rose up through fissures in the sea floor and spread out until a pile two miles thick had accumulated. At an early stage there was a pause in the building during which a cover of vegetation grew, the remains of which now form coal seams. The pile of lavas was a shield volcano rather like Hawaii, but it is now considerably eroded. The Faroe Islands thus have a much simpler history of development than the islands of Orkney and Shetland and are separated from them by the deep Shetland-Faroe Channel (Fig. 7).

Although the Viking graben ceased to develop 100 million years ago the area in which it occurs continued to subside and to collect sediment. The graben now lies buried beneath several thousand feet of sediment forming the East Shetland Basin. The oil in the Viking Graben is two to three miles below the sea bed.

Throughout Upper Cretaceous and Tertiary times the sea level periodically rose and fell. One of the greatest rises took place when chalk was deposited over a vast area to the south and east of Shetland. In general, however, the sea level gradually rose so that as the thickness of the sediments in the basin deepened they also spread more widely across the eroded platform towards Shetland (Fig. 6). The climate gradually cooled and about two million years ago finally became arctic as the Ice Age started. By then Shetland must have had very much its present appearance and vegetation and had probably been an island or island group for some time.

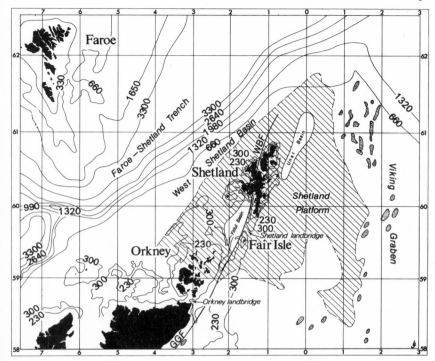

FIG 7. Bathymetric map. Dotted areas are oil-fields. Submarine contours in feet.

THE ICE AGE

Little is known of the history of Shetland during the Pleistocene period. The islands must have been covered by ice a number of times but only the last glacial maximum left much evidence of itself. However it did not destroy all evidence of earlier glaciations.

At Uyea, in North Roe and to the south of Melby small patches of peat underlie the till deposited by the last ice sheet. This peat was formed 37 to 40,000 years ago during the warm period before the last ice sheet. It overlies boulder clay deposited by ice which had covered Shetland before that warm period. There is other evidence for the existence of an earlier ice sheet. Not far to the north of Sumburgh is a boulder of Norwegian rock. It was found in a small roadside quarry in the till and is called the Dalsetter erratic (Fig. 8). It is composed of rock found only at Tönsberg just to the south of Oslo and weighs about 1.5 tons. Fragments of the Old Red Sandstone breccias found along the

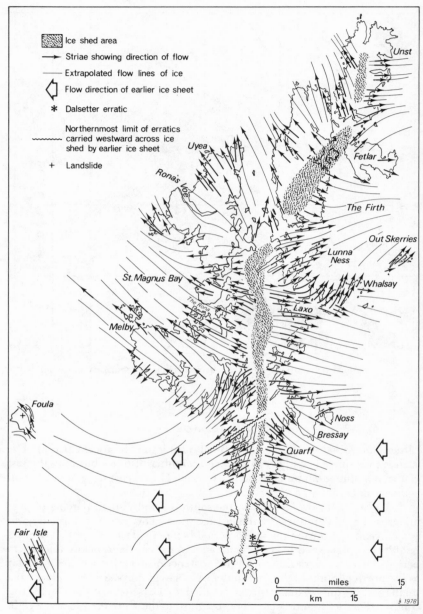

FIG 8. Flow pattern of the Shetland ice cap.

east coast of Shetland to the south of Quarff can be found also along the
watershed to the west and along the west coast beyond.

An ice sheet from Norway carrying the Dalsetter erratic overran at least the
part of Shetland to the south of Quarff, picking up Old Red Sandstone
erratics and distributing them over the metamorphic rocks to the west. This
ice sheet probably also crossed Fair Isle from east to west and farther south
neared the Aberdeenshire coast and may even have invaded England.
Orkney, at that time, was probably overrun by Scottish ice forced to flow
northwestwards across the islands from the Moray Firth because the Scandinavian ice sheet blocked flow to the east.

The last glaciation started later than 30,000 years ago and was over by
12,000 years ago. For part of this time the islands were covered by an ice cap
(Fig. 8), which flowed to the east on the east side, to the west on the west side
where it extended over Foula, and to the south where it covered Fair Isle.
South-west of Shetland this ice cap was blocked by a Scottish ice sheet
covering Orkney. In the southern part of Shetland the ice cap flowing
eastwards swept the eastern slopes of the Clift Hills more or less clean of the old
erratics deposited by the Scandinavian ice sheet but in the ice shed area the
lack of flow left them undisturbed.

As the ice flowed it picked up all loose rock and soil and nearly all the till left
by the previous glaciation. Armed with this embedded material the ice
attacked the bed rock, scouring and grinding the rock surface where the flow
impinged on it and plucking away blocks of rock from the lee sides of
protuberances. All this loose material was carried radially outwards and was
deposited on low ground as till when the ice melted. The largest block of rock
which the ice carried along with it can be seen on Lunna Ness broken into
several parts by weathering. It is called the Stanes of Stofast and weighed
about 2,000 tons. Most erratics were very much smaller.

The direction in which the ice flowed can be determined from a study of the
ice scoured surfaces and from a study of the distribution of the erratics. The
fact that the ice to the north of Lerwick moved eastwards on the east side of
Shetland was first discovered from the occurrence on Whalsay and the Out
Skerries of granite erratics from Laxo, North Nesting. Many rock types which
occur in Shetland south of Scalloway are to be found as erratics on Foula and
in Fair Isle.

By 12,000 years ago the ice cap had melted, leaving a layer of till in some of
the lower lying areas. If it left any moraines, these are now beneath the sea.
The climate became better than it is at present, the islands were repopulated
by plants and peat started to form in the bottoms of the lochs.

About 10,000 years ago the climate worsened again during the Loch
Lomond Readvance and small accumulations of ice started to develop in
parts of Scotland. In Shetland a small glacier formed in Loch of Voe,
overflowed westward into Olna Firth at Voe and left very slight traces of
moraine in the Wethersta area. Just to the south of Loch of Voe it left a barely

discernible but perfectly formed terminal moraine. In the Loch of Voe area and on the lower slopes of many Shetland hills there are small groups of hummocky moraine and groups of boulders which were probably formed during this period by small patches of ice. Accumulations of sand and gravel deposited by melt water from ice are almost confined to the Kergord area, but it is not clear whether these were formed by the main ice cap or during the Loch Lomond Readvance.

Other topographic features associated with glacial erosion occur in Shetland. On the north side of Ronas Hill are several incipient corries, possibly formed during the Loch Lomond Readvance. There are no other corries in Shetland. At times Ouvrefandal in Foula has been mistaken for a corrie, but there is no doubt that it is a large landslide of a hillside oversteepened by glacial erosion. The landslide may have taken place before the Loch Lomond Readvance in which case it would probably have accumulated a corrie glacier-like mass of ice, but it was certainly not formed by the ice. In the Cunningsburgh area is another smaller landslide (map reference HU 424291), the slide mass of which is sometimes mistaken for hummocky moraine. On the west side of the valley of Weisdale (at map reference HU 385524) is a giant landslide scar with no apparent slide mass. The landslide may have taken place before the last glaciation.

Most of Shetland's voes are drowned river valleys as described below. However Ronas Voe was formed by ice action and is a true fjord. Its trend is parallel to the general direction of flow of the ice which gouged out its bottom to 100 yards below sea level in the middle but it shallows considerably at the entrance in the west. Another such overdeepened valley is The Rona near Aith. Several valleys have U-shaped cross sections typical of valleys which have carried glaciers although most Shetland valleys lie across the direction of flow of the ice. However, Colla Firth, the eastern end of Dales Voe in Delting, and the Dale Burn valley at Sandsound are all parallel to the direction of the ice flow and probably owe their U-shaped cross sections to this fact. They show no other signs of glaciation by glaciers.

There are about 2,500 freshwater lochs in Shetland. A few have been cut off from the sea by beach-bars, many have been formed behind barriers of peat blocking the drainage of flat areas, but at least 1,000 occupy rock basins gouged out by ice.

Ten thousand years ago peat started to accumulate again in the lochs after the end of the Loch Lomond Readvance and has continued to accumulate there ever since, although it only started to form on the hillsides 7,000 to 5,000 years ago. In the lochs it overlies a layer of clay and gravel which was washed into them during the Loch Lomond Readvance, and which sometimes contains plant remains including fragments of large leaves. It is therefore possible that plants continued to grow throughout the Loch Lomond Readvance.

The melting of the ice sheets after the last glaciation caused a rise of sea level. In Shetland the sea rose so fast and the rocks are so hard that little erosion took place during the rise. The result was the coastline as we know it today: the hills and the valleys of the old landscape were partially drowned form the inner coastline, and the foot of the cliffs of the old landscape was drowned to form the outer coast (Fig. 9).

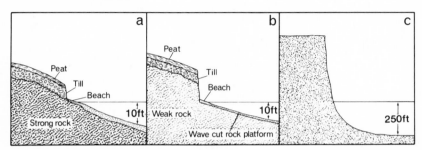

FIG 9.　Coastal profiles (diagrammatic).
a. & b. typical profiles of the inner coast. c. typical profile of the outer coast.

The inner coastline, composed of voes, firths and sounds, penetrates the islands so deeply that it is not possible to be much more than 3 miles from the sea anywhere in Shetland. As the sea rose it turned hills into islands separated by sounds, and turned river valleys and even whole drainage basins into voes and firths. These waters are so sheltered from the open sea that little erosion took place as the sea flooded the valleys. Usually the sea eroded the layer of peat and till but was unable to attack the bed rock (Fig. 9a). At the heads of many of the voes the sea has been unable even to erode the peat which now forms the beach. On some quite exposed beaches peat can be seen just below a protecting layer of pebbles. On the other hand, along some of the more exposed parts of the inner coast where the rocks have been smashed by faults, the sea has been able to cut into the bedrock. In such places a small rock cliff with a wave-cut platform at its foot is formed in the text book manner (Fig. 9a).

The action of the sea stripping the till and loose bedrock from the valley sides as it rose provided much gravel and sand which has accumulated in a series of spits, bars and tombolos. These are beaches or ayres which jut out into the sea as shown in Fig. 10. These features are characteristic of very recently drowned coastlines. Shetland provides one of the best examples in the world of this early stage in the development of a drowned coastline (Fig. 11). A particularly fine example occurs at Dales Lees in Delting where a tombolo connecting the island of Fora Ness to the Mainland has thereby formed a

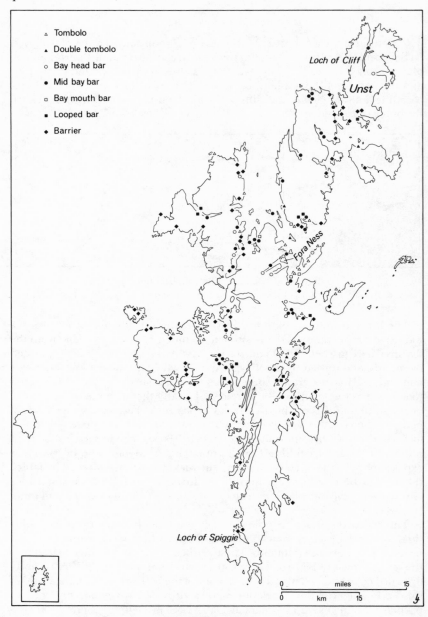

Tombolo
Double tombolo
Bay head bar
Mid bay bar
Bay mouth bar
Looped bar
Barrier

Loch of Cliff

Unst

Fora Ness

Loch of Spiggie

miles 15

km 15

FIG 10. Distribution of spits and bars.

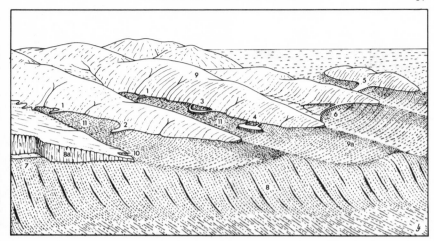

FIG 11. Coastal and submarine features characteristic of Shetland:
1. Bayhead bar;   2. Mid-bay bar;   3. Looped bar;   4. Double tombolo;   5. Tombolo;   6. Bay mouth bar and barrier forming brackish or fresh-water lake;   7. Cliff foot beach;   8. Marine erosion surface continuing above sea-level as cliff at 8a;   9. Subaerial erosion surface continuing below sea level at 9a due to drowning;   10. Geo;   11. Voe.

small voe to the east which has developed a typical bay head bar and a mid-bay bar. Continued development and accumulation of beach material in this way leads to the voes being cut off from the sea when a spit extends right across a voe to form a bay-mouth bar or barrier. The water behind the bar becomes a fresh water loch which gradually fills in with sediment. Quite a few Shetland freshwater lochs including Spiggie and Loch of Cliff owe their existence to this process.

Sandy beaches are prominent features of the Shetland landscape (Fig. 12). There are about 100 of them varying from little more than a few yards up to a thousand yards across. Some of the spit-type features described above are made of sand but most are made of pebbles. St Ninians Ayre, the most perfectly formed sand tombolo in Britain seems to be a pebble tombolo overlain by a few metres of sand. In Fetlar, Loch of Tresta is cut off from the sea by a bay-mouth bar of sand.

The sand on Shetland beaches is very variable in composition. It contains from 0 to 100% comminuted shells, but the average is about 50%. The shell component of the sands is derived from shells and echinoids living along the adjacent shores. The rest of the sand is made of siliceous mineral grains washed out of the local till or obtained from local smashed or deeply weathered rocks. The local origin of the sand is made obvious by the occur-

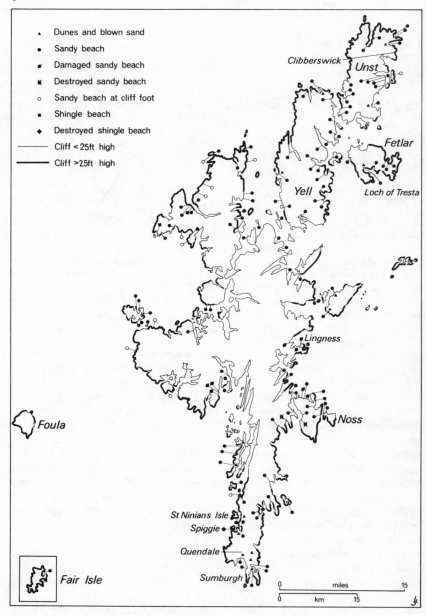

Dunes and blown sand
Sandy beach
Damaged sandy beach
Destroyed sandy beach
Sandy beach at cliff foot
Shingle beach
Destroyed shingle beach
Cliff < 25ft high
Cliff > 25ft high

Clibberswick
Unst
Fetlar
Yell
Loch of Tresta
Lingness
Noss
Foula
St Ninians Isle
Spiggie
Quendale
Sumburgh
Fair Isle

miles   15
km   15

FIG 12. Distribution of cliffs and of sandy beaches.

rence of the same minerals in the sand, the till and the bedrock: the beach sands and the rocks of Yell are particularly rich in garnet, streaks of red garnet sand being obvious on the beaches; magnetite sands occur in Fetlar; and magnetite-garnet and muscovite sands in Unst.

The sand accumulates as patches on the sea floor, and some spills onto the land to form beaches. This can only happen if there is a bench along the coast for the sand to build on. Therefore, cliff-foot sandy beaches on the outer coast are rare and most sandy beaches are found on the inner coast. The supply of sand available for beaches varies considerably. In the Quendale area it has filled a voe 1000 yards long and 1000 yards wide to form a machair area. A number of sandy beaches exposed to the winds and without a substantial cliff behind them have given rise to areas of dunes and windblown sand. The largest such area lies between Quendale and Sumburgh but others occur in Yell, Unst, Burra Isle and elsewhere.

The outer coast has a very different appearance from the inner coast although it is usually separated from it by less than a mile of transitional coastline. The outer coast at its most spectacular is formed of rock cliffs up to 1000 ft high facing the open sea. However the cliffs are usually very much lower because the outer coast truncates the landscape without regard to the height of the land, whereas the inner coastline follows the contours closely.

The underwater profile is more characteristic of the cliffs of the outer coast than their continuity. In general they plunge steeply underwater and only gradually flatten out to join the general sea floor at about 250 ft (Fig. 9c). The great cliffs of Clibberswick, Noss, Sumburgh and Foula all have smooth concave-upwards underwater profiles and reach a depth of about 250 ft within half a mile of the waterline. The same underwater profile is found along most of the outer coast irrespective of the height of the cliffs and in places continues underwater to link up stretches of outer coast separated by drowned valleys (Fig. 11).

As we have seen, the landscape drowned by the sea to form the inner coastline was formed by the action of rivers, rain, frost, ice and occasional drowning by the sea over time measured in hundreds of millions of years. The topography is almost entirely controlled by the geology, a fact which is immediately obvious from a comparison of the geological map with small scale aerial photos or even the topographic map. The two largest faults, the Walls Boundary fault and the Nesting fault tend to run along the bottom of voes and where they cross the land they do so in cols and the line of the fault is often marked by small features visible on aerial photos.

The larger scale layering of the East Mainland Succession is outlined from Unst to Fitful Head by long narrow ridges especially well developed in Delting and to the south. Aerial photos often reveal in extraordinary detail the much finer layering of these rocks and the offsets in them caused by small faults. Some of the larger igneous masses cause topographic heights and some lows according to their resistance to erosion. This topography seems to have been etched out of the rocks by a uniformly acting atmospherically controlled process. The topographic features do not cut across geological lines in the way that they would if (for example) rivers had been the dominant eroding agent. Even glacially formed features are all on a small scale. Aerial photos reveal patches of fluting on the hills caused by ice flow, but these are very insignificant features and the hills show no signs of being moulded by the ice flow. In Lunnasting the knobbly or knock and lochan topography may be ice formed, but it is on a relatively small scale. If the dominant form of erosion has, indeed, been atmospheric then the landscape has been forming very slowly, especially since plants evolved which could cover the hills with a protecting layer.

From Unst to Fitful Head and Fair Isle and from Bressay to Melby and Foula there are hills with summits at about 750 ft but varying up to 120 ft above and below this level (Fig. 13). A series of summits such as this spread over the whole area is possibly a relic of a very old erosion surface at a level of 750–900 ft. If this is so then the summits of Ronas Hill and of Foula which rise to about 1350 ft with steep sides above the 750 ft level would have been erosional remnants on an old erosion surface much as Shetland itself is an erosional remnant on the erosion surface which forms the seafloor around it.

There are several topographical features which are unrelated to geology. The most spectacular of these is the gap through the Clift Hills at Quarff. Less well developed east-west gaps through geologically controlled ridge-like hills occur at Voe and at Mid Yell (Fig. 14). These may possibly be remnants of deep valleys cut by rivers when Shetland was part of a much larger group of hills, as it was in Middle Devonian times.

The erosion surface which was drowned by the sea to form the outer coast has a very different origin. It is younger than the sub-aerial erosion surface because it truncates it, but it is far older than the present rise of sea level. The outer coast is exposed to the open sea and is, therefore, subject to very much stronger wave attack than the inner coast. Most marine erosion takes place at sea level in storms when the waves loosen and remove blocks of rock. Eventually the cliff is undermined and a mass of rock falls from above. In Shetland this rock usually falls into deep water because of the concave underwater profile. By the time it comes to rest it is too deep for the waves to have much effect on it. Even after storms, rocks not far below the surface can be seen to be still covered by apparently fragile seaweeds. Loose blocks of rock which come to rest at sea level are hurled around by the waves and help to batter loose other rocks. Not all the loosened rock falls downwards. In several places where the cliffs are less than 100 ft high fragments of rock are washed up onto the tops of the cliffs to form high level storm beaches. Good ones have developed along the cliffs on the south coast of the Out Skerries. At the Grind of the Navir there is a storm beach well back from the cliff edge composed of blocks which mostly weigh over a ton.

Stretches of low cliff joining the inner and the outer coast are prone to much

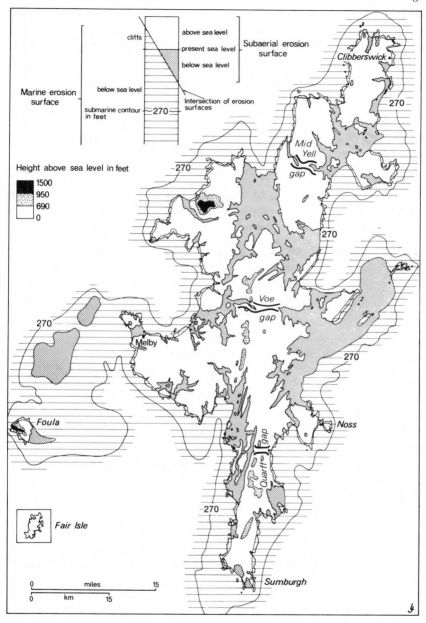

FIG 13. Erosion surfaces.

more selective attack by the sea. In these areas the sea is only able to erode along zones of weakness in the rocks, such as small faults and closely spaced fractures. The sea excavates these zones to produce caves and blow holes. Inside such narrow inlets the effects of wave action are magnified and erosion is able to continue inland along the zone of weakness. In this way the deep narrow inlets in the cliffs called geos are constructed. They are a very characteristic feature of the Shetland coastline (Fig. 11).

It is obvious that if any of the great cliffs of Shetland had retreated by even a yard or two as the sea rose after the last glaciation, the amount of debris which would have accumulated underwater at the cliff foot would have turned the concave-upwards profile into a convex one. In several places where the rocks are heavily shattered and weak the cliff has retreated significantly in front of the rising sea and a wavecut bench has been formed. This in turn supports a cliff-foot beach, and produces a convex underwater profile (Fig. 11). Examples occur on the west side of Ronas Hill at the Lang Ayre, west of Hillswick and on the south coast of Vaila (Fig. 12).

The cliffs of the outer coast form an erosion surface both above and below sea level which is younger than and surrounds the sub-aerial erosion surface (Figs 11 & 13). The two erosion surfaces intersect above sea level at the cliff edge and below sea level where the drowned valleys are truncated by steep underwater slopes. This younger erosion surface is dominantly of marine origin. It is the result of many rises and falls of sea level; during the falling phase the waves are able to attack and remove the debris which had accumulated since the previous rise.

It is unlikely that the cliffs have retreated in this way right across the continental shelf. As mentioned above, a few miles to the south of the cliffs cutting the Sandsting granite, the Fitful Basin is formed of sandstones which were deposited on a desert land surface about 280 million years ago. It seems likely that when the sea returned to the Shetland area in Jurassic times Shetland was already part of a range of hills rising steeply from a flattish land surface. Such land forms are common in some parts of the world and are called monadnocks or inselbergs. A rising sea level would rapidly turn such a range of hills into an island group ringed by cliffs. The rises and falls in sea level since then have caused the ring of cliffs to retreat, gradually truncating hills and valleys alike. Possibly the area may have been buried or partially buried beneath younger sediments at times of high sea level. However, these would have been much softer than the rocks forming the islands now and more easily eroded when the sea level fell again. As time passed plants evolved to forms able to form a protective cover for the hillsides so that subaerial erosion was slowed, and marine erosion became the dominant process in the area.

AFTER THE ICE AGE

It is very difficult to determine how far the sea level fell during the last glaciation. The fall was due to a combination of causes of which the transfer of water from the oceans to the land-based ice caps was just one. The ice sheets were unevenly distributed around the north pole and this probably caused the whole planet to tilt so that the geographic position of the rotation axis was changed. Since the distance from the centre of the planet to sea level at the pole of the rotation axis is less than the distance at the equator this tilt must have caused a change of sea level all over the planet. The weight of the ice caps caused the crust beneath them to sink and then to slowly recover after the ice had melted. The Hudson Bay area of Canada seems to have risen more than 900 ft as a result of the melting of an ice cap nearly two miles thick. Around Scotland raised beaches record the rise of Scotland after the melting of its ice cap. It is possible that areas peripheral to ice caps were uplifted to compensate for the sinking of the central areas. After the ice melted these areas would be expected to sink again and to have no raised beaches. Shetland was peripheral to the Scottish and Scandinavian ice caps, and shows evidence of sinking. It has no raised beaches. The relative levels of sea and land are further complicated by the fact that removal of water from the oceans during the glaciation caused the ocean floor to rise and its return afterwards caused it to sink again thus partially offsetting the changes of sea level.

Most estimates of the fall of sea level at the maximum of the last glaciation are close to 300 feet. The actual falls of the sea relative to the land in the Shetland area due to all these causes could be more, or less, than this. All that is known so far is that at Symbister in Whalsay peat formed 5,500 years ago at an unknown height above sea level is now 30 ft below sea level.

The islands were recolonized by plants after the last glaciation and before 12,000 years ago when peat began to form in lochs. If at that time the level of the sea relative to the land was more than 275 ft lower than at present, then the landbridge to Scotland via Orkney would have been open for colonizations to have taken place over land (Fig. 7). However the sea level must have been rising rapidly then and Shetland is more than 600 miles from the southern limits of the ice in England. It seems likely that even if there was a landbridge it was not of much significance for the repopulation. The plants growing in Faroe did not reach Faroe across a landbridge so that the plants of Shetland did not need a landbridge to recolonize Shetland. Plants in Shetland which need a warmer climate than existed at first, such as hazel, must have arrived later when the chances of the landbridge being open were very much less.

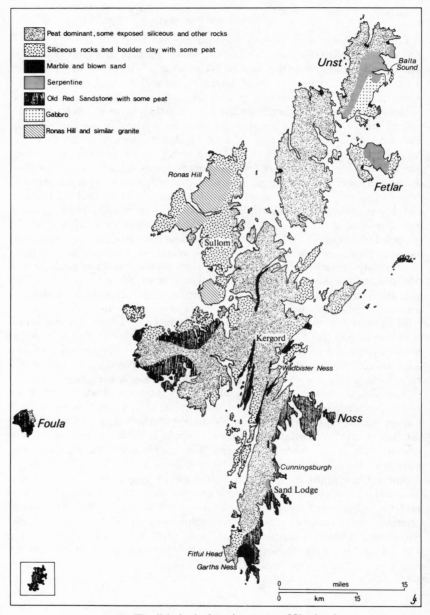

Peat dominant, some exposed siliceous and other rocks

Siliceous rocks and boulder clay with some peat

Marble and blown sand

Serpentine

Old Red Sandstone with some peat

Gabbro

Ronas Hill and similar granite

Unst

Balta Sound

Fetlar

Ronas Hill

Sullom

Kergord

Wadbister Ness

Foula

Noss

Cunningsburgh

Sand Lodge

Fitful Head

Garths Ness

miles

0   15

0   km   15

FIG 14. The lithological environment of Shetland.

GEOLOGY AND THE ENVIRONMENT

One of the most important factors controlling vegetation cover is the nature of the underlying rocks, because these break down to form the soil in which the plants grow. Fig. 14 is a geological map showing the distribution of the dominant soil-forming rocks. For this purpose peat and blown sand must be treated as rocks. Most of Scotland is covered by a layer of hill peat which has accumulated on till or on siliceous rocks such as Old Red Sandstones and metamorphic schists and gneisses. However, several rock types have created rather different environments.

Blown sand containing shell fragments and crystalline limestones have produced patches richer in lime than usual in Shetland. For example, intermittent exposures of a narrow limestone band to the west of the airstrip at Tingwall have produced a row of islands of green rising above the heather covered hill peat. Each island has had a croft on it at some time. Most of the limestone areas have been heavily cultivated for a long time. To the south of Kergord the Whiteness peninsula and the southern end of the Weisdale valley are particularly good examples. To the north of Kergord the Weisdale limestone passes beneath a thick layer of peat.

The large areas of serpentine in Unst and Fetlar produce a very poor soil able to support few plants and hill peat never formed on them. However, some of the larger areas of bare rock or almost bare rock especially to the east of Hagdale, have probably been produced by miners stripping the surface in search of chromite ore.

Another area which owes its special nature to the underlying rock is Ronas Hill. The Ronas Hill granite does not break down very easily due to weathering because of the interlocking nature of its mineral grains, and when it does it produces a very infertile soil. The resultant thin cover leaves the rock exposed to frost action to which it is particularly prone because it is already rather heavily shattered. The puffy soil, the looseness of moss and lichen on the rocks and of the surface layer of the rock itself all testify to continuing freeze and thaw activity making it even more difficult for a plant cover to be established. Foula at the same height and degree of exposure to the elements has a continuous and thick layer of vegetation which extends to the summit of the island and protects the rocks from frost. The difference between the two areas is that Foula is made of Old Red Sandstones which not only crumble to make a sandy soil but also contain a trace of lime. All sandstone areas are more fertile than the siliceous metamorphic and igneous areas.

HUMAN EXPLOITATION

Some of the Shetland rocks are sufficiently valuable to man to have been exploited. A number of small copper veins are scattered over the area between Fitful Head, Wadbister Ness and Noss. The copper occurs in the form of the mineral chalcopyrite ($Cu_2Fe\,S_4$). At Sandlodge the chalcopyrite is sparsely disseminated in a thick vein of ankerite (Ca,Mg,Fe) (CO_3). This vein was heavily weathered during the development of the landscape so that a high concentration of iron oxides and copper carbonate accumulated near the surface. The deposit was mined between 1789 and 1808 by a company controlled by a London cornfactor assisted by the laird, John Bruce of Sumburgh who was trained as a lawyer and was at the time a lieutenant in the Sea Fencibles at Edinburgh. A steam engine built by Trevithick was installed in 1802 to help work the mine. Much capital was put into sinking shafts in search of further ore at depths where there was none so that the enterprise failed.

A rival company supported by the laird of Quendale, Andrew Grierson, attempted to work the large mass of pyrrhotite (Fe_nS_{n+1}) at Garthsness for copper. This enterprise was kept going for some time by Shetland workers slipping copper pennies into the ore sent for assay. However, Thomas Williams of Llanidan in Anglesey, whose control of the world's largest copper mine at Parys Mountain in Anglesey had enabled him to gain control of the Cornish copper mines and thus to corner the market for copper, arrived. He realized what was going on and the mining stopped.

Mining was renewed at Sandlodge again in the 1870s. John Walker, who was at one time the factor for the estate of Cameron of Garth, had gradually become so widely involved in business in Shetland on his own account that he was known as the Director General of Shetland. He set up a company to open up Sandlodge mine. The rich ore near the surface was open-cast mined and shipped south, but the proceeds were again wasted on underground mining and Walker left Shetland in 1881 a bankrupt.

The mine was opened again about 1920 by a Belgium mining engineer. Soon a series of increasingly urgent editorials appeared in the *Mining Magazine* pointing out that his very optimistic prospectus was not supported by any reports from reputable mining consultants. After publication of an unfavourable report from one such consultant the mine closed again.

During the 1930s, D. Haldane, one of the Geological Survey officers, discovered some scarn-magnetite masses in the Sullom area. One was opened up by a Canadian army unit in the war. After the war the magnetite was taken out and used for coal cleaning. Later the scarn was quarried for road metal.

Chromite was discovered in the dry stone walls at Baltasound in Unst by Hibbert in 1817. However, it has been suggested that the skipper of a trading smack had been carrying cargoes of it south for some time in the form of ballast, the implication being that he knew its value. The chromite was mined intermittently in the last century for the manufacture of yellow lead chromate pigment and in this century for use as a refractory. This activity had a greater impact on the environment than the copper mining as it involved quarrying and so left a series of pits and spoil heaps on the hills around Baltasound. This tradition of mining led naturally to quarrying of serpentine and steatite in this century. There are large reserves of steatite in Unst and Cunningsburgh.

Sand beaches have been exploited for some time for building purposes and to a lesser extent for agricultural use (Fig. 12). During the war a beautiful shingle beach at Spiggie was completely removed as was Lerwick's sandy beach at Sandsound, while the Gulberwick beach was badly affected by exploitation. In recent years many sandy beaches have been worked as the need for building sand increased, though none has been destroyed so far. The very beautiful shell sand beach at Lingness in Nesting was almost entirely removed for agricultural purposes but it has since partially recovered. The most persistently exploited beach is the sand tombolo at St Ninian's, unmatched in Great Britain. It is clear that sand cannot be taken wantonly from Shetland beaches without spoiling or even destroying the beach which may take years to recover naturally, if it ever does. Exploitation of beaches should be stopped and consideration given to repairing the damage that has already been done. It is not usually possible to turn a stony beach to a sandy one by dumping sand on it, although this could be done at Sandsound since it was once a sandy beach. A shipload of sand equivalent in volume to what was taken in the war would give Lerwick its sandy beach once again.

In the Quendale-Sumburgh area there are vast quantities of sand which could be exploited with little damage to the environment. For agricultural purposes there are immense reserves of limestone in Shetland. Quarries at Voe and Girlsta have been used for this purpose in the past. Beach sand is not an economical substitute for crushed limestone or imported lime if the amenity value of the beaches is taken into account.

Since the discovery of oil in the area the quarrying of rock has become much more important than it was earlier. Before the days of tarmac roads in Shetland there were small quarries in the till beside the road every half mile or so. Now the roads are constructed from a few quarries. The biggest is at Scord near Scalloway, the other islands generally having smaller ones. In the Lang Kames granite, deeply weathered long ago under other climatic conditions, is being exploited because of its sand-like nature. The needs of the construction industry for rock fill have led to the opening of many new quarries and the reopening of old ones first used in the war for runway and camp construction. Some of these have been sited in naturally shattered rock. Some are more or less hidden from view while others could not be more obvious, such as the one which, with its plant, has turned Mavis Grind into an eyesore. Until recently Mavis Grind was one of Shetland's better known beauty spots. In contrast, one quarry used in connection with the construction of the Ninian pipeline, has been so well restored that it is difficult to find the site, but this was a recently made borrow pit. Little can be done to improve the appearance of the big rock quarries.

References for Chapter 2
(full citations are given in the Bibliography on p. 353)

Birks & Ransom, 1969; Black, 1976; Bott & Browitt, 1975; Bott & Watts, 1970; Chaloner, 1972; Chapelhow, 1965; Curtis & Brown, 1969; Finlay, 1926*a,b,* 1930; Flinn, 1958, 1959, 1964, 1967, 1969*a,b,* 1970*a,b,* 1973, 1974, 1977, 1978; Flinn, *et al,* 1972; Flinn, *et al* 1979; Hoppe, 1965, 1974; McKay, 1974; Mather & Smith, 1974; May, 1970; Miller & Flinn, 1966; Mykura, 1972*a,b,c,* 1974 1975, 1976; Mykura & Phemister, 1976; Phemister, 1978; Pringle, 1970; Read, 1934, 1937; Sissons, 1974; Westoll, 1937; Wilson & Knox, 1936; Ziegler, 1978.

CHAPTER 3

NATURAL HISTORY OF MAN
IN SHETLAND

MAN in Shetland has faced the same problems and similar vicissitudes to the other introduced species: difficulties from fresh colonizers, intra-specific competition, food shortage, isolation, but above all, the climate.

The chief conclusions from a study of his characteristics are firstly, the extraordinarily constant pattern of life in Shetland over many centuries; and secondly, the pure Viking origin of the bulk of Shetlanders.

The earliest colonizers of Shetland arrived towards the end of the 3rd millennium B.C., and were megalith builders with links in the eastern Mediterranean. They were followed by Bronze Age Beaker folk, and by Pictish broch-builders in the Iron Age (Table 5). At that time there was a considerable Pictish culture in Shetland: half the known total of Pictish ogam-inscribed Stones come from Shetland and Orkney. However, by the time of the Viking colonization of the islands in the 9th century, there seem to have been few Picts left. Brøgger (1929) believed that the Scandinavians came to a 'veritable museum' of deserted brochs, farms and outbuildings, while Shetelig (1940) claimed that 'the islands were at most only very thinly peopled when the Norwegians made their first settlements', since 'most of the Picts had earlier migrated to the mainland of Britain'. Traditionally, Cunningsburgh and parts of the West Mainland have been regarded as peopled by 'Spaniards wrecked from the Armada ships in 1588, although they are now considered to be evidence of non-extinction of the pre-Norse settlers' (O'Dell, 1939). In fact there is no firm evidence for the survival of either the early inhabitants or the inadvertent Armada settlers; the culture, sentiments, and almost certainly the genetical constitution of the Shetlanders are determined by the Scandinavian relationships.

There are three lines of evidence that Shetland was largely uninhabited when the Vikings arrived:

1. The lack of weapons in Viking houses and graves excavated in both Orkney and Shetland.

2. The enormous preponderance (about 99%) of place names in Shetland are of west Scandinavian origin.

3. Less convincing, the contemporary accounts of Viking activities in both British and saga literature.

There are a few Celtic place names in Shetland (the ones that survive are

59

TABLE 5. Early inhabitants of Shetland

Date	Climate	Population movements	Archaeology and culture	Reference
BC	Climatic deterioration: gales cleared Caithness forests			Lacaille (1954)
1800–1600	Sub-boreal period, permitting settlement on higher ground	First colonists from SW Europe and Eastern Mediterranean		Daniel (1941)
		Lengthy period of peaceful husbandry – progressive expansion of field system (barley grown; horse, ox, sheep, pigs bred)	Heel-shaped cairns (variant of chamber tombs) Stanydale and Yoxie Temples Neolithic houses on separated sites (unlike villages in Orkney)	Calder (1956)
700–600	Sub-Atlantic (time of peat formation)	Beaker folk (Bronze Age) – waves of immigrants displaced from Continent	No cultural change – two breeds of sheep at Jarlshof	Childe (1946)
c. 300	Climatic improvement		Seals and walrus hunted Birds and fish eaten	
AD Up to c. 150		Iron Age: peaceful immigrations (Northern peace following submission of Orkney to Claudius, AD 43)	Farming, fishing and piracy Brochs (95 in Shetland)	Hamilton (1956, 1968)
300–800		Further immigrations from south, and inhabitants become known as Picts	Wheelhouses	Wainwright (1962a)
800		Massive Scandinavian colonizations from SW Norway	Long houses	Brogger (1929) Wainwright (1962b) Berry, A. C. (1974)
			Primarily agriculturists, with fishing a reaction to poverty of agriculture	Small (1969)

principally those associated with Papa and the *papae*, which means a monk or hermit in Old Norse), and there can be no doubt that the Scandinavian colonization amounted to a mass migration which must have completely swamped any indigenous population. The Vikings arrived in numbers sufficient to overwhelm the earlier inhabitants, politically, socially, culturally and linguistically.

The sole legacy of the Picts seems to have been the Christian Faith. The evidence for this are the ogam stones which mainly belong to the 8th and 9th centuries, well after the original Viking movement; the lack of pagan burials (most of which date from the early part of the 9th century); and the number of early names incorporating 'church' in them, notably *Kirkabister* and *Kebister*.

Although settlers must have continued to arrive in Shetland from Norway throughout the Viking period, there is general agreement that the main immigrations took place during the decade either side of 800 A.D. It has been suggested that the *udal* system of land tenure, where a family holding was divided between all the sons and daughters, may have been a factor in precipitating emigration from Norway, particularly if the limits of taking in new land for improvement had been reached. Economic stresses of this sort would have been exacerbated by a westward shift in the migration route of the herring believed to have taken place at this time. For a people becoming dependent on the sea as shipbuilding technology improved and land availability became restricted, this may have been a critical factor. In other words, the migrations were triggered by a complex interaction of geographical, social, political, economic and even psychological factors.

Loot from the British islands has been found in graves from a large part of the south western seaboard of Norway, but mainly from Rogaland and Sogn og Fjordane (south and north of Bergen). From linguistic evidence, Jakobsen (1928) claimed that 'the character of the word-material in the Shetland Norn (*i.e.* old Norse) points so decisively to the south-west of Norway, that one can conclude that the Shetland islands were peopled to an altogether preponderating extent from . . . the stretch of country from Bergen down to Lister and Mandal, with its focal point in south Rogaland'. However, an analysis of the surnames of the inhabitants of the South Mainland indicates that about a third of the population there was of lowland Scottish origin, incomers in the years following the pledging of Shetland to Scotland by the King of Denmark in 1469.

The ABO blood groups for Shetland fall into the pattern of north Scotland – Orkney – Shetland – Faroe – Iceland, with a higher frequency of group O than in Norway (Table 6). On face value, therefore, the Shetlanders have a greater affinity with British people than with Scandinavians. However, the ABO system is known to be subject to a number of selective pressures. A great many of the geographically isolated peoples of Europe and neighbouring regions – in islands, on mountains, and in the desert – have particularly high group O frequencies. They include the Icelanders, the Scots, the Irish, the

TABLE 6. Gene frequencies (%) of blood groups and serum proteins

		Cumbria	Ireland		Orkney		SHETLAND	Iceland	Norway	Denmark
			Southern	Northern	Sanday	Westray				
	Approx. numbers of people tested*	800	1700	300	110	350	300	1600	200	430
Blood groups										
ABO	A_1	18	13	12	9	13	**13.1**	13	21	20
	A_2	8	4	5	6	6	**6.1**	6	10	8
	B	7	7	6	17	9	**8.9**	6	6	8
	O	67	76	77	68	72	**71.9**	75	63	64
MNS	MS	25	27	28	22	23	**31.2**	16	20	22
	Ms	29	29	26	40	34	**27.7**	42	31	30
	NS	6	6	5	2	6	**2.4**	6	9	7
	Ns	40	38	41	36	37	**38.7**	36	40	41
Rhesus	R_z	0.2	0	0	1.0	0.3	**0.2**	0	0	0
	R_1	42.0	40.0	40.0	46.3	44.5	**45.2**	44.1	43.5	39.8
	r'	0.4	0.4	0	0	0	**0.4**	0.4	1.0	1.0
	R_2	10.8	15.7	14.4	13.6	13.5	**13.6**	16.6	16.4	16.6
	R_0	1.9	1.4	1.4	0	0	**2.5**	1.2	0.6	1.5
	r''	1.9	3.6	0.5	1.5	0	**0**	0.8	0	0.8
	r	42.7	42.1	43.7	37.6	41.3	**38.2**	36.8	38.5	40.2
Duffy	Fy^a	38	42	41	50	44	**46.9**	43	42	41
Kell	K	5	4	5	4	3	**5.0**	5	4	4
Lutheran	Lu^a	4	2	2	2	—	**4.2**	2	4	4

P	P⁺	29	48	45	39	38		40	—	—
Proteins and enzymes										
Haptoglobin	Hp[1]	35	38	41	42	38	**43·5**	43	38	40
Adenylate kinase	Ak–1[a]	95	97	96	95	97	**95·8**	93	96	96
Acid phosphatase	Acp[a]	32	34	33	32	—	**31·4**	37	38	34
	Acp[b]	65	62	63	62	—	**63·6**	55	55	60
Phosphoglucomutase	Pgm–1[a]	72·9	74·3	78·6	68·3	82·0	**79·7**	83·7	77·7	80·1
6-phosphogluconate dehydrogenase	6–Pgd[a]	97·2	98·5	98·1	97·9	98·5	**98·7**	97·9	—	—
Transferrin	Trf[c]	99·5	99·0	98·7	100·0	—	**99·5**	99·9	—	—

*Varies for different genes

northern Welsh, the Walsers of the high Alps, the Basques, the Corsicans and Sardinians, numerous small tribes of the Caucasus, the Berbers of the Atlas Mountains, and the Arabs of the Arabian peninsula. These populations show a considerable range of frequencies in their Rhesus and MN groups. Frequencies in these two systems appear in general to be more stable in time than those of the ABO groups, and there is no question of close relationship between the various populations. The possibility must therefore exist that there has been parallel evolution in these isolates. The most likely mechanism would seem to be the elimination of A and B foetuses following immunization of the mother against her own baby. It would then be necessary to assume that high frequencies of A and B are maintained by counter-selection in non-isolated populations, presumably through exposure to epidemic infections preferentially attacking or killing persons of group O.

For Shetland, the most useful traits for measuring relationships have been 'non-metrical variations' of the skull. These are small variants of the bones where two or more alternatives exist – the presence or absence of a sutural bone, one or two foramina, the existence or not of small ridges, and so on. The alternatives are all 'normal' and they are recognized by their presence or absence rather than by measurement (hence 'non-metrical'). The frequency with which any variant occurs in a population is a genetical characteristic of that population. Since each variant is based on a number of different genes, a multivariate statistic based on the frequencies of many variants will describe variation in a substantial part of the genetical constitution and be a valuable indicator of the degree of relationship between population samples.

The frequencies of 30 non-metrical variants in skulls excavated from St Ninian's Isle have been determined. Most of the skulls are probably of mediaeval date, when the St Ninian's Chapel served as an ecclesiastical focal point for much of the South Mainland. The last burials were in the mid-19th century.

The St Ninian's skulls are much more like those in a sample from South Norway (Jaeren) than elsewhere (Fig. 15). This affinity suggests that the Shetland sample represents the old population of the island and not mediaeval incomers; and that the origin of the Shetland population (or at least that of the South Mainland) was in south Norway.

If the measure of divergence shown by the skull characters is a valid measure of genetical similarity, the next closest relatives of the Shetlanders are in Orkney and the Viking settled area of the Outer Hebrides. It is interesting that Orkney (which was much more a political centre than Shetland in Viking times, and therefore subject to greater population movements) is more like the Iceland sample than is the Shetland one.

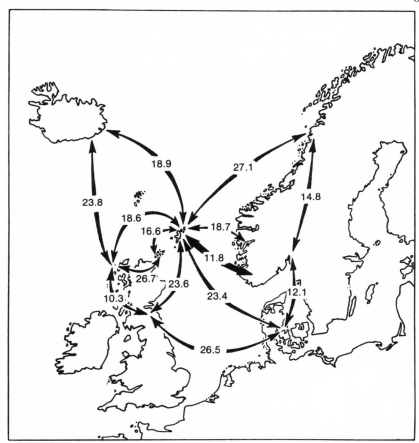

FIG 15. Relationships between the Shetlanders and other peoples. The figures are measures of divergence between population samples of skulls – low figures indicate close relationships (from Berry & Muir, 1975).

THE PRESENT POPULATION AND ITS DISEASES

We cannot regard the South Mainland as containing an entirely representative selection of the human population of Shetland. Even the small amount of information that we have on ABO blood group frequencies shows that marked differences exist between regions, quite apart from the subjective impressions of anyone who travels throughout the islands. However, we are forced for the moment to deal with 'Shetland man' as if everyone there had the same characteristics.

One fact we can assert confidently, and that is the recent history of the islands has not diluted the original Viking genes of the population to such an extent as to alter them significantly. In 1712 the British Government imposed a heavy duty on imported salt which finally destroyed the foreign trade of the islands and put the local landlords in a monopolistic position as agricultural superiors, buyers, and providers. They used this to exploit the 'haaf' (long line) fishing which required considerable manpower (see Chapter 5). The landlords manipulated their economic power to discourage emigration and promote early marriage, and thus the population increased from 10,000–12,000 in the early 18th century to a maximum of 31,670 in 1861. The pinnacle of landlord influence was reached at the end of the 18th century: even though some landlords were showing signs of enlightenment, there was still only one who did not make selling fish to him a condition of tenure. The power of the landlords finally disappeared with the passing of the Truck Acts (1872), followed by the Crofters Act of 1886. However, from 1880 the decline of the 'haaf' fishing as herring drifters were introduced, associated with both voluntary emigration and the 'clearances' contributed to a decline in popu-

TABLE 7. Population size in Shetland

Date	Population
c. 1600	9,750
1755	15,410
1801	22,379
1811	22,915
1821	26,145
1831	29,392
1841	30,558
1851	31,044
1861	31,579
1871	31,371
1881	29,149
1891	28,241
1901	27,736
1911	27,238
1921	24,117
1931	21,229
1951	19,102
1961	17,483
1971	17,298

lation which continued to the present apparently stable level of about 18,000 (Table 7). Although Shetland has had considerable contact with Scandinavia (especially through the whale fisheries, the armed forces and the mercantile marine), the present population of the islands – particularly the North Isles – still seems largely composed of the direct descendants of the original Viking colonizers. On the basis of the census returns, less than eight per cent of the permanent Shetland population was not born there, and most (c. 70%) of these incomers were born in either the fishing counties or midland valley of Scotland. A study of the fishing island of Whalsay showed that over 95% of the families had lived there for many generations.

At this point it is worth describing the appearance of those parts of the islands that have been settled by man, because they are so different from the farming landscape of Britain. The only old town in the County is Scalloway; other coastal villages are fishing ports around natural harbours; but until relatively recent times most of the population have lived in crofting 'townships' associated with fertile land.

R. L. Stevenson commented derogatively on these in 1869: 'The lowlands were cultivated after a skimble-skamble fashion; ruinous walls ran here and there, sometimes wandering aimlessly into the middle of the fields and there ending with as little show of reason, sometimes gathering into gross heaps of loose stones, more like an abortive cairn than an honest drystone dyke; for crop, it seemed that docken and the yellow wild mustard, which made bright patches every here and there, were more plentiful than turnips or corn. Mixed up with this unwholesome looking wilderness were thatched cottages bearing every sign of desertion and decay, except the curl of smoke from the place where the chimney should be and was not; and in some cases presenting bare gables and roofless walls to the bitter ocean breeze. The uplands were a sere yellow-brown, with rich full-coloured streaks of peat, and grey stretches of outcropping rock. The whole place looks dreary, and wretched; for here Nature, as Hawthorne would have said, has not sufficient power to take back to herself what the idleness and absence of man has let go. There is no ivy for the ruined cottage; no thorn or bramble for the waste wayside'.

Stevenson must have written on a bad day after a rough crossing from the south. Ruins there are in plenty in Shetland, but in sunshine the colours of the rock and fields more than offset the dereliction. Each croft or group of crofts is surrounded by arable infield and wet meadows cut for hay, by grassy rocky ground too uneven for cultivation, and outside a hill-dyke by common hill grazing or scattald. In sheltered spots "plantie-crubs" (closed stone wall circles) still occur, although they are rarely used for their original purpose of protecting newly planted seedlings. Nowadays, many of the old croft houses have been renovated or replaced by trim bungalows, and the fertile land from several crofts is often joined together to make viable agricultural units. But only in the South Mainland and the Tingwall Valleys are larger farms found, and in this Shetland differs even from Orkney.

The pattern of crofting has persisted with comparatively little change throughout historic times and we can still regard the Shetland human population as being more or less directly descended from a group of founders much smaller than the present population. If so, it would be expected that some of its gene frequencies would be significantly different from the ancestral population. The clearest evidence of this comes from the disease patterns of the Shetlanders, which have been relatively well recorded. These will be influenced to varying extents by the genetical composition of the population. Most conspicuously, Shetland has the highest recorded prevalence of multiple sclerosis in the world, followed closely by Orkney. Numerous speculations have attempted to relate this to climate, diet or geology. Genetical influences have been specifically rejected in the past on the grounds that Orkney and Shetland (with many cases), and Faroe and Iceland (with proportionately fewer) are all descended from the Vikings and hence, it has been inferred, they are genetically alike. This fails to take into account the colonization circumstances of the islands. The most plausible hypothesis for the causation of multiple sclerosis is that it is an inborn error of metabolism with a penetrance affected by immunological, dietary and possibly climatic variables. If so, the 'magnification' of a founder effect could produce the observed frequencies. Unusually high frequencies of some diseases have been recorded in a number of communities where the founder situation is better documented than in Shetland.

Two other conditions are especially common in Shetland.

1. Mortality from 'gastric and duodenal ulcers' is more than 68% higher than the population average for the United Kingdom, being more marked in males than females. This conclusion is based on death certification and could be suspect. A preliminary analysis of *post mortem* information of hospital deaths in Lerwick has shown that a significant proportion of patients presenting with haematemesis (and who might be recorded as ulcer sufferers on a death certificate) had no ulceration. In the absence of adequate morbidity data, it is probably best to conclude that any excess deaths from this cause were the consequence of isolation before treatment and the time taken to travel to hospital. If so, they will decrease with the improving interisland air and ferry service. However, the infant mortality is low, and since this implies easy access to medical help, this could mean that the Shetlanders are in fact particularly susceptible to alimentary ulceration. Carcinoma of the stomach has a higher incidence in Iceland than anywhere else in Europe.

2. Down's syndrome is six times more common in Shetland than Orkney. The 24 cases of this condition in Shetland living in the 1970s account for the difference in mental defect rate between the two island counties (4.6 per thousand in Shetland; 3.5 per thousand in Orkney), as well as the excess of lower grade defectives in Shetland: 13 of the Down's cases had an IQ of 20–50, 10 of < 20. All the Shetland cases were standard (trisomy-21) patients,

which occur at an increasingly higher frequency in the children of older women (in contrast to 'translocation' patients, which are equally frequent in the children of women of all ages). The mother's age was over 35 in 19 cases, and over 40 in 11. The suggestion has been made that the Shetland Down's patients are the result of the father being away from home for extended periods (*e.g.* at sea), so that the family is spread in time. Five of the patients were born before 1939, 5 in 1940–46, 3 in 1947–50, 5 in 1951–55, 4 in 1956–60, and the rest later. Two of the patients were sibs with first cousin parents; one other patient had first cousin parents; and one had second cousin parents.

With these exceptions, there are no unusual disease incidences. Mortality from lung cancer is less than two-fifths that in Aberdeen but is of the same order as in other rural areas of north east Scotland. Essential hypertension is believed to be common by local doctors, but the death rates from arterial disease are similar in all parts of north east Scotland and the islands. Psychiatric disease would be expected to be under-recorded in a close-knit rural county like Shetland, and therefore it may be significant that schizophrenia and depression are comparatively often diagnosed. Local tradition maintains that depression results from loneliness in intelligent crofters. In all the rural areas, the time of first psychiatric referral is later in life than in patients coming from the city of Aberdeen.

The causes of death have changed greatly over the past century, even when allowance is made for faulty diagnosis a hundred years ago. Arterial disease has replaced tuberculosis as the single most important cause of death. However, tuberculosis was only half as common in Shetland as in other parts of Scotland in 1862, according to Cowie who wrote his M.D. thesis on the inhabitants of Shetland. This was despite the fact that Shetland had more people living two or more to a room than any other county at the time of the 1871 census. In the 20th century the position was reversed: the death rate from tuberculosis in 1924 was 1.9 per thousand of the population, compared with 0.8 in Scotland overall. Surprisingly, cancer deaths have increased from only 4 to 6% of the total. Of the 23 cases in the 1855–61 period where the site of the growth was recorded, 8 involved the alimentary tract and 6 the face or lip. This could have been a result of mending tarred fishing nets, which were gripped in the mouth while being repaired. In earlier days, drowning was probably the greatest hazard for an adult man; this is now a comparatively slight hazard.

Infectious diseases seem to have been particularly rampant in Shetland's history. For example, a visiting clergyman (Brand) records in 1701 that 'upon one Lord's day there were 90 prayed for in the Church of Lerwick all sick of the same disease (smallpox); whereas, when we were there a few weeks before there was not one we knew sick thereof. They say a gentleman's son in the country, who had lately gone from the South and was under it when he came home, brought it with him . . . a third part of the people in many of the isles are dead thereof'. For most of the 18th century smallpox epidemics occurred regularly every 20 years. In 1720 the disease produced so much death that it was known as the mortal pox (or muckle fever). It is said that of the 200 or so inhabitants of Foula only 4 men were left to bury the dead, and the island had to be repeopled from the North Mainland by the landlord. Vaccination was introduced during the 1760 epidemic, and thereafter the disease was less often fatal. Between 1855 and 1861, only 7 people died from smallpox compared with 110 from 'hooping cough', 54 from measles, 25 from typhus and 24 from influenza.

One interesting disease which is said to have survived longer in Shetland than in other parts of Britain is leprosy. By the time of Edmonston (1809) it was becoming rare, but he recalls that 'formerly this affection was very prevalent. Unfortunate individuals who were seized with it were removed to small huts, erected for the purpose, and there received a scanty allowance of provisions daily, until the disease put a period to their miserable existence. The parish of Walls and the island of Papa Stour appear to have been the places in which it raged with the greatest malignity'. A visitor to Shetland in 1769 noted: 'A dry scaly eruption sometimes covers the whole body, while the hairs drop off the eye-brows. The people dread this distemper so much, that to secure themselves from infection, as soon as it begins to appear, the Patient is removed to a solitary hut in which he is confined for life, unless the disorder chances to give way. The neighbouring inhabitants by turns supply the wretch with provisions laid down at the door of his hut. In Unst I saw one of these miserable Patients who had been exiled from society for several months, but was afterwards removed to the Royal Infirmary of Edinburgh from which, after six months he was dismissed at his own desire, his complaints being much relieved. No person in the ship that carried him to Leith, no person in the Royal Infirmary was infected, so that the contagious nature of the disease is very doubtful. It may, however, be very proper to prevent the person affected with so loathsome a distemper from sleeping with a sound person and from marrying, but to confine him to a dirty, solitary Hovel is at once superfluous caution and the utmost cruelty. . . . The Patient whose case gave occasion to these remarks was most relieved by a solution of Corrosive Sublimate and a decoction of the woods. The first is a remedy so active and dangerous that it never ought to be employed except under the inspection of a skilful Practitioner. The decoction is safer and more manageable. It is composed of the shavings of Gulacum, the wood of Sassafras, and the roots of Liquorice. The roots of Sarsaparilla may also be employed for the same purpose. A light, thin diet, together with whey, barley-water or butter-milk ought to be employed during the cure.' The description fits well with a case of advanced lepromatous leprosy.

The last recorded Shetland leper died in 1798, although endemic leprosy still persists in Iceland. There are traditions of the importation of leprosy into the western coasts of Norway (especially around Bergen) by Vikings returning from the British Isles. There are now only three leprosy patients remaining in Norway from a considerable epidemic a century ago.

Older writers frequently commented on the longevity of Shetlanders. It is likely that a demographic trait of this nature might have been more characteristic of a crofting community than any particular disease (except inherited ones). In 1862, Cowie calculated that in Shetland the male death rate between 20 and 70 years of age was 51.2% compared with 90% in Scotland as a whole; in Shetland one fifth of the adult population survived to over 80 compared with one thirteenth in Scotland. Edmondston noted that women usually lived longer than men, and preserved their faculties better, 'It may be from having been less exposed to excessive and desultory labour'. The *Statistical Accounts* (1791, 1841) describe a Fetlar man who married in his 100th year and lived until he was 140; of another who died at 120, and a woman at 105; a woman of 98 who died in the house in which she was born, and had only slept two nights out of it; a seaman who received his discharge in his 96th year. Cowie was surprised to find that children were frequently born to women up to 50 years of age, and that menstruation continued up to 55 years. In the 1851 Census, the proportion of females aged 70 years or more was 10% higher in Shetland that in Scotland generally, while in 1951 the excess was even more marked. In 1761 6.6% of the population was over 75, and 1.3% was over 85; women outnumbered men 2:1 among the over 75s. In Scotland as a whole, only 4.2% of the total population was over 75, and 0.7% over 85. Modern figures are likely to be affected by emigration, and the relative life-span of Shetlanders and neighbouring peoples cannot be established without much more detailed demographic study.

References for Chapter 3
(full citations are given in the Bibliography, p. 353)

General
Baldwin, 1978; Balneaves, 1977; Barclay, 1965; Berry & Muir, 1975; Brand, 1701; Coull, 1967; Edmonston, 1809; Fenton, 1978; Goodlad, 1971; Heineberg, 1972; Hibbert, 1822; Nicolson, 1978; O'Dell, 1939; Sandison, 1968; Smith, 1977; Thomson, 1970; Venables, 1952, 1956.

Early history and colonization
Brøgger, 1929; Calder, 1956; Childe, 1946; Daniel, 1941; Donaldson, 1958, 1969; Goudie, 1904; Hamilton, 1956, 1962, 1968; Jakobsen, 1928, 1936; Lacaille, 1954; Laing, 1974; Shetelig, 1940; Small, 1967-8, 1968, 1969; Small, Thomas & Wilson, 1973; Stewart, 1954, 1965; Taylor, 1955; Toyne, 1948; Wainwright, 1962a,b.

Inherited characteristics and relationships
A. C. Berry, 1974; R. J. Berry, 1968, 1972a, 1974; Bjarnason, Bjarnason, Edwards, Fridriksson, Magnusson, Mourant & Tills, 1973; Boyce, Holdsworth & Brothwell,

1973; Brown, 1965; Cummins & Midlo, 1943; Donegani, Dungal, Ikin & Mourant, 1950; Fisher & Taylor, 1940; Hartmann & Lundevall, 1944; Mohr, 1951–52; Persson, 1969; Romanus, 1965; Tulinus, 1965; Welch, Barry, Dodd, Griffiths, Huntsman, Jenkins, Lincoln, McCathie, Mears & Parr, 1973; Welch & Mears 1972.

Disease

Acheson, 1965; Allison, 1963; Baldwin, Innes, Miller, Sharp & Dorricott, 1965; Benediktsson & Bjarnson, 1959; Berry, 1969*b*, Cowie, 1871; Cumming, 1968; Dungal, 1961; Ferguson, 1960; Field, 1973; Fog & Hyllested, 1966; Hall, Robertson, Dorricott, Olley & Millar, 1973; Howe, 1963; Innes, Kidd & Ross, 1968; Kurtzke, 1966; Ross, Innes & Kidd, 1967; Sutherland, 1956.

CHAPTER 4

VEGETATION

W H A T features of the Shetland landscape, represented by its cover of plants, are most striking on one's first visit from the South? Impressions will, of course, vary, but only the very unobservant will fail to mark the bright green of sea pastures, the small, often brilliant, patches of summer flowers here and there amidst the ubiquitous moorland, and the lack of trees in the natural and semi-natural vegetation. Together these form a memorable picture interrupted only by limited areas of cultivation and very few planted woods.

Awareness of Shetland's position in the North Atlantic and its surface geology (p. 55) may be enough to persuade our visitor that the lack of trees and predominance of moorland are the direct results of a cool climate and, away from the coast itself, of mainly poor soils. Now it is true that geographical position and geology have always exerted powerful influences on the vegetation, but over large parts of Shetland these factors have been rivalled for over 5000 years by man's influence, principally through his grazing animals. After outlining the plant communities this chapter discusses some of the important and perhaps surprising effects of man on Shetland's vegetation, including the rarity of many species which are common in the United Kingdom generally.

The flowering plants of Shetland have been studied by naturalists for over 100 years, from George Low's observations of 1774 to the current flora of Richard Palmer and Walter Scott which provides information on the distribution within the islands of about 600 species of flowering plants, ferns and their allies. However the first paper on the vegetation proper was published as recently as 1921 by W. R. Price; subsequent studies, including much otherwise unpublished work, are summarized in *Shetland's Living Landscape: a Study in Island Plant Ecology* by D. H. N. Spence (author of this chapter). That book contains a fuller account of soils and their development and of the vegetation than is possible here; it also has comprehensive tables of the composition of all the more important plant communities, grazed and ungrazed. These tables form the background to the present chapter and provide the detailed evidence, along with calendar-dated pollen diagrams by J. Johansen, for the assertion that Shetland's present plant cover is largely man-made.

ENVIRONMENTAL FACTORS

Climate is discussed earlier in the book (Chapter 1). Shetland's growing season at sea level is the same as that at Dalwhinnie (altitude 1200 ft) in the

Central Highlands of Scotland; an altitude of 1000 ft in Shetland has the same summer temperature as 2500 ft in the Central Highlands. Moreover Shetland is very windy: the summit of Sandness Hill (817 ft) has 80% of the mean annual windspeed at the top of Ben Nevis (4400 ft); on Ronas Hill (1475 ft) this annual windspeed is probably exceeded. Strong winter winds combine with an absence of prolonged snow cover in Shetland; since the air can be heavily salt laden, wind can damage plants at any time of the year.

Strictly maritime vegetation, however, which is made up of plants that can tolerate regular soaking by salt, is confined to small salt marshes, shingle beaches, the seaward face of sand dunes, and parts of sea banks and cliffs on the outer coast. Agriculturally the short growing season and exposure to wind and salt favour stock rearing, rather than arable farming. Most of Shetland below 500 ft in relatively sheltered valleys or below 250 ft on summit ridges has a submontane climate and possesses, *inter alia*, submontane heath, tall meadow and scrub, although the latter two community-types are now very scarce. Shetland's climate above the altitudes mentioned is subarctic-oceanic and supports some of the appropriate vegetation types.

SHETLAND SOILS

Within the constraints of climate and in the absence of practices associated with settled agriculture, *soils* determine the potential of a site for plant growth through their capacity to supply nutrients; the nature of the soils themselves in these conditions is based on surface geology, particularly the degree of drainage and the availability of calcium. In the outline that follows, well-drained Shetland soils are described first, then poorly-drained ones. The grouping of plant communities used is based on soil types, and the typical vegetation cover of each soil is mentioned.

On granite and serpentine there are extensive *debris soils*, composed of small fragments of rock which form a flat and often unstable surface. This is a subarctic, mountain-tundra soil which supports fellfield (areas with sparse plant cover) and *Rhacomitrium* (Hair Moss) heath; both communities frequently include many arctic and subarctic plants. On parts of limestone, serpentine and some sandstone outcrops there are *brown soils* (and a related sandy loam on links behind calcareous sand-dunes). However these soils are almost always cultivated in Shetland and comprise the main agricultural areas – the Vale of Tingwall, Weisdale, Whiteness and Dunrossness, along with parts of Baltasound, Melby, Reawick, Breckin, Catfirth etc. Even without cultivation, brown soils have good mixing by earthworms of their organic matter (humus) and inorganic matter. All casting earthworms have a positive requirement for calcium and such soils are therefore intrinsically fertile. In their 'unimproved' state, these soils at present mainly support grazed, species-rich grass heaths or grassland. The very few examples of ungrazed tall grassland and tall meadow on this soil type are enough to confirm the considerable growth potential its natural fertility would suggest.

The last soil of the well-drained group is *podsol*, derived from rocks low in calcium. A surface layer of organic matter or raw humus up to nine inches deep overlies the mineral soil rather than being mixed up with it; earthworms are absent. Generally these soils support grazed and/or burnt heather-moor and appear to be of low growth potential but this soil in rare ungrazed, unburnt places, can support tall vegetation of greater woodrush and buckler fern, with scattered scrub.

The remaining soils consist largely of *peat* and all have more or less impeded drainage. Peat is composed of partly decayed plant remains and their completely decayed residues; it builds up when lack of air discourages most of the soil invertebrates and micro-organisms that mineralize organic matter. This accumulation of decaying plants is hastened, again through effects on mineralizing organisms, by low nutrient supply and low temperature. Peat on hill tops and slopes began to develop about 4000 years ago as a result of soil deterioration, itself caused by a worsening climate and, possibly, mismanagement of hill land. The peat which covers so much of Shetland is called *blanket bog* because on hard rocks like gneiss and mica-schist it drapes all but the steepest and most unstable slopes.

Valleys contain two types of waterlogged peats, depending on the quality of nutrients reaching the soil surface: *nutrient-rich fens* or mires occur in limestone areas, while those in valleys receiving drainage off blanket peat are *nutrient-poor*. Blanket bog and nutrient-poor valley peats are soils of low growth potential and bear the commonest vegetation in Shetland, mixtures dominated by mat grass, heath rush, cotton grass, deer sedge and heather with prominent *Rhacomitrium*. Nutrient-rich fens are usually heavily grazed but a few ungrazed examples of tall fens and meadows exist to indicate the far greater growth potential of such sites.

Any attempt to understand Shetland's vegetation must start with the observation that for many centuries it has been stock-rearing country. Grazing and burning of hill land dates from 5300 years ago when stock-rearing settlers reached the islands, and still persists on the same land. Iron Age and Norse settlers were also stock rearers, and even to this day Shetland carries more sheep than the much larger former county of Caithness.

In addition to the raising of sheep, cattle and ponies and, until the last century, swine, hill land has been used since the Iron Age to provide peat for fuel. It also provided topsoil or turf for the infield or inbye until the last century (often being mixed with winter manure from the cow byre). Scattalds or common grazings originally laid out by the Norse settlers 1100 years ago have borne the brunt of all these activities. Turf scalping is responsible for the bare state of the hill land on Papa Stour and may also account in part for the thin soil cover on the areas around many townships, *e.g.* Muness in Unst. Failure to replace the top sod with its vegetated cover after removing the peat beneath may account for the bare, stony areas so commonly found in cut-over blanket bog (as at Staneydale in the West Mainland). Road-side areas with a similar appearance are usually the result of road widening and back-spreading of subsoil and stone, without attempts at revegetating.

Between 1957 and 1970, over 8000 acres of apportioned scattald were improved with funds allocated by the government for the reclamation of hill land. Surface reseeding with (for example) clover – rye grass mixtures, together with fertilizer and enclosure has created permanent pasture on blanket bog and degraded wet heath. Already reclaimed areas spread over large tracts of former moor in the South Mainland, with smaller enclosures in other parts. The other recent 'improvement' in the plant cover has been less widespread, although often just as successful: the creation of shelter belts by the Forestry Commission and by private individuals. Those at Sullom Voe and, particularly, upper Kergord show that remarkable growth can be achieved provided there is total protection from sheep and partial protection from the wind. On a wide enough scale, of course, such plantations might eventually shelter considerable numbers of stock in severe weather. A strong case can be made for an increase in shelter belts, especially if they consist of native Shetland trees and shrubs.

THE VEGETATION

The plant communities so far mentioned are predominantly those of grazed coast and hill land. However on both well drained and waterlogged sites, there are scattered fragments of ungrazed vegetation composed of species quite different from their counterparts on grazed sites. Land use and not soil accounts primarily for these differences. In addition, the enclosed land within townships often contains patches of marshy or drier ground which is un-cultivated, although commonly cut for hay. There are also ungrazed ditches between fields or alongside roads, including the road banks themselves. All these sites frequently bear tall grasses and herbs, including many uncommon Shetland plants, in what is really rich fen or tall herb meadow; they are described below. Furthermore, soils and vegetation generally form a mosaic on the hills which may, in some areas like that on the serpentines and metagabbro south of Baltasound in Unst, become complex and consist of five or six quite distinct types of vegetation.

In the following descriptions, plant communities are identified by one or two dominant species, using botanical names* which are not italicised, or if the plant community is common and known elsewhere, English names.

* English and botanical names of all higher plants follow Palmer & Scott (1969), *Check-list of Flowering Plants and Ferns of the Shetland Islands*. For flowering plants this list closely resembles names used in W. Keble Martin's *Concise British Flora in Colour* (Revised edition, 1969). Fern descriptions and keys, and fuller accounts of the species of flowering plants, are given in the standard work, Clapham, Tutin and Warburg (1969), *The Flora of the British Isles*. The Shetland flora contains a large number of subspecies (see Table 23).

Description is based on selected, uniform patches or stands of vegetation; sample areas covered 1 sq. metre in all but the most closely grazed swards where the sample area was 0.1 sq. metre.

Maritime plant communities

Maritime crevices. Lichens, dominated by the yellow-orange *Xanthoria parietina*, form a zone at the base of rocky cliffs and on rocky shores above the high tide mark. Crevices and patches of mineral soil on sea cliffs exposed to fairly continuous salt spray are colonized by thrift (*Armeria maritima*) and the dark coloured moss *Grimmia maritima*. Sea plantain (*Plantago maritima*), red fescue (*Festuca rubra*), and sea campion (*Silene vulgaris* ssp. *maritima*) are also common. Lovage (*Ligusticum scoticum*), Northern salt-marsh grass (*Puccinella maritima*), kidney vetch (*Anthyllis vulneraria*) and sea spurrey (*Spergularia maritima*) are typical here with, less frequently, moss campion (*Silene acaulis*) and roseroot (*Rhodiola rosea*). This open community grades beyond cliff tops and on sheltered grazed ledges into *Plantago maritima* sward or, on ungrazed but still rather exposed slopes, into a continuous sward of red fescue.

Coastal scree. This consists of gravel slides on crumbling cliffs, and is unstable, exposed to salt spray and often mineral rich, with or without the addition of guano from sea bird colonies. Typical species are sea campion, scurvey grass (*Cochlearia officinalis*), thrift, sea plantain, sea pearlwort (*Sagina maritima*), buck's-horn plantain (*Plantago coronopus*) and scentless mayweed (*Tripleurospermum maritimum*). Scentless mayweed, scurvy grass, nettle (*Urtica dioica*), curled dock (*Rumex crispus*) and mouse-ear chickweed (*Cerastium glomeratum*) are common on scree below sea-bird nests or roosts, and many also grow on shingle beaches; most are capable of rapid growth and appear to have high phosphorus and nitrogen needs.

Shingle beaches. Plants colonize shingle beaches that occur at the head of many voes and their roots are established in the remains of seaweed beneath a stony or pebbly surface. On sand and shingle foreshores characteristic species are the annuals, sea rocket (*Cakile maritima*), Babington's orache (*Atriplex glabriuscula*) and common orache (*A. patula*); and the perennial curled dock (*Rumex crispus*) and sea purslane (*Honckenya peploides*). Oyster plant (*Mertensia maritima*) survives precariously in a few places. Orache may extend as far as the shingle crest where it is accompanied by scentless mayweed, sow thistle (*Sonchus asper*), spear thistle (*Cirsium vulgare*), curled dock, bladder campion, chickweed (*Stellaria media*) and, notably, silverweed (*Potentilla anserina*). Goosegrass (*Galium aparine*) is frequent, along with field milk-thistle (*Sonchus arvensis*) while butter dock (*Rumex longifolius*) and rayless mayweed (*Matricaria matricarioides*) are occasional. A shingle ridge at Boddam supports almost the only wild population of herb robert (*Geranium robertianum*) in Shetland. Taking the list of shingle plants as a whole, many of them are species well-known as weeds in fields and gardens, another set of often nutrient-rich habitats which are colonized by these opportunist plants.

Salt marshes. These are confined to small areas at the head of some sheltered voes like Baltasound or Whiteness or the edges of brackish lochs like Strom Loch. Closed swards of marshes nearest the sea are dominated by common salt-marsh grass (*Puccinella maritima*) and greater sea spurrey (*Spergularia media*). Salt-mud rush (*Juncus geradi*) dominates in swards above the Puccinella zone with sea milkwort (*Glaux maritima*) and sea arrow-grass (*Triglochin maritima*). Sea aster (*Aster tripolium*), sea-blite (*Sueda maritima*) and sea grass (*Zostera marina*) are all rare.

Sand dunes. These are typified by the Quendale dunes, the most extensive in Shetland, which are composed of calcareous shell sand. Here a *foreshore* with occasional sea rocket is backed by a mobile dune of marram grass (*Ammophila arenaria*) which extends to 20 ft above sea level. The dune then drops over a distance of 300 ft to a dune slack about 5 ft above sea level, flooded in winter. Sandy hillocks extend from this slack inland to the Loch of Hillwell and to the top of Ward Hill (267 ft) about three-quarters of a mile from Quendale Bay. There is a *mobile dune* nominated by scattered plants of *Ammophila* and a few species such as dandelion (*Taraxacum officinale*), orache, creeping thistle (*Cirsium arvense*), angelica (*Angelica sylvestris*) and sow thistle; this gives about two species per square foot. A few yards from the dune ridge, red fescue and creeping clover (*Trifolium repens*) become constant and there are six species per square foot in this *early fixed dune*. In the *late fixed dune*, which develops landwards, mosses predominate (notably *Mnium undulatum* or *Rhytidiadelphus triquetrus*), and plant cover rises to 85 per cent or even 100 per cent. Marram is now replaced as the most common species by red fescue, and the mean number of species increases to 11 per square foot. Four further mosses are common, along with ten new herbs, including self-heal (*Prunella vulgaris*), Foula eyebright (*Euphrasia foulaensis*) and thyme (*Thymus drucei*). Festuca-Mnium or Festuca-Rhytidiadelphus dominates on the landward side of sand hillocks from the slack area to the summit of Ward Hill. *Dune pasture* is dominated by red fescue and bent (*Agrostis* ssp.). This contains a total of 40 species and occupies the seaward side of sand hillocks from the slacks inland. It is similar to the nutrient-rich sward found on Spiggie links or limestone. The dune slack pasture resembles that on grazed fens on limestone, notably in sharing the carmine-flowered orchid (*Dactylorhiza incarnata* ssp. *coccinea*). The dunes which Quendale most resembles outside Shetland seem to be those of Luskentyre in Harris and Balnakeil in Sutherland, in both of which creeping clover typifies the early fixed stage and *Mnium* and *Rhytidiadelphus* the late-fixed stage. These localities share the strong winds to which Quendale is exposed.

Norwick, Spiggie and St Ninian's Isle in the South Mainland, West Sandwick in Yell, and Burrafirth in Unst have smaller dunes with similar mobile and early-fixed stages, although lyme grass (*Elymus arenarius*) replaces marram in some of them. In every case there is a fairly abrupt transition to dune pasture which is not confined to sand hillocks as in Quendale but covers

instead notably level links. Rabbits are common and contribute to overgrazing and often severe erosion in several dune systems. Regrettably most of the
West Sandwick links had been removed by sand extraction by 1978.

Vegetation of mainly inorganic soils

Inland scree is rare in Shetland but supports broad buckler fern (*Dryopteris
dilatata*) and black spleenwort (*Asplenium adiantum-nigrum*) and also, in North
Roe, oak fern (*Carpogymnia dryopteris*), beech fern (*Thelypteris phegopteris*) and
mountain fern (*T. limbosperma*). Buckler fern, common and polypody
(*Polypodium vulgare*) occur among serpentine boulders on the Heogs in Unst.
Serpentine and limestone crevices have occasional green spleenwort (*A. viride*),
brittle bladder fern (*Cystopteris fragilis*) maidenhair spleenwort (*A. trichomanes*)
and hoary whitlow grass (*Draba incana*).

Fellfield and Rhacomitrium-heath

Debris is composed of small angular stones about 2 cm in diameter and
overlies finer material. It occurs in two characteristic situations. In the first,
the debris is poorly colonized, mainly by flowering plants. This occurs particularly in sites like ridges or summits that are snow-free in winter. It is liable to
'frost-heaving' and is therefore unstable. Such an open community is known
as *fellfield*; it is widespread in Faroe. It is commonest in Shetland on the granite
of North Roe (Ronas Hill in particular), and the dunite-serpentine of Unst;
small patches occur on Sandness Hill, the Sneug on Foula and some granitic
cliff tops in south-west Mainland. In the second situation the debris becomes
colonized by woolly hair moss (*Rhacomitrium lanuginosum*), with a thin black
layer of organic matter between the base of the moss mat and the debris
surface. This Rhacomitrium-heath forms a mosaic with fellfield on Ronas Hill
and the more exposed parts of North Roe and alone covers a summit plateau
like the metagabbro of Sobul, Unst. Rhacomitrium-heath is absent from
serpentine although the moss species is a common subordinate; it forms large
tussocks in damp-flush areas on that rock.

Festuca-Juncus trifidus fellfield and Rhacomitrium-heath

Above 220 ft on the north-west shoulder of Ronas Hill and at higher altitudes
in other directions fellfield predominates. Over 1000 ft viviparous fescue
(*Festuca vivipara*) and three-leaved rush (*Juncus trifidus*) typify fellfield and are
accompanied in the granite gravel by sea plantain, least willow (*Salix heb-
acea*), heath bedstraw (*Galium saxatile*), thyme, and the only Shetland plants of
spiked mountain woodrush (*Luzula spicata*) and alpine saussurea (*Saussurea
alpina*). Least willow also occurs in the fellfield on the Sneug of Foula and

Sandness Hill, along with some plants of filmy fern (*Hymenophyllum wilsonii*).

Rhacomitrium-heath with bell-heather (*Erica cinerea*) and rigid sedge (*Carex rigida*) occurs on Sobul between 300 ft and the summit at 368 ft. The undulating granite of North Roe also has Rhacomitrium-heath, here with occasional red bearberry (*Arctostaphylos uva-ursi*); as exposure increases on upper slopes, fellfield develops interspersed with crescents of *Rhacomitrium* and heather (*Calluna vulgaris*) (as described 60 years ago by Crampton in the mountains of Caithness). Rhacomitrium-heath reaches its highest Shetland altitudes on Ronas Hill, being confined near the summit to 'wind shadows' behind granite boulders. Beside rigid sedge, alpine club-moss (*Diphasium alpinum*) and the lichen *Cladonia uncialis*, there are several ericoid species: red bearberry, alpine bearberry (*Arctous alpinus*), prostrate azalea (*Loiseleuria procumbens*) and five species of *Vaccinium* and *Erica*. This heath is terraced, typical of the solifluction (or soil-movement) which is induced on moderate, exposed slopes by thawing and freezing – a subarctic-oceanic phenomenon.

Arenaria norvegica – Cardaminopsis fellfield

Many species of granite and sandstone fellfield are also common on the poorly colonized serpentine debris: sea plantain, thyme, and species of fescue and bent. The best-known area is that on the dunite Keen of Hamar on Unst where Thomas Edmonston of Buness found Norwegian sandwort (*Arenaria norvegica*) and the Shetland mouse-ear chickweed (*Cerastium arcticum* ssp. *edmondstonii*) more than 130 years ago. It is the largest area of fellfield in Unst and of this serpentine habitat in the United Kingdom.

In one kind of fellfield, sparse plant cover is probably maintained (as on Ronas Hill) by exposure and soil instability. Small areas like this occur all over the Unst serpentine. The Keen of Hamar represents a second kind where debris always lies around weathering bedrock, and a high rate of weathering, as well as nutrient imbalance (see below), may also be involved.

It is only on fellfield like Hamar that a rich assemblage of species occurs in Shetland. In addition to Norwegian sandwort and Shetland chickweed there are mountain rockcress (*Cardaminopsis petraea*) and alpine scurvy grass (*Cochlearia pyrenaica*); apart from sea cliffs these are the only serpentine habitats in Unst of thrift, moss campion and stone bramble (*Rubus saxatilis*). Many of these plants have an arctic or subarctic distribution and their joint occurrence at such a low altitude is unique in the British Isles.

As Hamar fellfield has probably persisted since the retreat of the last ice sheets: what has stopped grass-heath or other 'closed' vegetation from invading it? Compared with well-covered parts of the serpentine of Unst, the Hamar and other areas of similar debris show nutrient imbalance; there is an excess of nickel and chromium which can be toxic to plants, much magnesium and little calcium (which is the reverse of the usual situation) and low levels of nitrogen, potassium and phosphorus. Experimental evidence points to phosphorus deficiency as a main causal factor, with most improvement in natural plant cover where nitrogen and potassium are added. This is also shown by the successful pasture re-seeding that followed the application of these three nutrients over an extensive area of the Keen.

Vegetation of somewhat organic, usually well-drained soils

Herb-rich grazed heath (serpentine, limestone and metagabbro)

The Unst serpentine heath contains 36 species of flowering plant, fern and club moss and 12 of these occur in almost every sample. There are also at least 15 species of moss and liverwort. Purging flax (*Linum catharticum*), slender St John's wort (*Hypericum pulchrum*), violet (*Viola riviniana* and some *V. canina*), heath orchid (*Dactylorhiza maculata* ssp. *ericetorum*), tormentil (*Potentilla erecta*) and thyme all flower abundantly in July and August. The milkworts (*Polygala vulgaris* and *P. serpyllifolia*) show a range of flower colours, and bird's-foot trefoil (*Lotus corniculatus*) is a brilliant yellow. Calluna-Erica cinerea heath is common on the Unst metagabbro, except over 300 ft where Rhacomitrium-heath dominates, and in the south-west where an impoverished wet-heath occurs over a large area. The dry heath contains thyme, violet, flea sedge (*Carex pulicaris*) and alpine meadow-rue (*Thalictrum alpinum*) as well as cross-leaved heath (*Erica tetralix*), bog asphodel (*Narthecium ossifragum*) and mat grass (*Nardus stricta*), so it is intermediate between heaths on base-rich soils and those found on rocks producing a more acid soil.

Herb-rich bent-fescue (Agrostis – Festuca) grassland

The bent-fescue grassland of serpentine on Unst, Fetlar and Hoo Fell and of the Weisdale and Whiteness limestone consists of the same grazed, herb-rich plant community. Glaucous sedge (*Carex flacca*) is a co-dominant in Unst and abundant at the other sites. Most species occur in grass heath but notable additional species are kidney vetch, field gentian (*Gentianella campestris*), frog orchid (*Coeloglossum viride*) and moonwort (*Botrychium lunaria*), while moss campion is abundant on out-cropping rocks on Whiteness grassland. Crested dog's-tail (*Cynosurus cristatus*) is common in some limestone pastures while both these and Hoo Fell serpentine also support abundant primrose (*Primula vulgaris*) and lady's bedstraw (*Galium verum*); damper areas contain in addition lesser celandine (*Ranunculus ficaria*). Infrequent arctic-alpine species like alpine meadow-rue, alpine bistort (*Polygonum viviparum*), and moss campion indicate the submontane affinities of this grassland. Much of the grassland on serpentine at least has probably been derived by grazing from heath but there are also one or two areas of extant tall grassland.

Behind sand dunes at Spiggie, Norwick, Burrafirth, West Sandwick, etc. there are rather level links, similar to the machair of the Gaelic-speaking parts of Scotland. They contain most of the species already mentioned, along with grass of Parnassus (*Parnassia palustris*) and eyebright (as *Euphrasia arctica*) at Spiggie, sheep's-bit scabious (*Jasione montana*), thrift and meadow orchid (*Dactylorhiza incarnata*); moss campion is, however, missing.

Grazed coastal grassland

The remaining grasslands or swards are coastal, grazed by rabbits and/or sheep and provide the typical green pastures of cliff tops, sea banks and many offshore holms. One type is dominated by red fescue, another by sea plantain but they merge into one another. True coastal swards lack mat grass (*Nardus stricta*) and contain thrift, buck's-horn plantain and, often abundantly, spring squill (*Scilla verna*) (although this species also occurs in base-rich grassland and even on serpentine debris). Meadow grass (*Poa subcaerulea*) and Yorkshire fog (*Holcus lanatus*) are common, along with about 15 other species such as mouse-ear (*Cerastium diffusum* and *C. glomeratum*), ribwort (*Plantago lanceolata*), pearl-wort (*Sagina procumbens*) and ragged robin (*Lychnis floscuculi*). The sward is always close-cropped, often only an inch or so high.

The plantain swards may be a result of heavy grazing of fescue pasture; excluding sheep and rabbits rapidly converts a plantain-thrift sward to a fescue-meadow grass sward, because the new dominants overshadow the original ones. Thrift-sea plantain open communities occupy unstable ground to seaward of the plantain-fescue swards, often on the tops of stacks, etc where there are puffin burrows but no rabbits or sheep.

Tall grassland and tall herb meadow

False oat-grass (*Arrhenerathum elatius*) is a conspicuous dominant of this grass-land which is absent from ungrazed sites; it occurs in a few places on the Whiteness limestone, and in one place on the Unst serpentine. It is typical of limestone meadows in northern Britain. Reedgrass (*Phalaris arundinacea*) often accompanies oat-grass while ungrazed ledges and banks sometimes carry tufted hair-grass (*Deschampsia cespitosa*). Ungrazed grassland on nutrient-rich soils of cliff ledges, roadside and field edges and sea-banks is usually domi-nated by red fescue, sometimes by viviparous fescue. Common associates are bird's-foot trefoil, Shetland campion (*Silene rubra* ssp. *zetlandicum*), tufted vetch (*Vicia cracca*), bush vetch (*V. sepium*) meadow vetchling (*Lathyrus pra-tensis*), and angelica, often over three feet high. All these species flower freely in these conditions. Cow parsnip (*Heracleum spondylium*), sheep's-bit and lady's bedstraw also occur, tall in contrast to their dwarf forms in links' pastures. With occasional rose-root and Scots lovage on sea-cliffs, this composite list represents tall grassland and herb meadow of nutrient-rich soils. On damper sites they grade into mowing meadow cut annually for hay, and fen, with yellow flag (*Iris pseudacorus*) and meadowsweet (*Filipendula ulmaria*).

Heath and grassland of siliceous podsols (and some dry peat of steep slopes)
Grazed Calluna-Erica cinerea *with hypnoid mosses*

On some well-drained sandstones and, locally, on steep, free-draining peats and other low-calcium rocks is another 'dry' heath which differs from the herb-rich type in having a prominent moss-mat of *Hypnum*-like, or hypnoid species (particularly *Pleurozium schreberi*) and only about half the number of flowering plants and ferns. Thyme, purging flax, alpine meadow-rue and common violet are missing, for example, but slender St John's wort, cat's-foot (*Antennaria dioica*) pill-headed sedge (*Carex pilulifera*) and eyebright (*Euphrasia micrantha*) still occur whilst lesser twayblade (*Listera cordata*) is locally frequent.

Ungrazed Luzula–Dryopteris *with scattered scrub*

Greater woodrush (*Luzula sylvatica*) and broad buckler fern (*Dryopteris dilatata*) often dominate ungrazed ledges on siliceous rocks covered by thin raw humus. Species which occur in every site include common polypody (*Polypodium vulgare*), hard fern (*Blechnum spicant*), golden rod (*Solidago virgaurea*) and wavy hair-grass (*Deschampsia flexuosa*), while male fern (*Dryopteris filix-mas*) is occasional. The scattered shrub layer has prominent honeysuckle (*Lonicera periclymenum*) with dog rose (*Rosa canina*) and eared willow (*Salix aurita*); rowan (*Sorbus aucuparia*) and aspen (*Populus tremula*) are found on ledges in Ronas Voe, hazel (*Corylus avellana*) in a ravine in South Nesting. *Luzula*-dominated ledges occur on sea-cliffs or inland.

On ungrazed islands in freshwater lochs the peat slope which on moorland carries Calluna-Erica cinerea heath with hypnoid mosses, or is eroded and lacks plant cover, is dominated by dense greater woodrush and buckler fern, locally forming a field layer to rowan, eared willow or royal fern (*Osmunda regalis*); again polypody and wavy hair-grass are constant, rose and honeysuckle common.

Like tall grassland and herb meadow, this community type is fragmentary, but remarkably consistent in its make-up and bears witness to the soil and climatic potential for growth in the absence of grazing and burning.

VEGETATION OF LOCHS, SWAMPS, AND FENS OR MIRES

Aquatic vegetation occurs along a gradient from deep water to at least seasonally dry land. Under the best conditions a water depth gradient is accompanied by submerged, then floating-leaved and, finally, emergent vegetation. Swamps are sites where sedges, horsetails or reed-like grasses predominate and where the summer water table lies above the soil surface. Swamps lack a moss carpet but may have submerged bog-moss (*Sphagnum*) species. All vegetated sites which are flooded in winter but where in summer the water lies at or under the soil surface are called *fens*: a moss carpet is frequent. Nutrient supply and the presence of typical species differentiate rich fen from poor fen.

Shetland fens sometimes border cultivated ground and are mown annually as 'bog hay' or remain uncropped, but generally both fen and swamp are severely restricted by grazing. Floating-leaved and submerged plants are limited by strong wave action and rocky substrata. Since most freshwater lies in nutrient-poor drainage areas, low nutrient levels also restrict the performance of species but siliceous rocks with boulder clay (Grasswater) or agricultural ground (Loch Spiggie and Loch Asta), calcareous sand (Loch of Hillwell) and one of the lochans on the Whiteness limestone provide some nutrient rich water and sediments.

Submerged, floating-leaved and reedswamp vegetation

Peat pools: some appear to have no higher plant life but in others bladderwort (*Utricularia minor*) and floating bur-reed (*Sparganium angustifolium*) occur, or dense growths of submerged bog-moss as *Sphagnum subsecundum* var. *auriculatum* and occasional submerged plants of the bulbous rush (*Juncus bulbosus* var. *fluitans*).

Examples of rocky, ice-scoured lakes are Flatpunds Loch and Lunga Water. Floating-leaved and emergent plants are confined to several small inlets about 18 inches deep, which are isolated from exposed open water. These inlets have a floor of soft mud and carry reedswamp of common spike-rush (*Eleocharis palustris*) and marsh horsetail (*Equisetum fluviatile*), together with shoreweed (*Littorella uniflora*) and submerged bulbous rush; bogbean (*Menyanthes trifoliata*) is common, while white water lily (*Nymphaea alba*) is confined to a few sheltered but nutrient-poor localities in West Mainland. In the main lochs, the substratum is rocky with shoreweed, water lobelia (*Lobelia dortmanna*) and quillwort (*Isoetes lacustris*) in sparse pockets of gravel.

Improved nutrient status and smaller area allows better growth of floating-leaved and submerged plants. Thus Stanevatsoe Water has a dense stand of floating pondweed (*Potamogeton natans*) and floating bur-reed in three to six feet of water, along with various-leaved pondweed (*P. gramineus*). Grasswater has extensive stands of bulrush (*Schoenoplectus lacustris*) accompanied by submerged bulbous rush with beds of long-stalked pondweed (*Potamogeton praelongus*) beyond; in the south-west bay a grazed fen gives way to a Carex rostrata-Menyanthes swamp, then an underwater shoreweed 'meadow', with some bladderwort (*Utricularia vulgaris*) and, beyond it, bulrush. A lochan at West Burrafirth provides a rare example in Shetland of a reedswamp of common reed (*Phragmites australis*).

Loch Spiggie is a 'moderately rich' loch in nutrient terms, but has calcareous sands as well as the commoner brown muds. The whole of the shallow, sandy, northern end is occupied by an open Chara aspersa-Myriophyllum alterniflorum (stonewort-milfoil) community with frequent slender-leaved pondweed (*Potamogeton filiformis*), fennel-leaved pondweed (*P. pectinatus*) and seaside crowfoot (*Ranunculus baudotii*). This community type is common in shallow nutrient-rich or calcareous sediments in Scottish waters. At the sheltered southern end, draining a moderately rich fen, are three zones: Carex rostrata-Menyanthes, Equisetum fluviatile-Littorella and Potamogeton natans-Juncus bulbosus. Submerged vegetation in the loch comprises stands of various-leaved pondweed, Callitriche-Potamogeton pusillus (starwort-lesser pondweed), quillwort, the moss *Fontinalis antipyretica* and the stonewort (*Nitella flexilis*), to a vegetation limit at 12 feet below the surface.

There is only one marl lake, a lochan on the Whiteness limestone, which typically supports dense beds of common spike-rush, fennel-leaved pondweed and stonewort (*Chara* species) and one loch entirely on calcareous shell-sand, the Loch of Hillwell. It contains the only Shetland plants of spiked milfoil (*Myriophyllum spicatum*) and supports a dense, luxuriant swamp of bottle sedge and marsh horsetail. This shallow loch is undoubtedly enriched by its large bird populations.

Fens

Fens are influenced by ground water chemistry and by man's activities. In Shetland this means that, almost without exception, fens of uncultivated hill land are all heavily grazed while fens on reasonably nutrient-rich soils in townships are grazed, cut for hay or for sedge peat; ungrazed and unmown examples are very rare. What follows is an attempt to provide a composite picture from diverse fragments.

Ungrazed fens. Islands in freshwater lochs, poor in nutrients, provide most examples of ungrazed fen. Their shores are usually made of boulders or rock, covered to the water's edge with a layer of raw humus and roots, and bearing dense greater woodrush with meadowsweet and angelica, a luxuriant vegetation which contrasts with the sparse low plant cover of most loch shores. This 'boulder-fen' may not be strictly comparable with the usual fen of silted, peaty sites. On islands the latter are rare: one area on a Loch Clousta island supports the only willow-carr in Shetland and parts of four further islands on West Mainland lochs carry fens of dense royal fern, up to 18 inches tall. There are some examples, too, of moor grass (*Molinia caerulea*) fen, with bent, marsh marigold and creeping willow (*Salix repens*). In all, island fens contain 35 species of flowering plants.

A rare, extensive example of ungrazed rich (eutrophic) fen occurs at Gulberwick, dominated by marsh horsetail and yellow flag (*Iris pseudacorus*). Apart from the lack of common reed which occurs in a few other places, this tall vegetation contains at least 18 of the species which make up the many fen fragments in roadside ditches, etc at Tingwall, Whiteness, etc. A second good example occurs at Culswick. Iris-Caltha fen and meadows of marsh marigold and white bent (*Agrostis canina*) are mown or lightly grazed versions of the Gulberwick fen, sharing many of the potentially tall plants like ragged robin, marsh marigold, water mint (*Mentha aquatica*), monkey flower (*Mimulus guttatus*), spotted orchid (*Dactylorhiza maculata* ssp. *ericetorum* × *purpurella*), water forget-me-not (*Myosotis palustris* and *M. repens*), lady's smock (*Cardamine pratensis*) and angelica. Marshwort (*Apium inundatum*), mare's tail (*Hippuris vulgaris*), marsh speedwell (*Veronica anagallis-aquatica*) and watercress (*Nasturtium officinale*) are all rare in Shetland fens but marsh ragwort (*Senecio aquatilis*) is common in fen and drier pastures. These fens are amongst the most colourful plant communities in summer.

Grazed fen. On limestone and serpentine, open flushes are occupied by Schoenus nigricans-Molinia (black bog-rush – moor grass), having prominent thrift and yellow sedge (*Carex lepidocarpas*); this often grades into a mire of Carex dioica – Eleocharis quinqueflora (dioecious sedge – few flowered spike-rush). Both may be replaced in less rich sites by Carex panicea – C. demissa mire in which brown mosses, particularly *Drepanocladus revolvens* and *Scorpidium scorpioides*, become less abundant.

The commonest grazed fen is dominated by common sedge (*Carex nigra*), jointed rush (*Juncus articulatus*) and moor grass: marsh thistle (*Cirsium palustre*) is frequent and there are large clumps of yellow flag or soft rush (*Juncus effusus*). Peaty drainage channels are often full of bogmoss with bog pondweed (*Sphagnum subsecundum, Potamogeton polygonifolius*), lesser spearwort (*Ranunculus flammula*) and bulbous rush. These channels merge into the poorest fens, Sphagnum moss mires with cotton grass (*Eriophorum angustifolium*), round-leaved sundew (*Drosera rotundifolia*) and up to 16 other associated species, mainly mosses and liverworts which are typical of wetter blanket bog.

Vegetation of blanket bog and related habitats

The commonest vegetation in Shetland is that growing on the peat of blanket bog or on soils derived from it. Blanket bog covers most of Yell, the gneisses and mica-schists of Unst and a large part of the west and north-east of Mainland. It has been much cut over for fuel and higher areas show erosion. Many parts like the Muness phyllites bear thin peat on water-logged soil, which is the remains of former deep peat removed for fuel. Almost always the substitute plant cover is dominated by mat grass and heath rush.

The least common community type of peat, Vaccinium-Empetrum, is confined to parts of the summits of Saxavord, Hermaness, Sandness Hill and Fitful Head. Blaeberry (*Vaccinium myrtillus*) is dominant, crowberry sub-dominant, bog whortleberry (*Vaccinium uliginosum*) and greater woodrush locally dominant (the only moorland type in which the latter species reaches this status). Trichophorum-Eriophorum is the other, and commoner, community type of high altitude, relatively undisturbed blanket bog on, for example, Weisdale Hill or Hermaness. It is dominated by deer grass (*Tri-*

chophorum caespitosum) and cotton grass in which *Rhacomitrium* is usually common, notably along the tops of eroded peat scarps; poorly grown heather is frequent but *Sphagnum* species only dominate in a few places on this undisturbed peat; it is more typical of bog pools and drainage channels. In a closely related community type of deep peat, heather codominates with cotton grass while deer grass and hare's-tail (*Eriophorum vaginatum*) are subordinate and crowberry (*Empetrum nigrum*) is constant. Cross-leaved heath (*Erica tetralix*) and bog asphodel are restricted to deep peats.

On naturally or artificially drained peat, on redistributed peat (eroded and spread on fresh ground by rainwash) or formerly cut-over and deeper peat, Nardus-Juncus grassland is the characteristic dominant. Mat grass (*Nardus stricta*) dominates and heath rush (*Juncus squarrosus*) is subordinate. In a quantitative study of this community type there were 33 species of flowering plant compared with 10 in the same number of samples of Calluna-Eriophorum. Species like tormentil and heath bedstraw are very common. (The upland examples in gullies on Ronas and Sandness Hills may, depending on the cryptograms, belong to a separate subarctic-oceanic type). An extreme example of its development on disturbed ground is provided by the Nardus-Juncus wet heath of thin humus on shallow, badly drained soils, typical of surfaces where peat has been almost entirely removed, and of some overgrazed scattalds and outfields – it is particularly widespread near townships on a range of acid, non-calcareous rocks. *Rhacomitrium* is frequent, along with heather and cross-leaved heath and other small plants, and total cover rarely reaches 100 per cent; bog asphodel, crowberry, moor grass and deer grass occur in about half the samples.

Deep peat occurs on many ungrazed islands in freshwater lochs. Most bear a greater woodrush – hair-grass (Luzula sylvatica-Deschampsia flexuosa) community; in one, Calluna-Empetrum heath had colonized the burnt remains of the community. On two other ungrazed islands, *Rhacomitrium* is co-dominant with heather and crowberry and, on one of them, dense stands of prostrate dwarf juniper (*Juniperus communis* ssp. *nana*). Common polypody, wavy hair-grass and tormentil are constant to all sites, and green-ribbed sedge (*Carex binervis*) is abundant, while hay rattle (*Rhinanthus minor*), golden rod and devil's bit scabious (*Succisa pratensis*) are frequent and flower freely. Bog whortleberry and red whortleberry (*Vaccinium vitis-idaea*) occur occasionally as do shrubs of rowan, dog-rose and honeysuckle.

THE SHAPING OF THE SHETLAND FLORA

This chapter sets out to give an outline description of Shetland vegetation in terms of the dominant species on the limited range of soil types present. The general description leads to questions ranging from the causes of the rarity of certain Shetland plants to the likely future for the vegetation.

To return to the point made at the start of this chapter: a first-time visitor is likely to be struck by the brilliance of the flowers he sees and, one may add, by the luxuriance of natural growth in many places. These features are characteristic over a wide range of rock type and habitat – but only in situations where there is freedom from grazing and trampling, and usually a moderate degree of shelter from wind or, at least, salt spray. The brilliance of flower colour in, for example, the Shetland red campion (*Silene dioica* spp. *zetlandicum*) or in Shetland populations of bush vetch (*Vicia sepium*), tufted vetch (*Vicia cracca*) and sheep's-bit (*Jasione montana*) is undoubtedly inherited (although the formal genetics have never been studied in these cases).

Part of the overall effect on the observer is probably due to the actual size of the flowers in these uncropped situations – in other words, the luxuriance of the plants generally. This is related to the fact that the products of net photosynthesis (what is left daily after the plant has breathed or respired), are kept within the system. These products are moved continually down to the roots and the dead leaves drop onto the soil surface in autumn where the well-aired soil organisms can convert a large crop for their own needs as well as releasing minerals from the dead plant material for re-use by plants next year.

How does this differ from the more usual Shetland moor or hill? Most of the hill land is occupied by various groupings of cotton grass, deer sedge, moor grass, heath rush, crowberry, heather and bell heather. It has been shown (in some cases in Shetland itself) that each of these species is encouraged in the long term by burning, grazing and trampling, although heather and bell heather are reduced by over-grazing in poorly drained places. Most of these moorland dominants have low rates of growth. The soils they cover are nutrient-poor and often trampled and badly drained, all factors discouraging the activities of soil organisms. Moreover hill land soils receive little or no nutrient return in the form of leaf litter. Even worse, this export of nutrients as hoof and horn from hill land coupled with much trampling has been going on for over 5000 years. Many of today's unproductive soils, especially near townships, are the end result of long term grazing.

Study of the species present in fragments of tall fen, grassland and scrub in Shetland shows that 15 species of fern and shrub or small tree have been confined by grazing and burning to ledges, islands and inaccessible fens, while 36 species of grass, woodrush and herb are almost totally restricted to ungrazed, lightly grazed or mown localities. While some of these places are on limestone or similar areas, most are not and their common feature, as may be inferred from what has been said above, is enrichment of the soil surface by litter or downslope drainage. The list includes every native shrub and tree in Shetland, all the taller ferns except bracken, all the taller grasses, greater woodrush, and all the larger herbs.

The correct conclusion from this is that Shetland's plant cover has largely been modified by man but, although the ungrazed fragments give the clue to most of Shetland's present-day vegetation, they do not by any means tell the whole story. All the ungrazed sites have at least a moderate degree of shelter so we must now look at vegetation where exposure may reasonably be regarded as the major factor – for a start, think of the vegetation on the comparatively remote summit plateau of Ronas Hill. Undoubtedly exposure coupled with low summer temperature accounts for the succession up the hill of dwarf shrub heath, then Rhacomitrium-heath and finally fellfield on the plateau itself. The same effect occurs on the lesser summits of Sandness Hill and the even lower granite ridges in North Roe.

Rhacomitrium-heath and fellfield are subarctic-oceanic kinds of vegetation characteristic of (for example) the Cairngorm plateau, so one result of the winds to which Shetland is subjected is the occurrence of these community types at their lowest altitudes in the United Kingdom. Where Rhacomitrium-heath and fellfield are rich in arctic species as on Ronas Hill or the Keen of Hamar, they are relics from Late Glacial times of the kind of vegetation that once covered Shetland. Exposure gradients are steep near the open sea and on the higher hills. Consequently micro-relief can create shelter on a small scale (as by a boulder on top of Ronas Hill) or on a lárger scale – consider the fact that dunes occur two-thirds of a mile from the open sea at Quendale and 250 ft above it, while planted trees can grow well at the same altitude in a sheltered inland valley like upper Kergord.

It is typical of all floras that most species are rare or uncommon and that such rarity has several causes. An outstanding cause of rarity is endemism which follows from total genetic isolation of a population for a long period of time. The best known endemic plant of Shetland is a mouse-ear chickweed, *Cerastium arcticum* ssp. *edmondstonii* which is confined to the fellfield of the Keen of Hamar. Visualize it as forming part of a plant community that once covered Shetland, just as similar vegetation occurs today in central Iceland; when the climate improved with the retreat of the ice, heath or grass-like vegetation eliminated fellfield except on places like Ronas Hill and the Keen of Hamar. In the latter area, nutrient imbalance or deficiency kept the cover sparse and, over some 10,000 years, allowed this arctic chickweed to evolve in geographical isolation, as a subspecies recognizably distinct from all other subspecies. Thrift on the Keen of Hamar fellfield is another species that has evolved a distinct physiological race in response to the unusual soil – although different-*looking* plants have not yet evolved. Thrift is not so isolated as the mouse-ear chickweed since thrift also occurs on serpentine in nearby grazed grassland and sea cliffs.

Another unusual race is the Shetland campion *(Silene dioica* ssp. *zetlandica)* but it is not a rarity in Shetland, and also occurs in Orkney and West Norway. A connection with the Norse settlers of the 9th century A.D. seems indicated and even today in Orkney and Shetland it rarely occurs much more than a mile from a human settlement.

In Shetland too there occur a very large number of endemic hawkweeds or *Hieracium* 'species', 60 at the last count; 'species' because hawkweeds reproduce apomictically, or without fertilisation of egg by pollen, *i.e.* sexual reproduction of the normal type. Perpetuation of individual differences by mutation and other means therefore occurs and a whole series of small populations of similar plants arises, many of these being very rare. As a group, hawkweeds are a showy feature of Shetland ledges. Another conspicuously flowered genus is *Euphrasia* which freely produces hybrids and hybrid swarms and, no doubt, some rare endemic 'species', although these have not been studied in Shetland.

On the grounds of their distribution in Shetland it appears that 36 species of shrub, tree, fern, herb and grass owe their present scarcity to man. The pollen record in the peat reinforces this conclusion for those species with recognizable remains; and their present-day distribution in the rest of the United Kingdom confirms it. The rarity of at least these 36 species is a result of land use, not climate.

Examples of the effect of climate are given by a set of species which are abundant over most but not all of the United Kingdom. Thus harebell (*Campanula rotundifolia*), herb robert and wood sorrel (*Oxalis acetosella*) each have only one or two localities in Shetland but they are also rare in Orkney and the Outer Hebrides and infrequent in north-west Scotland. This distribution implies limitation by cool summers. On the other hand, plants like mountain azalea and three-leaved rush, which are arctic-alpines, are confined to the higher parts of Ronas Hill, and this suggests their exclusion from regions with warmer summers because of growth habit and slower growth rates.

Another group includes alpine rock-cress and Norwegian sandwort. In the United Kingdom this group is largely or completely confined to the north-west Highlands and the islands and no species is ever common. Their growth forms and their apparent need for base-rich sites at low altitudes in this region seem to account for their scarcity. For instance the survival of Norwegian sandwort and alpine rock-cress on serpentine debris has probably had similar causes to the survival in Shetland of the arctic mouse-ear chickweed. Interestingly, however, neither rock-cress nor sandwort appear to have evolved into endemic subspecies although they have presumably been isolated for as long as the chickweed.

The environmental impact of the arrival of the oil industry in Shetland is discussed in other chapters. Only two points need to be made here: first, most of the vegetation of Shetland which is unusual in the context of the United Kingdom is of very limited extent. Even the unique mosaic of grass-heath, Rhacomitrium-heath and fens, most of it grazed but offering some patches of taller cover, which forms the breeding area of whimbrel and many other waders just south of Baltasound, covers a comparatively small area. Vegetation that is unusual in a Shetland context, the few bits of scrub, of tall grassland and ungrazed fen are even smaller and without exception extremely vulnerable to any change in land, or freshwater, use.

Second, poor growth on most uncultivated ground which may seem, like treelessness, to be a result of climate is in fact due to the effects on plants and soils of stock rearing, a process over 5000 years old. This means that loss of plant cover is made good slowly in these mainly nutrient-poor, grazed places and perhaps not at all if exposure is severe. Since most of the constructional work in connection with the coming of oil, whether it be roads, the laying of pipes, or extraction of aggregate, is inevitably taking place on hill land, care should be taken to encourage the restoration of plant cover. Enough damage has taken place at the time of writing to make one worry greatly for the future of the Shetland environment – the correct answers must lie in treating the plant cover with as much respect as any other living system.

References for Chapter 4
(full citations are given in the Bibliography, p. 353)

Allot, 1971; Ball & Goodier, 1974; Barkham, 1971; Birse, 1971; Crampton, 1911; Denny, 1963; Druce, 1922, 1925; Edmonston, 1845; Erdtman, 1924; Ferreira, 1959; Goldsmith, 1975; Goode, 1974; Hawksworth, 1969, 1970; Hilliam, 1977; Hoppe, 1965; Hoppe, Fries & Quennerstedt, 1965; Johansen, 1975, 1978; Lewis, 1977; Neustein, 1964; Palmer & Scott, 1969; Price, 1929; Proctor, 1971; Proctor & Woodell, 1975; Rasmussen, 1952; Shewry & Peterson, 1976; Spence, 1957, 1958, 1959, 1960, 1964, 1970, 1974, 1979; Spence & Millar, 1963; Stewart, 1962; Swan & Senior, 1972; Tyldesley, 1973; West, 1912.

Background
Birks, 1973; Bullard, 1972; Fenton, 1937; Gimingham, 1964a,b, 1972; Gore, 1975; Grime & Hunt, 1975; Hansen, 1930; Lewis, 1907, 1911; McVean & Ratcliffe, 1962; Matthews, 1955; Metcalfe, 1950; Ostenfeld, 1908; Ostenfeld & Grontved, 1934; Perring & Walters, 1962; Poore & McVean, 1957; Rasmussen, 1952; Watt & Jones, 1948.

CHAPTER 5

THE SEA

BOTH history and natural history in Shetland are bound up with the surrounding seas. Were it not for the productivity of the neighbouring waters, the
islands would not be able to support their large seabird colonies and the
human settlers would have had a very different and much more checkered
time than they have.

A full understanding of the Shetland seas involves the oceanography of the
whole north-eastern Atlantic. In brief, they are dominated by a stream of
Atlantic water flowing southwards into the North Sea down the east side of
Shetland. This means that the seas round the islands are of almost undiluted
oceanic origin, and less productive than more enclosed coastal waters. A very
different body of water moves northward up the west coast of Britain from the
Mediterranean, and may upwell as far north as the Continental Shelf off
Shetland. These two streams are mixed by the strong tidal currents of the
islands, and by turbulence produced by storms moving east along the Polar
Front. This process raises nutrient salts to the surface and results in a rich
growth of plankton in summer, which supports large populations of fish and
the predators which feed on them.

The effect of this is to produce a situation described by Sir Alastair Hardy in
his New Naturalist on *Fish and Fisheries* as 'a great culture medium'. Near the
surface conditions are favourable for plant growth and 'the little plants of
the phytoplankton are spread through the upper layers; upon these graze the
members of the animal or zooplankton. Some fish such as herring, sprat and
mackerel, feed directly on the zooplankton, so also do the basking sharks and
the still larger whalebone whales. . . . From this teeming world of plankton
life there sinks the rich supply of nourishment to the animals on the sea-bed
. . . and these in turn not only support a host of worms, crustaceans and less
familiar creatures, but also form the food of the bottom living fish. . . . The
entire wealth that man takes from the sea is ultimately dependent upon the
plankton for its production.'

FISH

Herring (*Clupea harengus*), cod (*Gadus morrhua*) and haddock (*G. aeglefinus*) are
the fish species which have been commercially most important to Shetlanders.
Herring is a surface living (*pelagic*) fish, while cod are deeper living (*demersal*)
species.

Stomach analyses of herring from around Shetland show that three-

92

quarters of their diet is a copepod, *Calanus finmarchicus*. This species seems to thrive best in highly salty water (with salinities of over 35 parts per thousand), as where oceanic and North Sea waters meet. There is an increase in *Calanus* numbers around Shetland between July and September, probably due to mixed water in the area at the time, combined with the high production of phytoplankton in early summer.

The Shetland herring fishery has been based upon stocks of fish spawning south of Shetland, east of Orkney, and off the north-east coast of Scotland. Their migration follows an annual irregular cycle round the North Sea. The uncertainties of their movements lead to the recurring difficulties of knowing whether poor catches are due to over-fishing or varying migration habits.

Two other pelagic fish taken around Shetland are sprat (*Clupea sprattus*) and mackerel (*Scomber scombrus*). Sprats appear in bays in varying quantities each year in late November and December, and remain till about March. This coincides with the strongest period of water movement from the Atlantic and may be related to it. Alternatively they may be seeking out water cooled by land to incude lower metabolic rates and thus less need for food. In spring the shoals move or disperse, perhaps to spawn. All Shetland-caught sprats are young animals; it is not known where the older fish go.

Until recently, mackerel were not caught commercially. They come inshore in late summer and feed mainly on small fish. They are caught by line, and can contribute significantly to the earnings of small boat fishermen.

Sand-eels (*Ammodytes* spp.) occur in large numbers around the islands, and are the most important item in the diet of many sea-birds. They are increasingly fished for making into fish meal.

Basking sharks (*Cetorhinus maximus*) occur fairly frequently, feeding on plankton. They are hunted by harpoon boats, mainly Norwegian. Porbeagle sharks (*Lamna nasus*) are also sometimes caught to the west of Shetland.

Demersal fish were traditionally caught round Shetland on lines, the species taken depending to some extent on the size. Since the late 1940s seine netting has been increasingly used to catch deeper-living fish. This involves dragging a net with the lower edge on the seabed; it can only be used over soft ground to avoid damaging the gear. Seine netters catch mainly haddock and whiting (*Gadus merlangus*) around Shetland, with smaller catches of cod, ling (*Molva molva*), skate (*Raja* spp.) and in the past halibut (*Hippoglossus vulgaris*), but this is now almost rare in the area. Evidence from line catches suggest that the less common species in the nets prefer hard grounds.

Saithe or coal fish (*Gadus virens*) was an important species when fishing was a more significant part of the domestic economy of Shetland than it is today. It formed the staple diet of Shetlanders in the 17th century, while Low in 1774 recorded it being exported to Leith and Dundee 'cured with the heads on, like Scottish cured Keeling' (cod). After the spawning season in deep water, young approach the shore and dense shoals are often found in voes. Up to a year old, saithe are known as 'sillak'; between the ages of one and three, they are referred to as 'piltak'. Fish older than three years are rarely found in shallow water: large saithe are often taken by trawlers at over 50 fathoms near the edge of the continental shelf; by hand line from herring boats 10–50 miles to the east of the islands; and in the areas of strong currents in the Sumburgh Roost, Skaw Strings to the north of Unst, and a similar area to the north of Foula.

MAN AND FISH

The earliest (neolithic) inhabitants of Shetland, probably had too poor boats for much fishing. Limpets were a major part of their diet as shown by 'shell middens' in several places round the coast. However by the early Bronze Age, large cod and ling bones at Jarlshof suggest that fishing from boats may have taken place, since only small individuals of these species can usually be caught from land. Late Bronze Age settlements show less sign of fishing. This was a time of climatic amelioration and the establishment of inland farms in several parts of Shetland (see Chapter 3).

About 500 B.C. a phase of cold, wet weather overtook Shetland. The Bronze Age farmsteads were deserted in favour of coastal sites, and during the Iron Age era of round houses and brochs, the main food requirements were probably met by fishing and seal hunting. The introduction of efficient boats by the Vikings made offshore fishing much safer than hitherto, and net-fishing was known in Norway in saga times although there is no direct evidence for Shetland.

Commercial fishing

The period between the Viking settlement of Shetland and the pledging of the islands to the Scottish crown in 1469, is often looked back on as a Golden Age, when the islanders were self-sufficient for food and in control of their own affairs. This is not entirely true. At least as early as 1186 dried fish from long-line fishing was being exported through Bergen, and the trade (and hence the fishermen) was increasingly coming under the control of the Hanseatic League of Lubeck, Bremen and Hamburg merchants. By 1400 the power of the Hanse was at its peak and most trade of significance in northern Europe was organized through its gathering points (*kontors*). Shetland export was in practice completely controlled by the North German merchants through the Bergen *kontor*.

In the early 15th century signs of decline began to creep into the Hanseatic League. One of the mainstays of its activity, Baltic herring, disappeared from their usual haunts whilst large shoals were being caught by Dutchmen in the North Sea. Around this time the first known North German merchant is recorded in Shetland, living on Yell. By the early 16th century Boece recorded 'the marchandis of Holland, Zeland, and Almanic cumis yierlie to Schetland to interchange uthir merchandyis with the people thairof . . .' while there is a

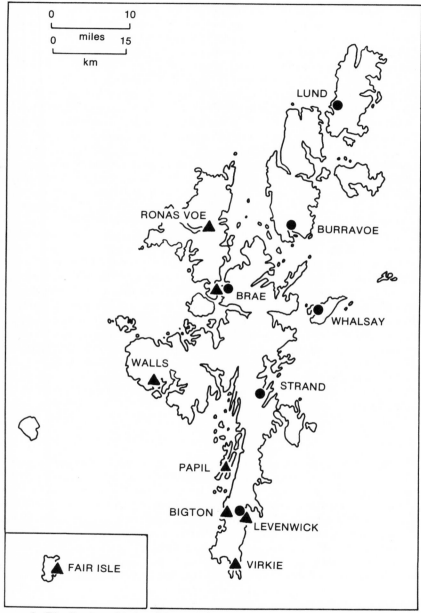

FIG 16. Distribution of *bods* – fish stores for trading with German merchants in the 17th century. Bremen merchants, Hamburg merchants (after Goodlad, 1971).

gravestone in Lung, Unst recording the death in 1573 of a Bremen merchant who 'had carried on his business in this country for 52 years'. Bergen ceased to be the only point of contact with northern Europe.

The German merchants now operating at the source of supply effectively broke the power of local traders and held sway for almost 100 years. They were represented at almost every haven around the island (Fig. 16) and their influence grew until it was broken by the raising of custom dues in 1712. Their typical pattern was to arrive in Shetland at the beginning of May and stay until the end of August. They rented *bods*, stores usually specially built by land-owners, into which they collected fish, butter, and saithe liver oil, and gave in exchange 'hooks and lines for the taking of cod and ling; Nets for the taking of Herring; Brandie and strong waters of all sorts; Mead, Strong Beer, Bisket, Wheat meal and Rye Meal, Barley, Salt, Tobacco, Fruits of all Sorts, Monmouth caps and the Coarser Sort of Cloth and Linen, and such like merchandise.'

The merchants also hired from the landowners stony beaches where fish could be laid out to dry. They were cured by either complete wind drying or part wind, part salt drying.

Changes in fishing practice were limited. The islanders still went to sea in small boats with two, three or four men in each, and they seldom travelled more than ten miles from the shore. However by this time they had been introduced to long-line fishing, in which a many-hooked line was buoyed near its end so that it spread over a greater stretch of sea-floor.

The replacement of the German by the Scottish influence in Shetland fishing came at the beginning of the 18th century. The power of the Hanseatic League had gone and with the union of Scotland and England, great obstacles were put in the way of foreigners trading on British soil. The imposition in 1712 of a tax on the salt necessary for curing finally removed the Germans from Shetland affairs.

The Lairds and the haaf (ocean) fishery

From the 1720s, a new pattern of fishing activity began to emerge concerned not only with simple trading, but also with problems of land tenure. It started with the ownership of large areas of land by incoming Scots, which meant that the native Shetlanders were more likely to be tenants than owners of their own land. When the tenants had an assured income from their trade with the German merchants, they could pay their rent and there was no problem; once the merchants disappeared, both landowner and tenant began to feel the pinch.

The only possibility for the landmaster to sustain his own prosperity was to 'take over' the export trade. This was spurred by the granting in 1727 of a bounty on all Scottish-caught cured fish, and by the opening of a Spanish market which was to remain the largest customer for Shetland caught and

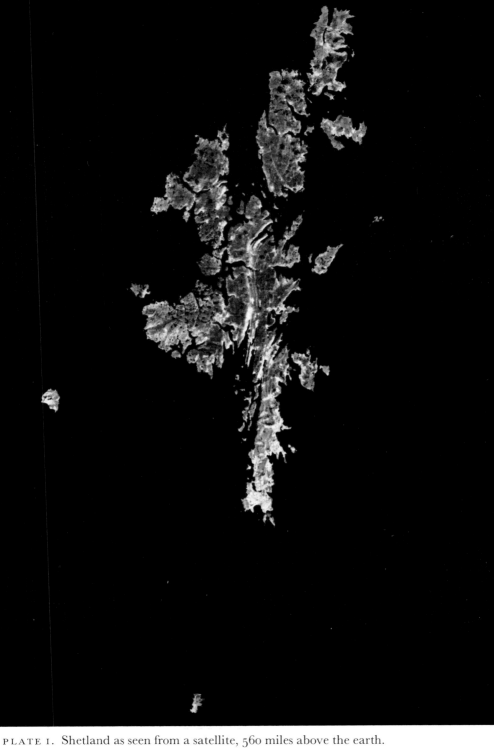

PLATE I. Shetland as seen from a satellite, 560 miles above the earth.

PLATE 2. *Above*, Voe, a typical peaceful township; *below*, the broch on Mousa.

PLATE 3. *Right*, the Tingwall Valley, a fertile limestone band running north-eastwards across the Mainland of Shetland. Scalloway is in the foreground. *Below*, part of the Walls Peninsula, showing the layering of the rocks and effects caused by small faults.

PLATE 4. The effect of grazing. *Above left*, an island in Hamari Water photographed in July 1958; *right*, the same island in 1978 photographed from a slightly different aspect. Sheep were given access in 1972, and all the tall ferns and herbs, and all the shrubs except one bush of Rowan, have been eaten and killed. *Below left, Nardus-Juncus* grassland on a peat cutting near Mail, Cunningsburgh with *Calluna-Eriophorum* in the middle distance (dark area). Surface re-seeding of hill land visible top right. *Right*, Kergord plantation from the south-west.

PLATE 5. *Above*, last Caain' Whale drive at Weisdale, 1903; *below*, Caain' Whales off Shetland.

PLATE 6. *Above left*, Otters; *right*, Shetland Otter trap. *Below*, Grey Seals.

35·3%

25·4%

15·9%

23·7%

PLATE 7. *Above*, view northwards across the Tingwall Valley, showing great differences in the frequencies of the melanic form *(edda)* of the Autumnal Rustic moth over a comparatively small area.

Right, Shetland melanics

ROW 1. Ingrailed Clay *(Diarsia mendica)*: *left*, typical form from Caithness; *right, f. thule* from Shetland.
ROW 2. Autumnal Rustic *(Paradiarsia glareosa)*: *left*, typical and *right*, melanic *(f. edda)* forms from Shetland.
ROW 3. Marbled Coronet *(Hadena conspersa)*: *left*, typical form from Oxfordshire; *right, f. hethlandica* from Shetland.
ROW 4. Northern Spinach *(Eulithis populata)*: *left*, typical and *right*, melanic *(f. fuscata)* forms from Shetland.
ROW 5. Ghost Moth *(Hepialus humuli)*: *left*, typical form from Caithness; *right, f. thulensis* from Shetland.
(specimens of J. C. Cadbury)

PLATE 8. *Above left*, juvenile Raven; *right*, Shetland Starling. *Below left*, White Wagtail; *right*, Shetland Wren.

cured fish until the end of the 19th century. Six-oared boats (*sixareens*) made their appearance, enabling fishing further away from land than hitherto. Outlying islands were inhabited, as they were nearer fishing grounds than mainland villages. By the 1740s the land-owners were contracting to sell and transport fish to London merchants, producing a more stable market, and giving encouragement for investment in boats and equipment. The problem was that this system was so profitable for the land-owner, that the selling of fish to him became a condition of tenancy on many estates, and was linked to a 'truck' system by which the necessities of life were provided in exchange for the tenants' fish.

The Danish governor of the Faroes, Christian Ployen, visited Shetland in 1839 to learn about Shetland fishing and marketing techniques. Ironically in view of the later development of Faroese fishing and the consequent prosperity of those islands, he found his people had much to learn from the Shetlanders, but he was surprised at the plight of the people: 'I must say to the credit of the proprietors that they use no harsh measures, and readily allow arrears to stand over, yet when a man is in debt to them, they get almost the entire produce of his labour, and still even beyond the time he is originally bound to fish for them, so that the Crofter, who at any time may be turned out, and therefore remains in debt to his landlord, has not an enviable lot. From this wretched state of dependence, from which the crofters are unable to extricate themselves, it follows that as a body they are poor, often miserably so; whilst the landlords live in luxury. . . .'

Big land-owners have had a bad reputation in Shetland since this period. There were good masters, but most were oppressive. Their power was outlawed by the Truck Acts of the 1870s, but already it was on the wane with the development of large decked trawlers and drifters. (A summer gale in 1832 caused the loss of many *sixareens* and over 100 lives in conditions where decked vessels survived.) Security of tenure and fair rents were assured by the Crofters' Holdings Act of 1886. Between 1871 and 1881 there were three major fishing disasters and 4640 Shetlanders emigrated.

Herrings

The first people to exploit herrings around Shetland were the Dutch, and they fished regularly until the wars of the late 17th century, increasing again at the end of the 19th century. Dutch herring was cured on board ship, and was much superior to British prepared fish. Perhaps because of this, and notwithstanding a great demand for herring from the West Indies as 'the food of negroes', there was little development of Shetland herring fishing until the 1880s; in 1874 the herring fleet was less than 50 boats and 1100 barrels of herring were cured in Shetland; in 1881 there were 276 boats and 29,586 barrels; and by 1884 932 boats and 300,117 barrels. This revolutionary change upset the relative stability of the preceding long-line fisheries which, together with the merchant navy and whaling provided employment for most of the male population. The early successes of herring netting gave possibilities for capital accumulation and reinvestment by fishermen and merchants which had never before been possible on such a scale in the islands, and which continued until the collapse of the herring fishing in the 1970s.

Before the great increase of the 1880s, curing stations had been established round the islands as near as possible to the catching grounds. These were expanded in size as the herring boom began, but later were displaced to the larger centres.

The recent story of herring fishing has been catastrophic. From a peak of 111,000 tons landed in 1924, the catch declined to around 10,000 tons in the 1960s to 2,000 tons in 1977. It is now accepted that this decline in catch is the result of overfishing following the development of new fishing methods and techniques for identifying shoals, but for a long time it was 'officially' argued that the falling catch could be due to a change in habits of the local stock. It may be that adverse environmental conditions reinforced the overfishing and hastened the final decline. Notwithstanding, the fall in catch coincided with trawling on the spawning grounds and the introduction of deep purse seine nets. The turning point in Shetland came in 1965 when catches in the early part of the season had been poor, but echo-sounders showed good shoals of herring below the level of the traditional drift nets. Local fishermen were hoping for better catches in July when out of the blue 200 Norwegian purse seiners arrived. By the end of the season these boats had taken 190,000 tons – most of it pumped ashore into fish-meal factories – compared with 10,000 tons by the British fleet. The Norwegians' success was short lived, since their catch declined thereafter in spite of ever more sophisticated gear. By this time the fish were being pursued on their spawning grounds, during their annual migrations, in their overwintering grounds, and back to the spawning grounds again. The Norwegian government introduced regulations to limit the amount of herring sold for meal but it was already too late, and in 1971 internationally agreed close seasons were introduced.

For some years British purse seiners raised the British catch to a level comparable with the interwar years, but the fate of the drifters showed the fate of the stocks. In 1972 only 17 drifters fished around Shetland; by 1975 the fleet was down to a single vessel, and her catch was so poor that she stopped fishing halfway through the season.

Shell-fish

The most recent marine species to be exploited around Shetland are shell-fish – first, lobsters (*Homarus vulgaris*) where landings increased from 289 cwts in 1955 to 3495 cwts in 1962, followed by the inevitable decline; second, crabs (*Cancer pagurus*), developed as a sideline to lobster fishing; and thirdly, scallops (*Pecten maximus*).

Shetland fishermen now have oil developments to contend with – developments excluding them from certain areas and raising the spectre of pollution. No one can be certain of the future of the fisheries; all that it is possible to say is that the fishermen have had a voice in the discussions about siting and environmental protection of the oil industry's works. Notwithstanding their stand against the oil companies, it is hard to avoid the conclusion that Shetland fishermen are suffering the fate of fishermen in too many parts of the world as a direct consequence of over-fishing. Some of this may be the result of local exploitation, although a large part of it can be put down to the depredations of large foreign fleets – Russian, German, Norwegian, French, Polish. But apportioning blame does not produce fish.

SCIENTIFIC INVESTIGATIONS

The knowledge about fish which has led to the plunder described in the first half of this chapter has come from marrying painstaking scientific enquiries to fishermen's lore. The background knowledge of the Shetland seas which must underpin these understandings is surprisingly under-developed.

Early studies were initiated by a Manxman, Edward Forbes (1815–1854). As a student he had been enthused by the results of his dredging in the Irish Sea – so much so, that he wrote a dredging song:

> Hurrah for the dredge, with its iron edge,
>   And its mystical triangle,
> And its hided net, with meshes set
>   Odd fishes to entangle!
> The ship may rove through the waters above,
>   'Mid scenes exciting wonder,
> But braver sights the dredge delights,
>   As it roves the waters under.
>
> *Chorus:*
> Then a dredging we will go, brave boys,
> Then a dredging we will go.

In 1839, Forbes dredged off Shetland and discovered at least a dozen invertebrate species previously unknown in Britain. He so impressed the British Association with his account that they set up a Dredging Committee which functioned for a number of years, and provided £50 in 1863 for 'Dredging, Shetland,' then £75 in 1864 and again in 1867.

Money from this fund was channelled through J. G. Jeffreys, a conchologist, who first visited Shetland in the 1840s and found several new British species as well as some previously known only as Pliocene fossils. This filled him with enthusiasm for determining the relationships of the Shetland fauna, and he dredged round the islands on six occasions between 1861 and 1868, usually from his yacht, and accompanied by Alfred Norman, a formidable Durham clergyman. In their final report Jeffreys and Norman added 204 species to the British list, as well as 40 entirely new to science. Norman wrote 'The marine fauna of Shetland has been proved to be extremely rich. The sea there would seem to be in an especial manner the meeting-place of northern and southern types. Many arctic forms not known further to the south are here found associated with numerous Mediterranean species which do not reach the Scandinavian coast, and some of these are remarkable in not having been found at any intermediate habitat.'

And there the matter rested. The Aberdeen Marine Laboratory of the Department of Agriculture and Fisheries for Scotland have monitored fish and plankton stocks off northern Scotland, and oceanographic cruises have passed near Shetland, but no major marine studies unconnected with commercial fisheries seemed to have been carried out for a century when Irvine reviewed knowledge of the Shetland marine algae ('In general the vegetation is much like that of the Faeroes. . . . The Orkneys have a richer flora than Shetland') at a meeting organized by the Nature Conservancy Council in 1974 (see also Table 19).

However a considerable number of studies of both sea and shore were carried out in the 1970s to lay down a baseline for any changes that might be produced by oil developments. Some of these are being regularly repeated to monitor the effects of oil. In this context, a survey of the bottom sediments of Sullom Voe carried out in the 1960s by the Aberdeen Laboratory showed that they were devoid of oxygen; if a similar study was carried out now, there is little doubt that this oxygen lack would be attributed to the adverse effects of oil!

Scientists from the Scottish Marine Biological Association (SMBA) have investigated the ecology of a number of voes. They found the occurrence of bottom living forms to be controlled by the presence of 'organically rich reduced sediment', *i.e.* peat is highly important in determining the species present. The peat comes both from submerged peat beds (*q.v.* Chapter 2) and from erosion of blanket peat on surrounding land. In contrast to sea lochs on the west of Scotland, the longer Shetland voes have very little change of water. This bodes ill for local oil spills, because it means pollution will not be rapidly flushed away.

Skin divers working from the shore have complemented the SMBA studies. Indeed the methods and results developed by a team working under contract to the Institute of Terrestrial Ecology of the Natural Environment Research Council are being used as a basis for encouraging sub-aqua clubs to collect biological data from all round the United Kingdom in a form to enable them to be used as the bases for conservation proposals.

As far as the Shetland results are concerned, four main habitat-species groups were identified in shallow water – faunas associated with clean sand; with muddy sand and gravel; one in the *Laminaria hyperborea* zone dominated by dead man's fingers (*Alcyonium digitatum*) and the anemone *Tealia felina*; and one dominated by brittle-stars. However the earlier claims about the particular richness of the Shetland sub-littoral fauna have not been borne out. The species present are less than those present on, for example, the north west tip of Ireland, and many of the species recorded are sufficiently rare to suggest that they do not have breeding populations in Shetland. For many groups the shallow sub-littoral has a markedly reduced species-diversity in comparison even with Orkney.

The shores themselves are dominated by rocks: the majority have some solid rock below high tide mark, and an appreciable proportion have boulders and pebbles or gravel. There are very few sandy shores and these have a fauna similar to that of the mainland of Scotland and Western Isles. Most of the rocky shores have fewer crevices and pools than other places and this reduces the faunal and floral diversity of exposed shores, since these form a niche for sheltered shore organisms on exposed shores.

The shores around Orkney have been more studied than those of Shetland – notably by the Orcadian poet and theologian Robert Rendall who attempted to summarize knowledge about them in his book *Orkney Shore*. The main differences from Shetland are the voes and deep water inshore of the latter. These have the effect that extreme littoral exposures occur in Shetland, but only rarely in Orkney and the Hebrides. Another consequence of life in the northern isles is that low daytime temperatures allow species which live entirely below the low-tide mark in England to extend into the littoral zone in both Orkney and Shetland.

Probably there are unique features of Shetland shores. Certainly the growth habit of *Fucus serratus* and *Ascophyllum* are different to similar habitats in Norwegian fjords and there are no unattached forms of *A. nodosum* in Shetland unlike both Norway and the Hebrides; certainly sea pinks (*Armeria maritima*) extend down to the upper *Fucus spiralis* zone of the extremely sheltered Shetland shores whereas in the south they are confined to well above the splash zone; there are likely to be many more local and significant features if the shores were better known. Many species grow to a very large size in Shetland: *Balanus balanoides* is two to three times larger in Shetland than in the south. Some species (*e.g. Elminius modestus* and *Littorina neritoides*) reach their northern limit in Shetland. Only one species of top-shell occurs, compared with four in the South. Many more small snail species (up to about half an inch long) than larger are found. An association not known outside Shetland is a commensal nemertean *Malacobdella grossa* in the cockle *Cerastoderma (Cardium) edule*.

An example of the extreme ecological pressures of Shetland shores is provided by shell banding in the common dogwhelk *Nucella lapillus*. Particular banding genes have a local distribution in different parts of the species range, to the extent that many small localities have a characteristic pattern of stripes; it is not clear why such genes should have restricted ranges in a species which has presumably been relatively stable since the end of the Pleistocene. There is a correlation of 33 per cent between banding frequency and exposure to wave action, but there are many highly exposed shores (such as in the Channel Islands and the west coasts of Orkney) where the whelks are virtually all bandless and white. In contrast the north coast of Cornwall shows an extraordinary range of banded and coloured forms. Now the immensity of wave action in Shetland is such that substantial differences in exposure occur over short distances. The frequency of banded whelks at the southern tip of Burra Isle (Groot Ness) is 14.0%; 500 yards up the sheltered east coast (at Sandy Geo Bight) it is 5.4%; and no banded shells occur at Duncanslade, a mile further along. Similar changes take place round Hillswick Ness. The environmental stresses are so great in these places that Shetland may be the only place in the United Kingdom where the determinants of whelk banding may be discoverable.

WRECKS

This is not a place to describe the many wrecks round Shetland. These range from *El Gran Grifon*, flagship of the store ship squadron of the Spanish Armada which was wrecked on Fair Isle and whose survivors are traditionally said to have introduced Fair Isle knitting to the islands (this claim is almost certainly wrong: 'Fair Isle' patterns were well known in Scandinavian countries long before the Armada), through the *Kennermerland*, a new ship of the Dutch East India Company which was wrecked on the Out Skerries in 1664 and much of whose treasure has been recovered in recent years, to assorted war casualties like the Dutch men o'war *Haan* and *Reiger* sunk by Spaniards in Lerwick Harbour in 1640, the *Oceanic* which ran aground on Foula in 1914, and the fishing boats which operated the 'Shetland bus' to occupied Norway in the 1939–45 war, to the North of Scotland steamer *St Sunniva* which hit Mousa in thick fog in 1930 and broke up in a gale two weeks later, and the many greater and lesser tragedies almost inevitable in communities fishing in northern waters.

However it is worth recalling the first known Shetland wreck when in 1148, according to the Orkneyinga Saga, the *Hjolp* and the *Fifa* ran aground on a voyage from Bergen to Orkney. A diving expedition searched Gulberwick, the most probable site of the wreck, for two months in 1972 and failed to find any definite signs that it took place there. However the seabed in the area is continually scoured so the bay cannot be ruled out as the place where Earl Rognvald and his colleagues came to grief. The failure of the searchers merely testifies once again to the powerful forces at work on the Shetland coasts.

References for Chapter 5
(full citations are given in the Bibliography on p. 353)

General: Fenton, 1978; Goodlad, 1971; Hardy, 1956, 1959; Johnston, 1977; Smith, 1977.

Historical: Jeffreys, 1869; Low, 1774, Mills, 1978; Nicolson, 1978; Norman, 1869; Ployen, 1896.

Shore and sub-littoral: Berry & Crothers, 1974; Burrows, *et al*, 1954; Dalby, *et al*, 1978; Earll, 1975; Irvine. 1974; Jones, 1975; Jones, Jones & James 1979; McIntyre, 1961, 1970; Pearson & Stanley, 1977; Rendall, 1960; Stephen, 1929–30, 1935.

Wrecks: Aston University Sub-Aqua Club, 1974; Balneaves, 1977; Eunson, n.d.; Morrison, 1973; O'Dell, 1939.

CHAPTER 6

WHALES AND SEALS

SHETLANDERS must have been familiar with whales for as long as they have voyaged. Particularly to the west and north of the islands, they would occasionally have come across both large baleen whales (such as the Fin, *Balaenoptera physalus* and the Sei, *Balaenoptera borealis*) feeding mainly on planktonic crustacea, and large toothed whales (such as the Sperm, *Physeter catodon*). Nearshore, the largest whale seen would probably have been one of the smaller baleen whales, the Minke (*Balaenoptera acutorostrata*), which grows to about 30 ft in length, less than half that of many of the larger species. Inshore they would have encountered the occasional Killer Whale (*Orcinus orca*) and the much smaller Pilot Whale (*Globicephala melaena*), as well as the abundant Common Porpoise (*Phocoena phocoena*) and several Dolphin species.

Although whales of all sizes are occasionally stranded, the traditional catching from Shetland was only for the Pilot or Caain' Whale, which is the most common whale off the coasts of North Scotland. This small black whale grows to 18–28 ft in length, and feeds mainly on cuttlefish. It often comes close to the Shetland coast around the South Mainland and in the area of the Sumburgh Roost. When this species ventured into the confined waters of bays or voes, boats were launched and the whales driven (or *caa'd*) into shallow water where they stranded and were killed. Only the blubber was made use of, being boiled and turned into oil, while the carcases were left to rot and attract the local carrion eating birds. In Faroe this practice still continues but there the meat is eaten as well, and considered a delicacy.

The largest known caa' was at Quendale in the South Mainland in 1845 when some 1540 animals were killed, while the last caa' was of 83 animals at Weisdale in 1903. Many caa's were of well over 100 animals, so the whale must have been fairly common in the 19th century. Today it is still the most common whale: between 1969 and 1973 Alan Whitfield the local Loganair pilot recorded over 2000 individuals, with schools from 7 to over 100 individuals.

In the late 18th and 19th centuries many Shetlanders were engaged at the Greenland whaling. At that time hunting was confined to open boats and the pursuit of the slower whales. These were harpooned and then killed with lances. In the late 19th century modern whaling was founded with steam-powered catchers, using an explosive harpoon fired from a cannon mounted on the bow of the catcher. This technique allowed the exploitation of the previously little hunted faster species, such as the Fin (and Sei and those such as the Blue, *Balanoptera musculus*, which sink on death). Whaling stations

sprang up all round the North Atlantic from Newfoundland to Spitsbergen.
At the turn of the century there were approximately 20 stations in Iceland
and Faroe and by this time the Greenland whaling was collapsing. In North
Norway whaling was banned as a result of bitter disputes with cod fishermen.
The Norwegian companies involved with whaling had to look elsewhere for
bases and in 1903 two whaling stations were set up in Shetland at Ronas Voe,
followed in 1904 by two more at Olnafirth and Collafirth. At the same time
whaling stations were set up in Ireland and in the Hebrides, but the Shetland
stations were always the most important.

The catches at these stations give us some evidences of populations and
seasonal distribution of whales in the eastern North Atlantic and northern
North Sea.

Species landed at Shetland

	Blue	Fin	Hump-back	Sei	Right	Sperm	Bottle-nosed
1903–1914	25	3287	49	1492	6	11	23
1920–1929	60	1069	2	347	0	8	2

Of the 4893 whales recorded in the 12 operating seasons before the Great
War, 67% were Fin and 30% Sei. Between the end of the War and the finish
of whaling from Shetland in 1929 some 1500 whales were caught in nine
seasons, the species ratio being similar, although all species except the Blue
showed a net decrease.

Before the 1914–18 War there was no evidence for over-exploitation, but
afterwards it became obvious that the stocks of whales passing through
Shetland waters, particularly the Blue, Humpback *(Megaptera novaengliae)*
and Right *(Balaena glacialis)* were not large enough to sustain the hunting
pressure.

Today whaling is still carried out from Iceland, mainly for Fin, Sei and
Sperm, but also for a very few Minke. The Norwegians also have small
catchers that hunt off Shetland mainly for Minke, Pilot Whales and small
Dolphins such as the White-sided *Lagenorhynchus acutus*. Protection has been
given to the Humpback since 1955, to the Blue since 1960 and to the Northern Bottlenose *(Hyperoodon ampullatus)* since 1977. There is no evidence for
overfishing of Sei or Sperm. Strandings on the British coastline are recorded
by the British Museum (Natural History). Since 1913 they have involved
mainly the Common Porpoise, Common Dolphin *(Delphinus delphis)* and the

TABLE 8. Cetacean Strandings in Shetland
(Common Porpoise, Pilot Whale and Common Dolphin are certainly under-recorded.)

Species	Date	Number	Size (feet)	Sex
Fin Whale	January 1943	1		
(Common Rorqual)	July 1949	1	60	
Minke	October 1935	1	26	
(Lesser Rorqual)	April 1938	1	13	
	August 1948	1	15	
	August 1951	1	20	
	July 1952	1		
	September 1952	1	13	
	February 1966	1	20	
Sperm	September 1946	1	60(?)	Male
	October 1946	1	49	Male
	June 1958	1	60	Male
	November 1977	1		Male
Bottle-nosed	August 1871	1		
	March 1883	1		
	March 1946	1	15	
Cuvier's Whale	August 1932	1	28	Female
Sowerby's Whale	April 1881	1	15	Male
	May 1885	1	15	Male
	July 1923	1	15	
	November 1949	1	12	Female
	December 1949	1	26	Male
	March 1968	1	15	Male
Narwhal	September 1808	1		Male
Common Porpoise	May 1930	1	3	Male
	May 1965	1	6	
	May 1975	1	4	
Killer Whale	September 1937	1	21	Male
	February 1944	1	25	Male
	March 1965	1	11	
	February 1966	1	8	Male
	August 1976	1	10	

Pilot Whale	October 1931	1	6	Female
	December 1951	1	15	
	April 1955	1	20	
	December 1963	1	18	Male
	November 1974	1	21	Male
	January 1975	1	18	
	December 1978	2	{ 16	Male
			14	Female
Risso's Dolphin	May 1947	1	8	
	June 1969	1	11	Female
White-beaked Dolphin	January 1960	1		
White-sided Dolphin	August 1918	1	6	
	July 1919	2	8	
	July 1924	1	6	
	July 1926	30	8	
	August 1929	35	8	
	February 1933	1	8	Male
	July 1956	1	8	
	November 1964	1	5	Female
	March 1967	1	5	Male
	May 1967	1	9	Female
Common Dolphin	February 1936	1	5	Female
	June 1966	1	5	Female

Pilot Whale. Dolphin species appear to have decreased in relative occurrence while the Pilot Whale has increased. The whale catch in the North Atlantic in 1976 as recorded by the International Whaling Commission was 281 Fin, 5 Sei, 2520 Minke, and 111 Sperm Whales.

The whaling season in Shetland lasted from April–September, not because of the restrictions of winter weather, but because this is the season that the larger whales generally make their appearance in northern waters. As the spring sunshine warms the surface waters of the sea a relatively dense phytoplankton 'soup' develops on which growing numbers of zooplankton graze, and on which the Herring, Mackerel, Sprat and Whales come to feed. Towards the end of the summer, the baleen whales at least, depart to warmer waters. It is clear from the catches of the British whaling stations that most of the large whales, such as the Right and the largest of all, the Blue, were caught to the west of Britain and few were to be found in the north around Shetland. These larger whales have an annual migration from warmer waters, where they have their young, to colder waters in the North Atlantic where they come to feed on zooplankton. The migration routes of the Blue and the Right lie to the west of Britain and Faroe. Both these species are now extremely rare and neither has been stranded or observed at Shetland, although both used to be landed at the whaling stations. The Humpback appears to follow a similar route but it has been extremely scarce since before the First World War and has not been recorded at Shetland except at the whaling stations.

The Fin and the Sei, which were the commonest species hunted, appear to migrate through the Shetland-Faroe channel, although both appear to prefer to remain far offshore outwith the 100 fathom contour, and there are only two records of stranding for the Fin in Shetland (in 1943 and 1949). None of the foregoing species was seen in the North Sea in a recent survey; the most common species there was the smallest of the baleen whales, the Minke. This often frequents inshore waters on its migration up the west coast of Scotland and around Shetland. It is the largest baleen whale regularly seen from the islands and there are seven records of stranding between 1933 and 1966, mostly in late summer and early autumn. In four years Alan Whitfield recorded four sightings, one of mother and calf in June and another of from 10 to 14 off Fetlar in October 1973. R. Tulloch has also seen it off the east coast in late summer.

The largest of the toothed whales is the Sperm, the males of which measure up to 60 ft. Solitary males probably visit offshore Shetland occasionally. It has been stranded on four occasions. Large whales were observed twice by Alan Whitfield but not positively identified. Unlike the baleen whales, the Sperm feeds mainly on cuttlefish and has its own monthly cycle of movement.

The Beaked Whales are mostly under 30 ft in length. They also feed predominantly on cuttlefish. The most common around Shetland is the Northern Bottle-nose whale. Apparently this species was regularly seen during whaling days but there are no records of it being landed although it was hunted in the Greenland whaling. There are two records of stranding in the 19th century and one for 1946. There is a single record of stranding for Cuvier's Whale (*Ziphius cavirostris*) in 1932 and one was caught at Eshaness in 1870. This was the first British record. Sowerby's Whale (*Mesoplodon bidens*) has been stranded at least five times. Alan Whitfield once recorded a Beluga (*Delphinapterus leucas*) off Shetland and there is one record of a Narwhal (*Monodon monoceros*) which was driven ashore in Weisdale Voe in 1808.

The Killer Whale was the most frequently sighted whale by Alan Whitfield, with 127 sightings involving over 600 individuals in four years, generally between April and October and usually in fast tidal streams around headlands and between large islands. This large and fast predator hunts all the Whales, Porpoises and Dolphins, also Seals and large fish. Males grow to 30 ft although females are only half that size. They are very distinctive with several large white markings underneath and behind the dorsal fin on an otherwise black background. The dorsal fin of the male is extremely conspicuous, being nearly 6 ft in height. They may be seen as solitary males, or in small parties of one male to several females, but they also join in packs of 30 or more to hunt larger prey. They sometimes herd Dolphins to attack them, producing very spectacular sights as the prey jump clear out of the water in their attempts to escape. When Seals are attacked their reaction is either panic or indifference; it is obvious that they are much less familiar with the Killer.

The only other cetaceans commonly seen in Shetland waters are Risso's Dolphin (*Grampus griseus*) and the White-sided Dolphin. The former is the larger at 13 ft in length and is seen regularly offshore and occasionally passing through the sounds, usually in small family parties. Compared to the other Dolphins and Porpoises it is a slow moving animal with a distinctive bulbous head and numerous small scars, white against the generally grey colouring. In contrast the White-sided Dolphin is possibly the most exuberant of all the smaller cetaceans, often leaping clear of the water and earning the name 'Looper Dog' from Shetland fishermen. It is the most frequently stranded cetacean in Shetland, possibly because of its behaviour. This is the animal often seen racing the bows of boats. It can also be distinguished by grey and white streaking on the side and underside. Like the others it is rarely seen in confined waters. It usually occurs in small family parties, although schools of over 100 are sometimes seen, and two of the records of stranding are of parties of over 30.

Other members of the Dolphin family occasionally sighted and stranded are the White-beaked Dolphin (*Lagenorhynchus albirostris*), Bottle-nose Dolphin (*Tursiops truncatus*) and Common Dolphin (*Delphinus delphis*). This gives 16 species known from strandings and inshore sightings, plus four that have only been recorded when caught 50–100 miles offshore.

SEALS

In the month of June, at the height of the simmer-dim when the summer day stretches into and almost through the night, when the breeding birds are sitting on eggs or feeding young and the Shetland flowers are at their most colourful, the Common Seal (*Phoca vitulina*) has her pup. She may haul out in one of the small colonies under cliffs or skerries, or on an uninhabited island such as Mousa, or she may even give birth in the sea. Although she is wary of enemies such as the Killer Whale or man, she rarely fears for the weather.

Curiously the other seal which breeds in Shetland, the Grey Seal (*Halichoerus grypus*) chooses to have her young in late autumn in October/November, when the weather is at its most variable and often its worst. When the migratory breeding birds are returning south, when even the tenacious Fulmar has vacated the cliffs and the boats are in their winter nousts, Grey Seal females haul out in colonies of up to a hundred on exposed cliff-foot beaches, in caves, on skerries and very occasionally onto grassy islands such as Gruney and produce their young as far as possible from the reach of the long swells pounding the shore.

These two seals are the only ones normally found on the coasts bordering the temperate seas of the North Atlantic, although other vagrant species appear from time to time. To the non-expert and sometimes even to the expert, they are quite difficult to distinguish. However they are relatively quite different in size and colouring and have different social habits as well as habitat preferences.

The Grey is the larger animal with bulls up to 8 ft and females usually just under 6 ft; the Common bull is slightly smaller than the female Grey, while the female Common reaches only 5 ft. The differences between the sexes is therefore much greater in the Grey than in the Common.

The old Shetland name for the Grey is the 'haaf' (deep sea) fish and the Common the 'tang' (seaweed) fish, indicating the former's preference for open sea conditions and the latter's preference for more sheltered shores and islands. The Grey is also sometimes known as the Atlantic Seal, as it is found only in the North Atlantic; while the Common Seal may be referred to as the Black or Harbour Seal, due to its darker colouring when wet and its frequenting of estuarine conditions, outwith Shetland, such as The Wash, and more sheltered sounds and voes in Shetland.

The Grey male generally has a dark coat although the female tends to have a lighter coat with dark blotches. However these are only very general descriptions as coat colour varies considerably with age as well as sex (particularly in the Grey where the female and immature are usually lighter in colour than the bull), with state of moult, and whether or not the animal is wet and the coat shiny, or hauled out and dry in which case the coat is matt.

One of the clearest distinguishing features is the shape of head. The Grey, especially the bull, has a high muzzle giving it a Roman Nose. In contrast the Common has a low dog-like muzzle with a relatively rounded head and distinct forehead producing a much more appealing and expressive appearance. The Common's nostrils form a V shape while those of the Grey are more parallel. The immature Grey is similar to the adult Common in size, and one can only definitely separate the two from head shape, although the Grey is usually the lighter in colour.

Whereas the Grey is largely confined to the eastern side of the North Atlantic (apart from small populations in Eastern Canada and Greenland), there are five recognised sub-species of the Common in the North Atlantic and North Pacific Oceans. In the British Isles the total population of the Common is approximately 20,000 while that of the Grey is estimated at 60,000 in Scotland alone. The latter however represents some 55% of the world's population. The Shetland populations of the two species are approximately 3800 and 3500, representing respectively 20% and 5% of the British population. The Shetland Common Seal population is of ecological interest in a British context as it occurs in much more exposed situations in the islands than it does on the mainland.

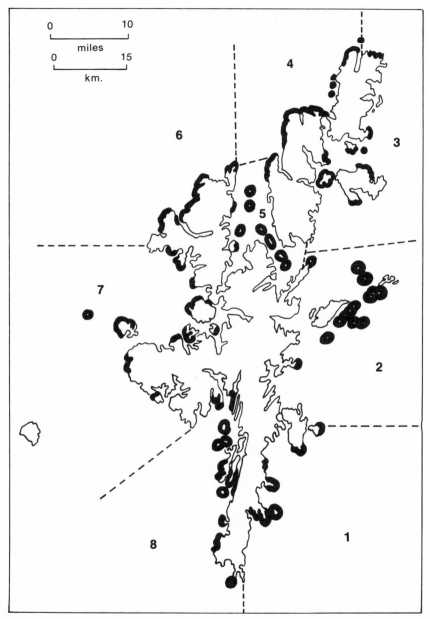

FIG 17. Common Seals. The numbers counted in each area in 1973 were: 1 225; 2 250; 3 225; 4 225; 5 250; 6 100; 7 250; and 8 225.

Seal histories in Shetland are long, and the bones of both Grey and Common have been found from Iron Age levels at Jarlshof, while the prefix 'seli' (seal) in the names of many localities attest to their former abundance, although in many such places they are nowadays comparatively rare. In the past Shetlanders have hunted seals with nets in the sea, with clubs in the caves, and latterly with rifles, but there has always been an ambiguous attitude towards them. Folklore of the northern and western islands has it that 'selkies' possess magic powers and are able to cast off their skins and come ashore as beautiful people.

> I am a man upo' the land
> I am a selchie in the sea
> And when I'm far frae every strand
> My home is on Sule Skerry

Traditionally this only occurred in Shetland at Johnsmas (midsummer) and many an islander is said to have fallen in love with a selkie and gone to the sea.

Notwithstanding, the seals were killed, their blubber used for oil, their skins for garments and 'rivlins' (footwear), and their flesh occasionally eaten. In recent years the main purpose of hunting has been for skins for the fur trade and for local tourist nicknacks.

The most valuable skins are those of the pup, particularly the Common pup, followed by adult skins just after moult. As Commons pup in accessible sites in June, they have been the main target since shooting began. It was also the case that whereas hunting the Grey Seal has required a permit since 1914, the Common Seal has only very recently acquired protection. This was sought specifically because of the Shetland situation.

After the Second World War the demand for sealskins increased and their price rose sufficiently to encourage the rather hard pressed Shetlanders to take part in the skin trade. In the 1950s and 1960s the price continued to rise and many individuals took to hunting part-time at the weekends quite apart from the existing hunting groups. Between 1960 and 1970 over 700 pups were culled annually, and it has been estimated that of the 1000 or so pups born in 1968, 900 were culled. By then it was obvious that the population was decreasing. For example the Fitful Head population declined four-fold:

Year	Maximum Count	Authority
1954	414	Venables & Venables
1955	304	Venables & Venables
1956	428	Venables & Venables
1967	141	Wilson
1968	132	Tickell
1971	99	Johnston
1977	120	Sea Mammal Research Unit

This pattern was repeated throughout the islands although the figures available are less accurate. Interestingly a delay in the date in breeding took place, presumably brought about by human predation since it was similar to that which occurred with exploited Elephant Seals in South Georgia. With the experience of Faroe in mind, where Common Seals were hunted to extinction this century, a Seals Conservation Bill was passed in 1970 to protect the Common Seal, requiring permits for hunting. A survey in 1971 revealed a very low population of 1800 animals, excluding the young of the year. In 1973 a total ban on hunting was introduced for a five year period. Happily, a survey carried out in 1978 showed a marked improvement in the population to 3800 seals with many more young animals. This figure and the recovery at Fitful Head indicates a much healthier state of the population.

Although the Common pup is a proficient swimmer at birth, the Grey pup is not, and their respective developments are very different. The typical picture of a new born Grey pup is of an appealing animal with large soft eyes and a white furry coat. In the Common this white, foetal coat is shed before birth and the animal is born with its second dark coat, which the Grey only acquires after birth by shedding its white coat over a three week period.

At Common Seal breeding sites there is little segregation by sex and maturity and all ages of animals may be present. In the Grey Seal however, the bulls fight to hold harems, while the immature stay out of the way. There are approximately ten cows to each bull (although this varies greatly at different sites). They haul out on the shore above the tide line to give birth. After parturition the cows may remain with their pups, but normally they spend most of their time in the water, only coming ashore to nurse every five hours or so, in response to the wail of their pups. Both the male and the female are very aggressive in this situation and pups are not infrequently killed accidentally by trampling. The Shetland colonies of both species vary from a very few animals to over one hundred although the colonies of the Common are generally small and widely scattered. The largest Grey Seal colonies are on long, narrow beaches on the west side of North Roe and on Fetlar, while the smallest are in deep and narrow geos or in caves.

Grey pups weigh an average of 32.5 lbs at birth which is ten pounds heavier than Common pups. Over the ensuing suckling period, Greys put on weight at the rate of nearly 4 lbs a day, so that at the end of the three week period of lactation they weigh from 80 to 110 lbs. At this point the Grey pup is a roly-poly dark skinned animal and the mother deserts it. In some pups growth is much slower and unless they have reached about 60 lbs by this time they are unlikely to survive the following winter. The relationship of the Common Seal pup and its mother is a much closer one, the pup accompanying and feeding from the mother in the water for possibly 4–6 weeks and probably being in contact for an even longer period. It does not increase in weight like the Grey pup, and year old Commons are not very much larger in size from pups of the year.

It is during the period when the pups are helpless on shore that hunting takes place. The exploitation of Grey Seal pups in Shetland has never been so intense as that of the Common, partly due to the season of breeding and partly to the general inaccessibility of the sites (Fig. 18). The highest recorded number of Grey Seal pups killed in any one year was 365 in 1964 although during the 1970s not more than 75 were taken in any one season and often many fewer. However natural mortality at the infant stage is high. In one season I counted over 100 pups at a cliff-foot colony on the west side of North Roe at an early state of moult. A few days later after a severe autumn gale only half-a-dozen pups could be found scattered over a wide area. Similar occurrences are known for the Fetlar colonies. Although specific localities are favoured for pupping, the actual site chosen may sometimes depend on the strength and direction of the weather at the time.

During the breeding period neither of the Grey Seal parents feed and this puts a heavy strain on the bull, who spends additional energy in defending his territory. The moult (which takes place in March) and the rigours of the winter weather also take a heavy toll. During the moulting period Greys may gather in a few sites, but afterwards they disperse widely throughout the islands until the onset of breeding season. However large numbers of Greys are often present at some sites, such as the Vee Skerries, during the summer months. First year Greys disperse widely and apparently randomly outwith Shetland – east to Scandinavia and south down the west and east coasts of the British Isles. Commons on the other hand have a much greater tie, although they may move in September from the immediate neighbourhood of their breeding sites.

Sexual maturity is reached in both species between the 4th and 7th year with the Common slightly earlier than the Grey seal. Mating takes place in the Grey at the time of breeding, but the Common appears to mate in September, a couple of months after the end of its breeding season and following the moult. The Venables have recorded Common Seals mating in Shetland in May and June. This has not been observed elsewhere, and they suggest that it may have been between young animals. The embryos of both species delay implantation until November/December for the Common and February/March for the Grey.

It has been suggested that Commons remain hauled out for particularly long periods in Shetland because the food resources are so ample it need not spend long periods feeding. When on shore they can be seen perched on the rocks in a very characteristic manner, balanced on their sides with heads and tails up forming a long 'U'. It looks extremely awkward but is presumably comfortable for the seal. They are frequently seen sleeping in the water also, rising vertically to the surface with their heads emerging every so often like fat black bottles.

In at least their first few months the young of both species seem to favour invertebrates such as crabs and squids, but as they get older they turn to fish

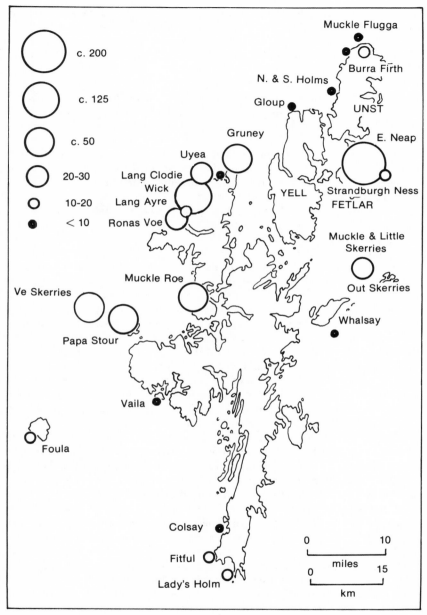

FIG 18.　Annual numbers of Grey Seal pups born.

for their main diet, the Grey feeding mainly on the larger species. The Common takes Whiting, Haddock, flatfish and Herring; while the Grey concentrates on Saithe, Skate, Cod and is known also to eat more squids and Octopus than the Common. When available both probably take Salmon and Sea-trout.

In both species the female is the longer lived, surviving approximately 30 years for the Common and 35 for the Grey, while a 46 year old Grey cow has been recorded from Shetland. The males of both species live to about 20 years, although the strain on the Grey is presumably much heavier than that on the Common.

As already noted the Common Seal population is now recovering from its past heavy exploitation in Shetland, but numbers of the Grey appear to be rather static, possibly limited by heavy juvenile mortality in their exposed pupping sites and maintained by recruitment from the large Orkney colonies. Indeed there has been a dramatic upsurge in the Grey Seal population of the British Isles as a whole. It has been suggested that this increase was already taking place before 1914 when it received statutory protection. Whatever its cause and timing, in recent years the increase has been exponential at the Farne Islands, in the Outer Hebrides and Orkney. In 1963 the Scottish population was estimated to be about 30,000; in 1978 it was 60,000. It is mainly because of this factor that there has been a call to reduce the population lest the commercial fish species go down more seal gullets than human gullets. Overfishing and subsequent reduction of the fish stocks have exacerbated this conflict between man and seal. However, little is known of the feeding habits of Greys when dispersed offshore, although there is a reasonable amount of information on their diet in inshore waters. (If the population is to be reduced simply because of the pressure of fishing interests should we prepare to reduce the Porpoise and seabird populations next?) The population explosion has brought overcrowding with associated malnutrition and disease to the more dense colonies such as those on the Farne Islands.

Another reason for culling seals is that the Grey Seal particularly is an intermediate host for the nematode worm *Terranova decipiens* which has its larval stage in the Cod. Although this is harmless to humans if the fish is cooked, no-one likes to see cysts in their food and fishing interests are understandably concerned that we are not put off eating their product.

As the populations of both Seals are not large it is unlikely that they cause much damage in Shetland, except to nets and lobster pots on occasion. Such damage is, of course, a sign that we are dealing with animals of considerable intelligence. One has only to watch Seals at play with buoys and ropes to appreciate this, which, along with their appealing appearance, is what raises such strong feelings over their destruction. Our attitude to Seals remains ambiguous, despite our persecution of them for several hundred years.

Vagrant seals from the Arctic appear in Shetland from time to time but there is no evidence at the moment that they appear more often here than on

British mainland coasts. The Ringed Seal (*Phoca hispida*) which has a circumboreal distribution from the Baltic to the Pole has been recorded only once – in 1968 when one was shot off Whalsay. This species is however not easily distinguished from the Common Seal and may have occurred unnoticed. The Venables give several records in the 19th century for the Harp Seal (*Phoca groenlandica*) which breeds no nearer than Jan Mayen island, but it has not been recorded this century. The Bearded Seal (*Erignathus barbatus*) has been recorded only once, in 1977 at Yell. The Hooded Seal (*Cystophora cristata*), so named for the bladder on the head of the male, has been recorded twice in the 19th century, identified by men familiar with it on their trips to the Greenland Whaling. The most recorded Arctic vagrant to Britain and Shetland is the Walrus (*Odobenus rosmarus*) of which there are ten records from 1815 to 1926 and two unsubstantiated ones at Sumburgh in 1976. Its nearest breeding ground is at Spitsbergen.

References for Chapter 6
(full citations are given in the Bibliography on p. 353)

General: Corbet & Southern, 1977; Laws, 1977; Tulloch, 1978; Venables & Venables, 1955.

Whales: British Museum (Natural History), 1913–1978; Brown, 1976, 1978; Christensen, 1977; Evans, 1976*a,b*; Haldane, 1905; Jonsson, 1965; Sheldrick, 1976; West, 1972; Whitfield, unpublished ms; Williamson, 1948.

Seals: Anderson, 1974; Berry, 1969*c*; Bonner, 1971, 1972, 1976, 1978; Bonner, Vaughan & Johnston, 1973; Boyd, 1963; Consultative Committee on Grey Seals & Fisheries, 1963; Davis & Anderson, 1976 Edmonston, 1809; Harwood, 1978; Harwood & Prime, 1978; Hewer, 1964, 1974; Laws, 1973; Lockley, 1966; Marwick, 1975; Smith, 1966; Summers, 1978; Summers, Bonner & van Haaften, 1978; Tickell, 1970; Vaughan, 1975, 1977; Venables & Venables, 1955, 1957, 1959.

CHAPTER 7

LOCHS AND BURNS

THE DISTINCTIVENESS of much of the inland Shetland landscape comes from its mosaic of water surfaces and smooth, rounded hills. The relatively high rainfall, low evaporation, mainly impermeable rocks and large areas of peat, plus the glacially eroded plateau and numerous coastal deposition processes, have given rise to a vast number of lochs and lochans. There are 1577 waterbodies marked on the OS 1:50,000 map, ranging from large valley-trough lochs to a myriad of peaty pools less than half an acre in extent.

However, apart from the *Check List of Flowering Plants*, published in 1969 by Scott & Palmer, and a few unconnected studies by visiting biologists, there has been little systematic investigation of these freshwater bodies until quite recently. In 1973 R. Britton carried out a brief study and in 1974 the Institute of Terrestrial Ecology a larger scale survey, of a cross-section of lochs and streams. Much of the information in this chapter leans heavily on their results, but a lot of the data collected has not yet been fully analysed, so any conclusions must be tentative.

The majority of Shetland's waterbodies are less than an acre or two in extent, the highest density being on the ice-scoured plateau of North Roe where open water occupies about 30% of the land surface. There are also locally dense aggregations of peaty pools on areas of deep blanket peat, particularly on the island of Yell. Only a relatively few lochs occupy valley troughs and these are generally the larger lochs, such as Girlsta, Tingwall and Cliff. The lines of the valleys give shape to such lochs, while the sinking of the land by over 200 feet since the last glaciation means that many of these valleys have been drowned and become arms of the sea, in the shape of voes. Occasionally silt blocks off these inlets (for example at Spiggie) and fresh-water accumulates on the landward side. Landscape formation has prevented large catchments, limiting the development of large river systems, most streams being short, steep and fairly fast flowing.

The greatest concentration of lochs lies between 350 and 500 ft above sea level, with very few over 700 ft. The highest is at 1220 ft on Ronas Hill. This clumping of lochs means that there is little altitudinal variation in the flora and fauna.

BIOLOGICAL POVERTY AND CLIMATIC EFFECTS

Because of the complex geology (Chapter 2) there is a greater variety of freshwater types in Shetland than in any comparable area on the Scottish

Mainland, but for a number of reasons the flora and fauna are impoverished and fairly uniform.

Firstly, the isolation of Shetland hinders the immigration of many groups and species. For example, although 12 of the 13 acid water specific plants of Scotland are present (the absent species is the Lesser Yellow Waterlily, *Nuphar pumila*, which has not been recorded farther north than Caithness), there are numerous absentees among those with a preference for more productive habitats. There are also considerably fewer species of aquatic invertebrates than for the mainland: there is only one species of Dragonfly (*Ennalagma cyathigerum*) (and this is the most widespread species of the British Isles), four species of Stonefly, three of Mayfly and four of Leeches, compared with 43, 31, 47 and 14 species respectively in mainland Britain. Since there are few calcareous lochs in the North of Scotland and Shetland, their fauna and flora is particularly poorly represented; of the invertebrate fauna, the only calciphile molluscs are the Pea-Shell Cockle (*Pisidium henslowanum*) and the Great Pond Snail (*Limnaea stagnalis*), and the latter is confined to the only marl loch, on the limestone peninsula of South Whiteness. It might be thought that the absence of habitats contributes significantly to this general situation, but in fact there are available habitats for many other aquatic insects (at least). Organisms with efficient means of dispersal are well-represented. For example, there are ten species of Stoneworts (*Chara* and *Nitella* spp.) in Shetland, although they are confined to the more productive lochs. (The reason for this high number of species must be that these plants are easily wind dispersed.) Notable absentees from Shetland are the Canadian (*Elodea canadensis*), Curled (*Potamogeton crispus*) and Grassy Pondweeds (*P. obtusifoluis*) which occur in Orkney, and Water Plantain (*Alisma plantago-aquatica*) which occurs in Caithness.

Secondly, the combination of wind and sea means that all freshwater lochs are to some extent affected by salt spray, and have a higher concentration of sodium and chlorine ions than lochs a similar distance from the sea in mainland Scotland. In fact all lochs in Shetland up to 300 ft from the sea and less than 30 ft above sea-level are brackish. This raised salt content in the more acidic lochs reduces the biological distinction between them and the more productive lochs by allowing colonization of the former by organisms normally restricted to the latter and permitting some organisms characteristic of acid waters to replace absent species in the nutrient-rich lochs.

Sixty-five species and hybrids of aquatic vascular plants (including both submerged and emergent types) have been recorded from Shetland. These include 27 highly adaptable species with a widespread British distribution which occur in both nutrient-rich and nutrient-poor lochs (eutrophic and oligotrophic respectively). For example the Water Milfoil (*Myriophyllum alterniflorum*) and Shoreweed (*Littorella uniflora*) extend from fairly peaty waters to those that are quite productive; the Stoneworts also (*Chara aspersa* and *C. delicatula*) extend into much more acidic waters than in Scotland.

There is also only one truly freshwater Shrimp (*Gammarus lacustris*), although there are many brackish species and some such as *Gammarus duebeni* are found nearly a mile from the sea! The maritime influence has also a distorting effect on the phytoplankton populations.

Species diversity is not directly related to loch size: some small peaty lochs have a comparatively rich flora, while large productive lochs influenced by sea spray have only a very few species. Generally though, the blurring of distinction between lochs, the general paucity of species diversity, and the fact that the microclimate varies little between lochs, means there is an overall simplification of ecology affecting all groups. The most diverse and varied floras are found in a few of the large productive lochs, such as the Lochs of Cliff and Tingwall (which each have 24 recorded species) but also in the tiny machair Loch of Hillwell and some small mesotrophic lochs such as Kirkiegarth and Bardister.

A further characteristic of the Shetland lochs is that the summer water temperature is on average 2.5°F cooler than at a similar height on the Scottish mainland. This allows organisms normally restricted to higher altitudes to survive at much lower altitudes in Shetland. For example a Flatworm (*Crenobia alpina*) which is confined to springs and high altitudes in most of Britain replaces the normal lake dwelling species in lochs near sea-level in Shetland. The lower temperatures have also allowed colonization by arctic aquatic organisms, for example the Water Flea (*Eurycerus glacialis*), which occur in the highest loch on Ronas Hill and has otherwise been recorded only once in Scotland.

Wind, the ever present wind, contributes to the biology of the Shetland lochs except in very sheltered situations or in small shallow lochs, in more ways than as a vehicle for salt spray. The water surface is rarely still and continual wave action hinders the development of emergent plants so that their overall importance in the biology of the lochs is much less than that of the submerged species. Very often the only emergent species in the more acidic lochs is the Bottle Sedge (*Carex rostrata*) and in more productive lochs, Quillwort (*Isoetes* spp.) and Spikerush (*Eleocharus* spp.).

The winds also create a certain amount of vertical water movement, and even in the deepest loch (Girlsta, 75 ft) there is no obvious thermal stratification. Lochs which are classified as 'eutrophic' therefore, are so in a peculiarly Shetland definition of the term, indicating a relatively high nutrient content with an associated diversity of flora and fauna, and in contrast to the less nutrient-rich 'oligotrophic' and the peaty 'dystrophic' lochs, it does not indicate that these lochs are eutrophic in the classical sense. That is, there is no deep layer, or hypolimnion, of organic material to reinvigorate these lochs in spring.

The distribution of trophic types depends largely on the underlying geology of the lochs and their catchment (Table 9). Large areas of Shetland on the most

TABLE 9. Classification of Shetland Lochs into Trophic Categories based on the Geology of the Catchment (after Britton, 1974)

	Number	% of lochs
Dystrophic	547	34.7
Oligotrophic	661	41.9
Mesotrophic	212	13.4
Eutrophic (excluding serpentine)	39	2.4
Serpentine	72	4.6
Brackish	45	2.8
Marl	1	0.1

acidic and impermeable rocks have a covering of blanket-peat with numerous peaty lochs and lochans. These dystrophic waterbodies, particularly those of half an acre and less are by far the most numerous of all the waterbodies and form a quite distinctive group. Generally they are shallow with dark brown peaty water, low in nutrients, alkaline, and with a high concentration of iron and phosphorus. In these peat stained waters light penetration is extremely limited even one inch below the surface, and submerged aquatics are found to a depth of only three feet. In the clearer acidic lochs they may be found down to about ten feet. Typically these lochs have soft edges and are the habitat of nesting Red-throated Divers, which because of their limited manoeuvrability on land construct their nests just above the waterline where they can slip easily in and out of the dark protecting waters (Chapter 9).

Characteristic submerged species are Bog Moss (*Sphagnum cuspidatum*) and Bulbous Rush (*Juncus bulbosus*), associated with emergents such as Cotton Grass (*Eriophorum angustifolium*). In the larger lochs, with deeper and less cloudy water the pink and white flowers of Bogbean (*Menyanthes trifoliata*) are very common, accompanied often by Bottle Sedge, Shoreweed and the relatively tall and branched Jointed Rush (*J. articulatus*). The slow-moving streams that issue from and connect these lochs have a very similar flora, often sharing with the lochs the Bog Pondweed (*Potamogeton polygonifolius*) and sometimes containing a unique Gnat, *Simulium zetlandese*.

Other common species are Lesser Spearwort (*Ranunculus flammula*), Floating Bur Reed (*Sparganium angustifolium*), Star Sedge (*Carex echinita*), Creeping

Bent (*Agrostis stolonifera*), occasionally the Great Bladderwort (*Utricularia vulgaris*), and in the West Mainland lochs Awlwort (*Subularia aquatica*). In a few sites, also mainly in the West Mainland, somewhat unexpectedly and sheltered often behind the protection of Bogbean, are the exotic white flowers of the White Water Lily (*Nymphaea alba*) giving in the summer white faces scattered on the dark skin of the water. Very occasionally thick stands of Bullrush (*Schoenoplectus lacustris*) also occur, which species extends into the intermediate mesotrophic lochs.

The next most abundant loch-type is the oligotrophic loch. These are usually larger and deeper than the dystrophic ones. However dystrophic lochs and the small oligotrophic ones (up to two acres) make up more than half of all the Shetland lochs. Oligotrophic lochs are common on the acidic igneous rocks in the absence of peat. They are particularly common in North Roe where they lie in ice-scoured basins, surrounded by small, smooth hills with much exposed rock. Imprisoned in the hard rocks, lacking suspended peat particles and solutes generally, they are sparkling clear. To some eyes these are the most attractive lochs in Shetland, the clarity of the water contrasting with its rugged surroundings. On still days the landscape north of Ronas Hill lies reflected in a host of broken pieces.

All the oligotrophic waters have a rather similar flora. The cover of aquatics, except in very shallow sites, is extremely small and even in the large, typically stony-edged lochs, the vegetation is restricted to a narrow peripheral band up to about six feet from the side. In the largest lochs this may occur only in sheltered bays and on sheltered shores. Two species which occur but are absent from dystrophic lochs, are Common Quillwort (*Isoetes lacustris*) and Water Lobelia (*Lobelia dortmanna*); while species characteristically absent but which are found in the mesotrophic and eutrophic lochs include Stoneworts and the Pondweeds other than Broad-Leaved Pondweed (*P. natans*). Other species in common with the dystrophic lochs are Shoreweed, Floating Bur-weed and Bulbous Rush. Sheltered edges may carry Water Horsetail (*Equisetum fluviatile*) and the Common Spike-Rush (*Eleocharus palustris*). These sites are generally poor in their invertebrate and phytoplankton populations, although many of them carry appreciable numbers of catchable Trout, which must be influenced by factors other than the geology of their catchment.

Mesotrophic lochs lie on comparatively basic rocks, but these are often hard and insoluble and if their catchment is on acidic moorland, such lochs may be little more productive than the oligotrophic lochs. However they usually have more species than the last type, although the species diversity is less than in more productive oligotrophic ones. They are found mainly on the crystalline limetones and harder and more insoluble sandstones of the West Mainland. Examples are Girlsta, Cliff, Tingwall, Kirkiegarth and Bardister.

Mesotrophic lochs have many species in common with the more extreme types, such as the Alternate-Leaved Water-Milfoil (*Myriophyllus alterniflorum*), Shoreweed, and some of the Stoneworts (*C. aspera* and *C. deliculata*). Typical

Pondweeds are Various-Leaved (*P. graminus*), Perfoliate (*P. perfoliatus*), Long-Stalked (*P. praelongus*) and in one loch the Reddish Pondweed (*P. alpinus*), all of which are northern continental species.

Of these lochs the more interesting are Girlsta, the deepest loch and the only Shetland site for the Arctic Char (*Salvelinus alpinus*); and the Lochs of Tingwall, Cliff, Kirkiegarth and Bardister for their variety of flora and for their importance as wintering wildfowl sites. The Lochs of Cliff and Girlsta are not as important for wildfowl as the others due to their large areas of deep water. Tingwall and a few other mesotrophic lochs in the Sandness area are noted for their breeding Tufted Duck.

The most productive or eutrophic lochs are generally small, with the exception of Spiggie in the South Mainland. These lochs lie on and within the catchments of the more basic and soluble sandstones (such as on Bressay), on limestone and areas of blown shell sand (at Quendale and Breckin), and on the serpentines of Unst and Fetlar.

Generally, the eutrophic lochs are those with the highest alkalinity, indicating a high proportion of $CaCO_3$ (greater than 30 parts per million). The serpentine lochs have a high alkalinity caused by the presence of magnesium rather than calcium salts, as well as having exceptionally high concentrations of nickel and chromium salts and low ones of potassium, phosphorus and nitrogen. As the lochs on the serpentine are not particularly nutrient-rich, they should not properly be classified with the other eutrophic lochs. Very little is known of their biology, since there are very few of this type of loch in Britain as a whole, but since the chemical nature of their environment is very distinctive, it is quite possible that their biology may also be unique. For example, Shetland as a whole is a favoured habitat for the zooplankton *Draptomus wierzejski*, but a small serpentine pool in west Fetlar supports a uniquely dense population ($210,000/m^3$ in May 1975).

Eutrophic lochs are characterized by a wide range of species and a generally dense cover of submerged species, up to 100% at shallow sites such as the Loch of Hillwell above the Quendale sands. This site is the only Shetland locus for two vascular plant species, Spiked Water Milfoil (*M. spicatum*) and a pondweed (*Potamogeton x zizii*). In addition the Flat-stalked Pondweed (*P. friesii*) and Mare's Tail (*Hippuris vulgaris*), two very rare Shetland plants, have recently been found in this loch. It is noteworthy also for populations of two of Water Bugs (*Sigara dorsalis* and *Callicorixa praeusta*) which are much smaller than elsewhere in Britain. For its size, it is probably the most productive loch in Shetland, and is extremely important for wildfowl, both breeding and wintering.

Species always present in these lochs are the Stonewort (*C. aspera*) and the Slender-Leaved Pondweed (*P. filiformis*). Other common species of the deeper water are the Stonewort (*Nitella opaca*), the Autumnal Starwort (*Callichtre hermaphroditica*) and a moss (*Fontaninalis antipyretica*). In shallower water, Various-Leaved and Perfoliate Pondweeds, Small Pondweed (*P. berchtoldi*) and Floating Sweet Grass (*Glyceria fluitans*) occur. Emergents are numerous and include many of the more colourful flowers such as Marsh Marigold (*Caltha palustris*), Water Forget-me-not (*Myosotis repens*), Amphibious Bistort (*Polygonum amphibium*) and Flag (*Iris pseudocarus*).

A number of rare species and species at the edge of their European range are to be found in the Shetland eutrophic lochs but usually in only a very few, e.g. Mare's Tail (*Hippurus vulgaris*), the Stoneworts (*Nitella confervacea* and *Tolypella nidifica*) and the Shetland Pondweed (*P. rutilus*) which is found elsewhere only in the Outer Hebrides and one place in Easter Ross.

Eutrophic lochs are uncommon in northern Scotland, but plant species which occur in Orkney and not in Shetland include Shining Pondweed (*P. lucens*), Glaucous Bulrush (*Schoenoplectus tabernaemontani*) and Bur-reed (*Sparganium ramosum*).

The richest eutrophic lochs, particularly those least influenced by sea spray, have a high biomass of both zooplankton and phytoplankton. The diversity of these groups appears to depend more on the size of the loch than other factors, the greater the size and depth of the loch, the less the proportional biomass. Notwithstanding, the greatest biomass of phytoplankton is found in the physically very disparate Lochs of Spiggie and Kirk, the latter lying on the edge of the Breckin sands in North Yell and supporting a unique association of blue-green, euglenoid algae.

Like the eutrophic lochs, the brackish lochs are usually small, but again with one exception, the Loch of Strom at Whiteness. They are formed by coastal depositional processes, so common in the islands, such as bar, spit and tombolo formation. There are very many small lochs of this type, Easter Loch in Unst being a good example of one of the more productive. Brackish lochs differ from eutrophic ones in the absence of the almost ubiquitous freshwater species, Shoreweed and Bulbous Rush, but share with them the Stonewort (*C. aspera*) and Sea Arrow Grass (*Triglochin maritima*). They are characterized by the presence of Slender Spike-Rush (*E. uniglumis*), occasionally Tassel Pondweed (*Ruppia maritima*), and rarely Coiled Pondweed (*R. spiralis*). The last has a very restricted range in Britain.

As these sites grade into a more marine situation there is an increase in the seaweeds, typically the Wracks – Bladder Wrack (*Fucus vesiculosus*), Serrated Wrack (*F. serratus*) and *F. ceranoides*, but also the Red Seaweeds, particularly *Chondrus crispus* and *Polyides rotundis*. These brackish sites are also important for wintering wildfowl, but only where they are reasonably productive.

STREAMS

Of all the freshwater situations, the burns and streams have been least investigated. For reasons already indicated the majority are short and steep, and pass over either peat or hard insoluble rocks, giving them a stony, gravelly or peaty base. The last has a flora akin to the lochs in slow moving situations, but in the absence of sediment and on unstable substrates the others are unsuitable habitats for large vascular plants and some burns have no macrophytic vegetation at all. The flora of these burns is therefore quite distinct from the lochs and is dominated by leafy liverworts such as *Scapania undulata*, while plants on the edge may include the Lesser Spearwort and certain Rushes, such as the Bulbous Rush.

In low lying and particularly in agricultural land, burns may be slow and depositing, often grading into ditches or the marshy margins of lochs. The dominant species is usually the Marsh Marigold, the ditches lining the green croft land with ingots of gold. Altogether the flora is rich and diverse with a wide variety of flowering plants such as Wild or naturalized Mints (*Mentha* spp.), naturalized Monkey Flowers (*Mimulus* ssp.), Redleg (*Polygonus persicaria*), Speedwell (*Veronica* ssp.) and Water Forget-me-not.

FISH AND AMPHIBIANS

Although the majority of the burns and lochs of Shetlands are unproductive in the biological sense, the islands are famed among anglers for their fishing. In particular the Brown Trout (*Salmo trutta*) is ubiquitous in all but the smallest peaty lochans. Their colour and markings vary a great deal. For example at Spiggie the Trout tend to be silvery and almost indistinguishable from Sea Trout; those on the serpentine are often tinged with red on the belly; while those from more dystrophic waters are dark and brightly spotted with red. Sea Trout too are common, but restricted to larger burns and lochs close to the sea. They return to spawn from about early September onwards. When rain falls heavily and the burns are amber in spate, there is a rush of both fish and anglers to the burn mouths. In Shetland there has been a tradition and a crofting right for many centuries to net the Sea Trout, but unfortunately the short-sighted and greedy have netted over-heavily for commercial gain in recent times and nowhere are the fish as numerous as they once were.

There are a few sites for Salmon (*Salmo salar*) but only at the largest burns, which one can hardly call rivers. Rainbow Trout (*Salmo gairdneri*) have been introduced to a number of lochs, but there are no signs of them becoming naturalized and spawning. A near-relative, the Char (*Salvelinus alpinus*) is predominantly a deep water fish and occurs only in Girlsta where presumably the temperature is most suitable for it. Shetland is (obviously) their most northerly British occurrence.

Other common fish species are the Eel (*Anguilla anguilla*), found in lochs and burns; the Three-Spined Stickleback (*Gasterosteus aculeatus*) in all situations from fresh to brackish water, except the most acidic and peaty lochs; and the Flounder (*Platichthys flesus*) in lochs with an easy access to the sea and with suitable substrate. The only other fish species occurring in Shetland is the Lamprey (*Petromyzon marinus*). There are doubtful records for *Salmo clarkii* (introduced into a Loch on Vaila, but not known whether it survives), and the

Ten-Spined Stickleback (*Pungitius pungitius*) (reported from the Lochs of Cliff and Watlee). As with other groups, it is clear that the number of species is highly restricted. It is no doubt significant that all these fish species either have a marine phase in their life-cycle or are tolerant of high salinities. It is also of interest that the species composition in Shetland is effectively identical to that of Iceland.

There are no amphibians native to Shetland. The Common Toad (*Bufo bufo*) has been introduced in small numbers on a number of occasions but has never become naturalized. The Common Frog (*Rana temporaria*) has been released several times this century and breeds successfully. It has been carried (probably by children) to most parts of the Shetland Mainland and to Yell.

AQUATIC ECOSYSTEMS

Limited as the information is about Shetland invertebrates, it is possible to draw some conclusions about the faunal poverty of the islands. Although 124 taxa have been recorded, the diversity of the invertebrates is extremely small in comparison with both Orkney and Scotland, and many groups and species have not been found. For example there are only 22 species of molluscs known whereas there are well over 700 native to Britain; and in the Crustacea there is only one freshwater Shrimp. Most of the common species are non-specialists, found in both standing and running water (*e.g.* the Wandering Snail (*Lymnaea pereger*)), while rarer species appear to be confined just to one or two sites.

In the zooplankton there are again a relatively few species and these recur in varying combinations in a whole range of conditions. Five cladoceran and five copepod species have been recorded, with only two of each group appearing in appreciable numbers in any of the 56 lochs sampled. These are the copepods, *Cyclops streuus abyssorum* and *Diaptomus wierzejski* and the cladocerans, *Bosmina corgoni* var. *obtusirostris* and *Daphnia hyalina* var. *lacustris*, the first being the most abundant species in each case. In general the majority of lochs at the time of sampling contained only one species of each group (population numbers vary according to the season), with one species representing over half the total zooplankton population. Only four species altogether are found in any one loch. Although the species composition is generally uniform, obvious distinctions are that large lochs, except the most acidic, and those with a maritime influence, tend to have the greatest diversity. An improvement of trophic status of a sample is always associated with a greater abundance.

Of the 58 lochs studied for their phytoplankton, all are different to some extent in their species composition and diversity. Four hundred species have been recorded and some of these seem to be new to science. Certain general features are extremely interesting, for example in nearly every loch two groups predominate – the Chlorococcoles (green algae) and the Chrysophyceae (brown algae), with the latter of more importance. There is a relative paucity of desmids and diatoms. The predominance of the Chrysophyceae, which thrive in nutrient-poor conditions is a common feature in the Fenno-Scandian region, but is rare in Britain, although few similar areas to Shetland have been studied. The strong maritime influence may have something to do with this situation.

The phytoplankton abundance decreases with an increase in depth and size, but exceptionally Spiggie Loch is one of the richest lochs, while another is the tiny Kirk Loch. In these eutrophic lochs the phytoplankton are mainly of the blue-green euglenoid type, in contrast to the predominance of brown algae in more acid lochs.

The overall picture of the Shetland lochs is of an immense number of waterbodies with great variation in trophic status but distinctions between them are not great, and their biologies tend to be impoverished, uniform and simple in comparison to the Scottish Mainland. The main points of interest for future study are isolation, marine influence, simplistic ecosystems and the unusual chemical conditions prevailing in the largely unstudied serpentine lochs.

References for Chapter 7
(full citations are given in the Bibliography on p. 353)

Blackburn, 1874; Boycott, 1936; Britton, 1974; Druce, 1922; Flinn, 1974; Fowler, 1977; Friend, 1959; Goode, 1974; Gorham, 1958; Hall, 1954; Jones & Mortimer, 1974; Macan & Worthington, 1951; Maitland, 1972; Mercado, 1967; Murray & Pullar, 1910; Oldham, 1930, 1932; Palmer & Scott 1969; Poppius, 1904–05; Scott & Duthie, 1894; Spence, 1964; Swan, 1957; Tulloch & Hunter, 1972; Venables & Venables, 1955; West & West, 1904.

CHAPTER 8

LAND ANIMALS

THE LAND animals of Shetland are extremely patchily known. There are few mammals and only the Otter and Field Mouse have been in the islands longer than written history. The Lepidoptera have been relatively well studied because many local forms exist in Shetland. With the exception of the Spiders, other invertebrates have been only studied piecemeal, and no general reviews have been undertaken.

MAMMALS

The land mammals illustrate particularly well the limitations and fascinations of the Shetland fauna. There are only a few species present, and all of them must have been introduced since the Ice Age. Some species have been intentionally released (Table 10); others have colonized the islands following a chance landing. Once ashore all the animals have had to adapt to the Shetland environment in order to survive. Unfortunately the amount of this adaptive change is impossible to determine unless specimens are available from different times during the history of the animals in Shetland, since the genotypes of the original colonizers is inevitably unknown. Only for sheep is anything known about the differences between the breed in past centuries and nowadays. All other species have to be compared with their relatives in other areas. Differences between the Shetland form and the typical form elsewhere can be established in this way, but they may have arisen either by an initial genetical difference in the colonizing group (the 'founder effect', see Chapter 1) or subsequent adaptation.

Apart from these uncertainties much of the mammalian fauna of Shetland may be of no greater interest than indicating the interests or prejudices of past naturalists. For example the Brown Hare (*Lepus europaeus*) was introduced into both Orkney and Shetland by their Member of Parliament, Samuel Laing about 1830. By the 1890s it was very common in parts of the Mainland and crofters were having to shoot numbers to protect their crops. In 1882 Hares were released at Windhouse and Reafirth on Yell, but they soon died out, and after the turn of the century, the species began to decline on the Mainland, becoming extinct about 1937. In contrast, the Blue or Mountain Hare (*Lepus timidus*) was introduced from Scotland to the Kergord estate about 1907, and exists now in moderate numbers throughout the Mainland. In recent years some animals were introduced on Ronas Hill, and their descendents now flourish in Northmavine. It is abundant on Vaila where two pairs from

Perthshire were released about 1900. The Shetland Hares share the characteristic of the Scottish race of not turning completely white in winter, although individuals with only their ears remaining brown are frequently seen until May.

There are two carnivores in Shetland (apart from dogs and domestic cats) – the Stoat (*Mustela erminea*) and the Otter (*Lutra lutra*). The Stoat is known as the 'Whitrit', which presumably means 'White Rat'. This has been present since at least the early 17th century, when a Zetland Court Statute (dated 1st August 1615) ordered that the head of a 'Quitred' (*i.e.* Whitrit) be presented to the Court by every local minister and gentleman. Brand records 'There are no weasels (stoats) in all the Northern Isles of Zetland, as I am informed, tho' numerous in the Mainland, which they report thus came to pass: The (King's) Falconer having a power given him, to get a Hen out of every House, once in the Year: but one year they refusing, or not being so willing to give, The Falconer out of Revenge, brought the next year two Weasels with him, which did generate and spread, so that now they are become very destructive to several goods of the Inhabitants, whereof a Gentleman, our Informer, told us he had killed several half an Ell long'. The Venables somewhat prosaically suggest that this story may be apocryphal, and that Stoats may have been intentionally introduced to control rabbits. Certainly Stoats were once released on Whalsay in an attempt to control rats and rabbits, although they are now extinct there. They are found today only on the Mainland and Muckle Roe.

Otters are almost marine mammals in northern Scotland. Analysis of spraints (faeces) collected in Fetlar has shown that 90% of the diet of otters there was fish (half being 'long fish' like Blennies, Butterfish, and Eels), and the remaining 10% was crabs. They also prey on breeding duck and Black Guillemots. This means that the distribution of the species is almost entirely coastal. It has been estimated that there is at least one otter every three-quarters of a mile on the more remote Shetland coasts, which means that the islands probably have a higher otter density than any other part of the British Isles. They are particularly fond of small uninhabited islands, but they also occur inland by loch and burn sides.

In the past they were caught for their pelt in 'Otter-houses', a stone box-trap on a known run, with a trip-wire releasing a trap-door from above once the Otter is inside.

The Shetland equivalent of the phrase 'Live and let live' is 'Lat be for lat be, as Robbie Glen said to the Otter'. The story is that the unfortunate Robbie Glen once stunned an otter (they are surprisingly often seen in the day-time for such shy animals), and thinking it dead he slung it over his shoulder and set off home, holding the creature by its tail. Unfortunately for Robbie the Otter recovered and gripped Robbie's own tail from behind – and this made him make his bargain.

The mammals which have the longest history in Shetland are farm animals

TABLE 10. Mammals (excluding domestic and farm animals)

	Origin	Distribution
INSECTIVORA		
Hedgehog *Erinaceus europaeus* L.	Introduced by a Tingwall farmer *c.* 1860.	Widely distributed on most inhabited islands (except Out Skerries, Unst, Fair Isle).
CHIROPTERA		
Bats	At least 5 species recorded, but only vagrants.	
CARNIVORA		
Stoat *Mustela erminea* L.	Introduced in 17th century.	Mainland and Muckle Roe (formerly also Whalsay).
Otter *Lutra lutra* (L.)	?	Widespread.
LAGOMORPHA		
Brown Hare *Lepus capensis* L.	Introduced in Cunningsburgh district *c.* 1830.	Common on Mainland around 1900 but hunted because of damage to crops; last seen alive in 1937. Survived only briefly on Yell after release there in 1882.
Mountain Hare *Lepus timidus* L.	Introduced to Kergord *c.* 1907; separately to Vaila from Perthshire *c.* 1900.	Widespread on Mainland hills. Changes from winter coat in mid-May.
Rabbit *Oryctolagus cuniculus* (L.)	Warrens on Burra and Scalloway islands by 1654.	Widespread, but has become extinct on some islands (said to have been elim-

RODENTIA

Species	Origin	Distribution
Field or Hill Mouse *Apodemus sylvaticus* (L.)	Originally from Norway, presumably *via* Viking ships.	Rocky hillsides and dry stone walls on all larger and many small islands (except Out Skerries). Separate races described on Yell (*A. s. granti* Hinton), Foula (*A. s. thuleo* Hinton) and Fair Isle (*A. s. fridariensis* Kinnear). Invade croft land in autumn.
House or Grey Mouse *Mus musculus* L.	Originally from Norway.	Widespread, although soil of South Havra, Hascosay and Uyea believed to exclude mice – soil from these islands was often spread round houses and corn ricks in other parts of Shetland as a preventative measure.
Black or Ship Rat *Rattus rattus* (L.)	Recorded as present in early accounts *c.* 1650; Brand (1701) refers to rats going ashore from ships in harbour. Whalsay rats reputed to have come from Baltic traders in haaf fishing era.	In Whalsay until at least 1951. Probably in Lerwick and Scalloway Harbour areas.
Brown Rat *Rattus norvegicus* (Berk.)	Origin unknown. Reached Britain (allegedly from Russia) in 1728–9, and Faroe in 1768 from a ship wrecked on Lewis but which grounded in Faroe.	On all large inhabited islands except Yell (extinct within living memory), Fetlar.

which were presumably brought by the earlier settlers: Rabbits; and Field and House Mice. The date of introduction of the Rabbit is not known, although warrens were present on West Burra, and the isles of Oxna, Hildasay, and Papa Little were 'somewhat stored with Coneys' by 1654. Shetland Rabbits are unusual in being polymorphic for coat colour – blacks, chocolates, spotteds, and even true albinos occur in significant frequencies. Dominantly inherited blacks survive on islands and headlands in other parts of the United Kingdom in situations where food is limited, apparently because they are more stolid than normal agouti animals, and continue feeding when their sibs are scared into their burrows. The extra food they get in this way presumably more than offsets their risk of being predated. The reason for the survival of the other colour forms is completely unknown; the occurrence of wild-living albinos is particularly surprising. Both the mouse species have probably been on Shetland since early Viking days, and come as close as any mammals to being indigenous.

FIELD AND HOUSE MICE

The Field Mouse (*Apodemus sylvaticus*) is common throughout the larger islands of Shetland, in all places away from the larger townships. Indeed it is usually called the 'Hill Mouse', which fairly accurately describes its habitat – certainly more accurately than its European and English name of 'Wood Mouse'. One of the reasons for its success in Shetland is that there are no Voles, and it shares the drier areas where Voles would live with the House Mouse. Shetland *Apodemus* are among the more brightly coloured races of the species, and are often referred to as 'Red Mice' in distinction to the House or 'Grey Mice'. Field Mice are more common than in Orkney, where they have to compete with Voles (*Microtus arvalis orcadensis*). The only small mammal in Faroe is the House Mouse.

Both Field and House Mice in Shetland are large forms of their species (Table 11). Indeed the House Mice are among the biggest recorded in the world. No-one knows why this should be so, although increased size is an almost invariable characteristic of mice living on small islands. The most likely reason is that mice are usually smaller than their most efficient physiological size because of the need to escape down small holes when chased by predators who are themselves capable of squeezing into holes. The relative absence of such predators in places like Shetland means that the larger animals are not continually eliminated, and the mean size of the mice is consequently able to increase. The main advantage of larger over smaller size is that body surface is reduced in relation to body volume, meaning that the proportion of energy lost as heat is reduced. Since the main cause of death in mice is cold, even a small increase in size is likely to be important. Other effects of greater body size will show in intraspecific fighting and intra-uterine competition between embryos.

The rapid change in body size of island mouse populations is of general

TABLE 11. Average sizes of Shetland Mice with other populations for comparison (mature animals only)

No. in sample		Weight (g)	Head & body	Tail	Hind foot
			Lengths (mms)		
Apodemus sylvaticus					
60	Iceland (*A. s. grandiculus*)	—	103.0	90.8	23.2
95	Foula (*A. s. thuleo*)	26.8	101.2	92.1	24.0
5	Yell (*A. s. granti*)	—	100.9	88.2	23.6
30	Fair Isle (*A. s. fridariensis*)	32.1	112.9	98.6	23.9
76	St Kilda (*A. s. hirtensis*)	42.6	114.4	99.2	25.1
38	Rhum (*A. s. hamiltoni*)	30.1	105.9	92.9	24.6
33	Perthshire	18.4	92.3	82.6	21.8
40	Surrey	20.4	87.6	86.2	21.9
Mus musculus					
55	Mykines, Faroe	25.4	96.1	87.9	19.0
49	Sandøy, Faroe	20.9	96.7	84.4	18.6
54	Foula	25.1	97.7	82.5	18.2
95	Bressay*	16.7	86.5	78.5	18.7
53	Scalloway*	15.5	83.2	72.8	18.1
91	Dunrossness*	17.4	86.5	75.1	18.4
12	Fair Isle	21.1	98.5	82.9	18.6
77	Sanday, Orkney*	17.9	87.6	73.1	17.7
64	Harray, Orkney*	14.8	84.0	69.5	17.7
104	Somerset*	13.5	86.6	74.3	16.8

*Caught when ricks threshed, and hence from a different environment to the other House Mouse samples, which were trapped in fields and on the cliffs.

interest. Some years ago, a Finnish palaeontologist, Bjorn Kurten attempted to measure evolutionary rates in recent geological time by comparing the size of fossil and living members of a range of species. The majority of forms had either not changed in size, or had altered to a comparatively small extent. From the amount of size change, Kurten was able to conclude that most rates of change were reasonably constant. However one species comparison was an order of magnitude greater than most: that was size change in Icelandic Field Mice in the millennium that they would have been isolated following the first human contacts with the island after the end of the Ice Ages. However, no early or sub-fossil Iceland mice are available, so Kurten was forced to compare the Icelandic mice with their putative nearest relatives, modern-day

Scandinavian animals. These latter are much smaller than the island mice. Consequently Kurten calculated that evolution had proceeded at a very much higher rate in Field Mice than in all other species he studied. This is a cautionary tale: it is dangerous to base any major generalization on a single trait (such as body size), which may be liable to rapid modification in particular conditions.

Shetland mice differ in more ways than size from other forms of the same species. A new species of *Apodemus* (*A. fridariensis*) was described in 1906 from six adult mice caught on Fair Isle. They were large animals, with a brain case longer and narrower than in typical *A. sylvaticus*, and a less developed coronoid (articulating) process on the lower jaw. The dark pectoral spot usually found on the white ventral surface between the forelegs was reduced or missing. In 1914 another subspecies (*granti*) was described from Yell, and in 1919 *thuleo* from Foula. Both the Yell and Foula races were smaller than the Fair Isle one, the Yell form having in addition a slightly shorter tail and the Foula one particularly large hind feet.

The Shetland subspecies were part of a general recognition during the early years of this century that a great deal of differentiation has occurred in small mammals on the islands of the western North Atlantic (especially the Hebrides, Orkney, and Shetland). As far as *Apodemus* is concerned, three species containing 16 subspecies were set up, all of them on small islands. This diversity becomes significant when contrasted with the uniformity of the species on the continent of Eurasia, where it extends from the Atlantic Coast to western China. Thus Barrett-Hamilton, one of the founding fathers of British mammal studies, wrote '*Apodemus* appears to be a form which in its long standing and successful struggle for existence has attained to a height of specialization from which it has either very little power of variation, or else which is such as to fulfil all the needs of the species in almost any conditions with which it may be brought into contact. The possible range of its variations, whether individual or geographical, would seem to be narrow. Unlike some of our common mammals, it is not subject to either melanism or albinism. In the whole series of the "Zoologist" and the volumes of the "Field" for the last twenty years, there is not to be found a single recorded instance of a well-marked sport of this species – a result which would have been very different had the object of the search been *Sciurus vulgaris*, *Talpa europaea* or *Mus musculus* (Squirrel, Mole or House Mouse). This, of course, does not prove that conspicuous sports do not occur, but it undoubtedly emphasises their rarity.'

The mainland uniformity of *Apodemus* highlights the separateness of the Shetland races of the Field Mouse. It led previous writers to ascribe to the latter a status which they do not possess. For example, the Venables believed 'the Shetland field mouse is indigenous, that is to say that mice of this genus were already on Shetland when the islands first separated from the main land mass of Europe, and have since evolved into a distinctive type not found elsewhere . . . they appear to be the only indigenous land mammal in the islands'; in his New Naturalist on *British Mammals*, Harrison Matthews argued 'one is forced to the conclusion that these populations probably entered the islands at the earliest possible moment after the last glaciation and that the islands were not cut off before the early part of the post-glacial period'; the authors of the *Highlands and Islands* New Naturalist go even further, 'if *Apodemus* is isolated for centuries in a small island it will begin to show differences from the main stock through the process of natural selection . . . *Apodemus* is a true relict.'

These conclusions are mistaken, but they have strongly influenced views about the antiquity and moulding of the Shetland fauna: if *Apodemus* could colonize Shetland by walking there, so could other animals. Entomologists, for example, have taken the existence of *Apodemus* in Shetland as indicating a post-glacial land-bridge, and gone on to date the origin and nature of some of the northern butterflies and moths by it.

But *Apodemus* did not walk to Shetland. As we have seen, there is no geological evidence for a post-Pleistocene connection between Scotland and Shetland (Chapter 2). Indeed the Shetland mice are more closely related to Norwegian animals than to Scottish ones. The way to show this is to compare as many gene frequencies as possible in population samples. This can be most conveniently done by using the frequencies of non-metrical skeletal variants as indicators of variation in a large number of genes. There are a number of technical advantages in doing this, not least the fact that the skull of a mammal is relatively imperishable and is the part most frequently present in museum collections. It is important to use a large number of genes when attempting to measure relationships in order to dilute the effect of adaptation (as in increased size) or chance in altering the frequencies of some genes.

Differences in non-metrical skeletal variant frequencies between two samples can be combined into a single multivariate statistic, which gives a measure of the degree of relationship between the samples. When the Shetland populations are compared with Norwegian and Scottish Highland samples, Yell mice are found to be much closer to Norwegian than Scottish animals. Comparisons within an island (or between samples collected on a single land-mass, such as the Scottish Highlands) consistently show little or no divergence – the statistic is around zero. The Fair Isle and Foula populations are unlike both Scottish and Norwegian mice, but are more like the Yell mice than anything else (Fig. 19). These relationships seem to indicate that the Yell *Apodemus* population was derived directly from Norway, and that the smaller islands were colonized from Yell (or one of the other large islands; no large collections have been made from the Mainland, which is the most likely source). Since each colonizing event presumably involved a few animals getting ashore, their gene frequencies will almost inevitably differ from those in the ancestral population (Fig. 2). The *founder effect* is the most powerful way there is of changing gene frequencies (p. 20). Consequently it is not surprising

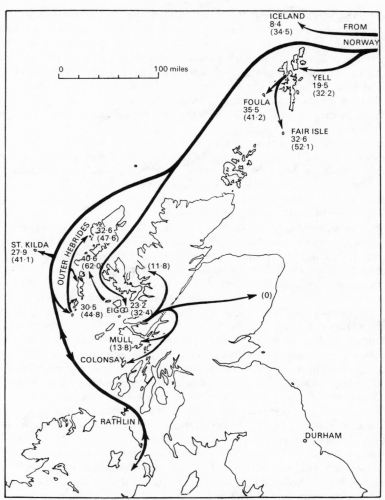

FIG 19. Map to show the suggested routes by which Shetland and the Western Isles were colonized by Field Mice (*Apodemus sylvaticus*). The figures are estimates of divergence (the higher the value, the more distant the relationship), those without brackets being the 'genetic distance' from the closest related population, and those in brackets the 'distance' from the Loch Sunart population (taken as typifying Scottish Highland Field mice) (from Berry, 1969).

that the Foula and Fair Isle populations are as distinct as they are. Now discussion about relationships between populations leads us back to the question of how long mice have been on the Shetland islands. Since massive genetical change can take place so easily, there is no need to assume that the distinctiveness of the Shetland forms implies they have been isolated for a very long time. The maximum antiquity for the Yell population will be a time when boats began sailing from Norway to Shetland; the Foula and Fair Isle populations could have been established at any time since. Probably *Apodemus* got ashore from one of the early Viking ships – perhaps in a cargo of seeds, or in the bedding of animals being introduced for the settlers' farms – about 1200 years ago.

The *Apodemus* situation is important, not only because of the confusion that has arisen through assuming that Field Mice are 'relics' rather than being introduced into Shetland, but also because of the light it throws on the mechanisms of biological change in general. If subspeciation can happen suddenly, new gene combinations can be 'tried out' by natural selection, and evolution will be able to proceed much more rapidly than forecast by the classical mechanisms of genetical change.

Not surprisingly, House Mice show a parallel situation to field mice in Shetland. Both the House Mice of St Kilda (where House Mice became extinct in 1932, but had previously been separated as the only distinct British species of *Mus*, *M. muralis*) and Faroe have a narrowing of the mesopterygoid fossa on the ventral surface of the skull (*i.e.* the place where the internal nostrils open). Magnus Degerbøl of the Copenhagen Museum and one of the most learned scholars of Scandinavian and island mammals, has speculated that this trait might be an allometric result of large size (which it is not because laboratory mice often attain the same size without showing it), or an indication of a previously widespread North Atlantic population exterminated on the mainland by a later invasion of mice. In fact both these suggestions are wrong: it is a sign of common ancestry, since Shetland Mice also possess it. As would be expected from the operation of the founder effect, its frequency is different on different islands: on Fetlar it occurs at 91%, on Foula at 9%. There are two stories of the introduction of House Mice to Foula – that they were released there by some Walls fishermen in dispute with Foula men about fishing rights, or that they came over in a packing case when a shop was first opened on the island. Both stories put the introduction about 1830. Narrowing of the mesopterygoid fossa has not been found in Orkney mice.

FARM ANIMALS

At one time Shetland had its own characteristic breeds of Pigs, Cattle, Ponies, and Sheep. In mediaeval times every township had a few Pigs, but no Pigs are kept in Shetland now. Small black Shetland Cattle (related to primitive Norwegian beasts) still exist, but they are thin-skinned and do not withstand cold weather well. More important in these northern latitudes where winter feed is often critically scarce, is that the traditional breed is very slow growing: a Shetland calf takes two years to mature, in contrast to the usual one year. A fat Shetland cow weighs two to two and a half hundredweights, and gives 5–8 quarts of milk a day. A first generation cross with a Shorthorn weighs up to five hundredweights and produces 10–14 quarts. It was said of the native breed in the 19th century that their only virtue was their 'capability to withstand improper treatment, and it will not under any circumstances, pay for artificial feeding'. In our days of better husbandry they are increasingly being replaced by Herefords and Shorthorns, but even these are dropping in numbers with on the one hand the increasing cost of freight to the markets of mainland Scotland, and on the other the growing use of deep freezers to reduce the local dependence on fresh meat.

Ponies are probably the most well known Shetland animals outside Shetland. Basically they are the same breed as those of Norway, although it is said that they crossed with Spanish horses from Armada wrecks. A skeleton of a pony of 12 hands was found in a midden at Jarlshof, and ancient stones from Bressay and Papil have a carving of a pony, ridden by a hooded figure, presumably a priest or a monk. The Shetland Court Books of the 16th century have a number of mentions of 'horsis' in connection with offences committed in the islands. These show the importance placed on the hair of the tails: this was of great economic value, and was used for making cords, fishing lines, and so on. Early in the 17th century, an Act was passed making it an offence to 'row or cut' the hair from the tail of another man's horse.

A 'Shetland Pony Study Book Society' was formed in 1890, and has published a register of horses and breeders most years since. The objects of the Society are to maintain the purity and promote the breeding of Shetland ponies. In 1956 a Premium Stallion Scheme was set up in collaboration with the Scottish Department of Agriculture. Under this, up to 18 registered stallions are placed on scattalds (common grazings) in the islands, and these have produced a great improvement in the present stock.

In the 18th century, the largest animals were exported and complaints were made that the breed was becoming smaller. However, the Marquis of Londonderry established stud farms on Bressay and Noss in 1870–1899 to produce horses for use down coal mines with the appearance but not the prohibitive size of the Clydesdale. In fact selection for big feet seems to have led to an overall increase in body size and even today decades after the introduction of more careful breeding, ponies in Shetland are frequently larger than 'Shetland ponies' in other places. The traditional use of ponies was as pack animals, particularly for bringing home peats from the hills; nowadays they are bred for riding and export. The first mention of the Shetland pony for road transport seems to have been made by Christian Ployen,

Governor of Faroe, who visited Shetland in 1839. He tells that he was driven in Lerwick by his host in a carriage drawn by a pony, and that he rode a pony for trips further afield – and that he was much impressed.

As cattle declined so sheep increased in Shetland. In the early 17th century a typical family would keep nine cows and 22 sheep on average. The ratio of cows to sheep was about 1 to 4 in 1870, but by 1970 the sheep population had trebled to about 200,000 and the ratio was about 1 to 250.

Shetland sheep are world renowned for their fine, soft wool. They are also small, very hardy, and produce good mutton. Only the rams have horns, and the breed has several primitive features which suggest an affinity with the even more primitive Soay sheep of St Kilda. One of these is the short tail, another is the tendency for the fleece to be moulted annually, and a third is the occurrence of coloured wool.

The average fleece weight is about 2 lb, and has increased $\frac{1}{2}$ lb through selection during the past 40 years.

Only about two per cent of Shetland sheep are coloured today, and of those the most common colour is the brown 'moorit'. However there are also black, piebald, and grey sheep and some variations. One of these, known as 'shaila' is greyish-black and is said to resemble hoar frost on old, rain-sodden snow. In the past there was a hairy variety of Shetland which may have been the result of Norse influence. This may survive as the 'hardback' on Foula. A similar method of inheritance of colour in Orkney and Icelandic sheep suggests they have a common origin. Shetland sheep are not very different to Orkney ones, including the well-known seaweed eating animals of North Ronaldsay. However precise relationships are difficult to ascertain. For example, the range of fleeces from hairy to woolly was a common feature of primitive sheep, and provides the basis for selective breeding everywhere.

The tendency to moult the fleece is due to a cyclical activity of the skin follicles. In the past it led to the custom of 'rooin' or plucking the wool, so that the fleece would not be lost. Complaints about the cruelty of this practice are periodically made, but always rejected, since the sheep moult naturally. As long ago as 1619 the Scottish Privy Council forbade rooin on the ground that it was 'grievous and noisome to the poor harmless beasts'. The Shetlanders protested, explaining 'that the undirgrowth of young woll cast off the auld groith of the awn accord, without pulling or clipping, and as naturallie as gif the wool wes taen off by industrie or art', and that consequently their practice was not 'grievous to the puir beastis'. The Council appointed a commission which confirmed the facts were as stated by the islanders, whereupon the prohibition was withdrawn.

The Shetland sheepdog perhaps ought to be included with the other farm animals. It probably originated from a cross of a Scottish collie with the all-purpose 'toonie' dog, which scavenged the crofting townships. At some time crosses with the 'Yakkie' dog of the Greenland whalers must have also taken place, giving the Shetland dog a black muzzle. Since 1908 breed standards have been established, and the modern selected dog probably bears little resemblance to the early crofters' scavenger.

There is no bat colony in Shetland, but occasional vagrants are reported in the islands. A Parti-coloured Bat (*Vespertilio murinus*) turned up on Whalsey in 1927, and another one appeared on an oil rig in 1965. The Whalsey occurrence was only the second time the species was recorded in Britain; it probably came from Norway. In 1947 a Long-eared Bat (*Plecotus auritus*) was disturbed hibernating in a Lerwick factory. A male Leisler's Bat (*Nyctalus leisleri*) was found at Ollaberry in 1968, a very long way from its northernmost colonies in Yorkshire and Northern Ireland. It appeared after a period of south-easterly winds which would have helped a flight from eastern England. However at least one 'assisted passage' has been reported: when a Swedish vessel in Scalloway Harbour in the early 1920s raised her mizzen sail for the first time since leaving home, a large bat flew out of the folds and was seen around the Castle on several subsequent evenings. It was most likely a Noctule (*Nyctalus noctula*) or a Serotine (*Eptesicus serotinus*).

Towards the end of the 19th century professional collectors began to visit the Outer Hebrides, Orkney and Shetland to search for rare specimens which could be sold in the south. The first lepidopterist to visit Shetland seems to have been a certain MacArthur, sent by E. G. Meek. He visited the Mainland in 1880 and 1881, and Unst in 1883. Following publicity about some of the distinct forms caught, Shetland acquired a fame which attracted a host of lepidopterists: C. A. Briggs, Meek himself, E. Roper-Curzon, P. M. Bright, J. F. X. King, W. Reid and W. Salvage.

The chief peculiarity of the Shetland moths which attracted so many outsiders was a high frequency of melanic forms. About a third of the non-migrant species are represented in Shetland by a form much darker than the typical (*e.g. Standfussiana lucernea, Diarsia mendica, Hadena confusa, Eupithecia venosata*) or by a range of forms between melanic and typical (*e.g. Amathes xanthographa, Eulithis populata, Apamea monoglypha*). At the same time as collectors began to visit Shetland, they also went to Orkney, usually to Hoy, but the Shetland forms were more spectacular (and saleable) than those found in Orkney, and Shetland was much more intensively collected. Melanics apparently identical to some of the Shetland forms occur as industrial melanics in England. For example, 4% of the black form of *A. monoglypha* occurs at Bradford, 17% at nearby Guisley. However industrial melanism is a result of changes in the day-time resting-places of moths as a result of pollution (eliminating, among other effects, vegetative lichens from trees and fences), and there is negligible air pollution in Shetland. In fact melanics are found in both Orkney and Faroe, but at a much lower frequency than in Shetland (only 2% of indigenous species in Faroe). The occurrence of melanism is high at the same latitude as Shetland in both Norway and Canada, and must be an adaptation to climatic or biological conditions at 60°N.

The Shetland lepidopteran fauna contains about half the species known from Orkney, and about three times the number known from Faroe (which has been poorly studied from the lepidopteran point of view) (Table 12).

TABLE 12 Number of species of Lepidoptera (after Wolff, 1971)

Norway	1700
Great Britain	2567
Orkney	282
Shetland	145
Faroe	56
Iceland	76

Orkney has no resident species which are not found in Caithness, but Caithness has more than 50 species which are not found in Orkney (almost all being deciduous woodland forms). Clearly the Shetland fauna is much more isolated from regular large-scale immigration than the Orkney one. There are a few species in which variation in Orkney is intermediate between that in Shetland and on mainland Britain (*e.g. Diarsia mendica* and *H. confusa*). It is impossible to know for certain in these cases whether the intermediacy in Orkney is a consequence of gene-flow or adaptation, although it may be of significance that the species with a great difference between Orkney and Shetland populations tend to be the more fragile (*e.g. Eupithecia venosata, Perizoma albulata*).

As already noted, entomologists have traditionally regarded the Lepidopteran fauna as having entered Shetland in early post-glacial times over a landbridge from the Scottish Mainland, and their reason for postulating a landbridge has been that the Field Mouse would have needed one to colonize the islands. (The survival of invertebrates in ice-free areas or nunataks through the Ice Ages is considered to be highly improbable – see Chapter 2.) Since the Field Mouse was almost certainly introduced by man (p. 135) and there is no geological evidence for a post-glacial land connection with Scotland (p. 53) we are forced to conclude that all the Shetland Lepidoptera reached the islands by flying (or at least by wind) or 'hitching a lift' on water transport. (It is said that the Cabbage White was introduced on NAAFI cabbage during the 1939–45 war.) A study of immigrants into Finland has shown that most were carried on aircurrents more than 500 miles from the south or south-east.

There would clearly be no problems for even poor fliers to be introduced to Shetland from either Scotland or Scandinavia. This means there is no certain way of establishing the date of colonization by any particular species. This is a great pity because it would be fascinating to know how quickly melanism has evolved in Shetland. More than 100 trunk-sitting cryptic species became largely melanic in industrial Britain during the second half of the 19th century, and geneticists assume that this very rapid change was possible because the species concerned had experienced conditions favouring melanism at some previous time in their history, when their adaptation was presumably much slower. (The reason for assuming widespread pre-industrial melanism is that virtually all melanic forms are inherited in a dominant fashion, and dominance itself has been shown to be the result of an evolutionary process in a number of moth species.) The uncertainty about the history of the Shetland Lepidoptera and the knowledge that the constituent species can have colonized the islands only after the final retreat of the Pleistocene ice, increases the fascination surrounding the origin and maintenance of the Shetland melanics.

Experimental Studies on Melanism

The reason for the high number of Lepidopteran melanics in Shetland is still unknown. The most reasonable hypothesis is that the long twilight period in summer means that nocturnal moths are flying before darkness fully falls, thus exposing them to predation by insectivorous birds. Under these conditions, a dark moth could have a cryptic advantage. However there is no evidence for this suggestion: the correct explanation could as easily be that the coloration is a physiological response to the cool conditions of Shetland.

A determined attempt to discover the factors maintaining the melanics was made by Bernard Kettlewell and collaborators using the Autumnal Rustic (*Paradiarsia glareosa*). This species was chosen because it has a distinct melanic (*f. edda*) which cannot be confused with the typical form (*f. typica*) except in very worn specimens. It is unusual in this respect; most of the Shetland melanics do not have a sharp distinction between the dark and light forms. Presumably special factors must have operated to bring about this distinction. As with most industrial melanics, the melanic phenotype is dominant over the grey typical one.

Until 1959, the melanic *edda* was not known to occur outside Unst; *f. typica* was known from Dunrossness. The original plan of the Autumnal Rustic study was to collect *f. edda* from Unst and *f. typica* from the South Mainland; to release the melanics in the south and typicals in the north; and then sample the population near the release points in order to measure the differential survival of the two forms in conditions where they did not normally occur. These experiments showed that in Unst the dark form had an advantage of 7.0

± 6.5% over the lighter one, while in the South Mainland there was no advantage of either form.

The mark-release-recapture experiments were later extended to two more sites (Hillswick and Tingwall). In no place was there much difference in the proportion of dark and light moths recaptured, although moths released at their site of capture always survived longer on average than moths from elsewhere. For example, at Hillswick marked *f. typica* and *f. edda* of local origin both survived 3.4 days on average between release and recapture, while morphs originating from the South Mainland survived 2.6 and 2.5 days respectively and Tingwall ones 2.8 and 2.6 days. *F. edda* tended to have a slightly higher survival than *f. typica* at its home site, but always survived less well than *f. typica* when moved. As far as the Autumnal Rustic is concerned, home is best. Being interpreted, this suggests that there is a degree of local adaptation which cannot be recognized from a simple inspection of the two morphs.

At an early stage in the study, *f. edda* was found in the South Mainland and further sampling throughout Shetland revealed that it occurred in all parts of the islands with decreasing frequencies towards the south of the archipelago (Fig. 20). It has now been found also in Orkney and Caithness. When the 'moth distance' in Shetland is plotted, the frequency of *f. edda* falls smoothly

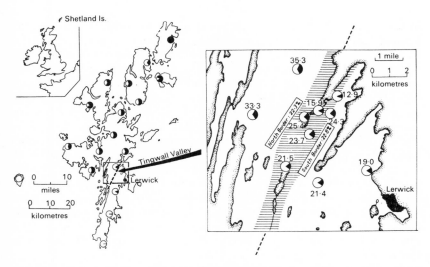

FIG 20. Frequencies of the melanic form (*edda*) of the Autumnal Rustic Moth (*Amathes glareosa*) in Shetland, showing the situation in the Tingwall Valley in detail. Numbers in the Tingwall Valley are frequencies of *f. edda*. In this region frequency differences are maintained despite virtually no movement of moths across the valley (based on Kettlewell & Berry, 1961, 1969).

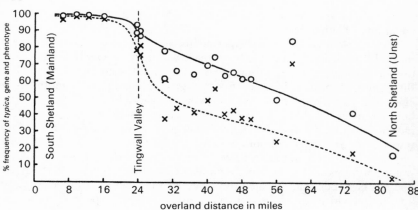

FIG 21. Decline in frequency of the wild type (*typica*) morph of the Autumnal Rustic northwards in Shetland, and its replacement by the melanic morph *edda*. Phenotype frequencies are represented by X, allele frequencies by O. The dotted line shows the cline in phenotype frequency, the continuous line that of allele frequency (from Kettlewell & Berry, 1961).

from 97% at Baltasound to less than 1% in the South Mainland (Fig. 21). ('Moth distance' in this sense means the shortest distance between sampling sites over land.) The frequency of *f. typica* on the opposite sides of the channels separating different islands was consistently similar, *i.e.* 38.2% at West Sandwick on Yell and 37.7% at North Roe on the Mainland; 42.6% at Burravoe in South Yell, and 48.7% at Mossbank on the Mainland opposite. This again suggests local factors adjusting phenotype frequencies, with similar pressures operating in similar sites separated by water.

Notwithstanding, the rate of change of allele frequencies is so smooth that it invites an explanation of common but uniformly changing factors acting throughout the Shetland range of the moth. Indeed the observed frequencies fit a theoretical model of a cline proposed by J. B. S. Haldane, based on a population divided into two parts by a barrier such that one homozygote is at a disadvantage on one side of the barrier but has an overall advantage on the other. In any cline, the rate of change of gene frequency is the result of migration decreasing the slope of change, while selection acting differently on the two phenotypes increases the slope. Since these two forces must be equal in an equilibrium situation, Haldane was able to derive an expression for the relation between the intensity of selection, the mean distance migrated per generation, and the slope of the cline.

On the evidence of the phenotype frequencies alone, there is a good case for a barrier between the population in two parts of the Shetland population. The incidence of *f. edda* remains high over the whole of the northern half of Shetland, falling only gradually (40% in 45 miles) in a southerly direction; in the South Mainland *f. edda* is much less common and the rate of change of frequency even less. However there is an intermediate region where *f. edda* frequency drops 35% in, about eight miles (Fig. 20). This region is centred upon the Tingwall Valley, which runs right across the Mainland, varying from a half to two miles in width. The valley itself contains little of the short heather in which the Autumnal Rustic lives in Shetland. If Haldane's arguments are accepted, the *net* advantage of *f. edda* over *f. typica* north of the valley is less than 1% which seems very small even though it refers to the equilibrium situation at any point in the cline.

The applicability of the Haldane model depends on a reversal of advantage of the two morphs at the Tingwall Valley. We carried out an experiment in which moths of both morphs were released on the two sides of the valley with different marks and their movement measured by recording the recaptures in traps situated along the two sides of the valley, and in the middle. Three conclusions emerged:

1. Individual moths frequently flew over a mile, judging by the number of individuals recaptured some way from the site of release.

2. Despite the facts that 65 moths were recaptured (out of 1682 released), that the wind during the experiment would at times have tended to blow moths from one side of the valley to the other, and that many moths moved much further than the distance between the two sides of the valley, only a single moth was recaptured on the opposite side of the valley to the one on which it was released.

3. The frequency of *f. edda* on the northern side of the valley was 22.3%, whilst on the southern slope it was effectively the same (22.8%), although the frequencies in the sparse colonies in the middle of the valley ranged from 15.9% to 25.4% over a distance of less than a mile, and these values did not change from year to year. However the frequency of *f. edda* increased up to 35% over two or three miles immediately to the north of the valley in an area of apparently uniform heather moor.

If the Tingwall Valley was really a barrier between a northern and a southern population of the Autumnal Rustic, *either* there should be considerable movement across the valley associated with a rapid elimination of the unfavoured form on each side; *or* the frequencies on the two sides of the valley should be markedly different. As it is, there can be no doubt that the valley does operate as a considerable barrier to moths, but that this barrier merely shows up the distinct populations existing over short distances in an apparently continuous area on the two sides. Far from being a situation of a cline maintained by diffusion of migrant moths, the *f. edda* cline is much closer to a network of partially isolated islands with local factors controlling the genetical constitution in each.

Clearly different factors operate in different places. Kettlewell shot birds (mainly gulls) searching the ground in Unst where moths were very dense, and found that their crops had 21% of *f. typica* in them although the local frequency of typicals was only 3%. Selective predation by birds is clearly an important factor for the Autumnal Rustic in Unst, although it is probably less in other parts of the islands. Indeed there are at least three other pieces of evidence of selective factors acting independently of the main cline in melanism:

1. Most important is the typical pattern of recaptures in north Shetland. With recapture experiments in general there is an exponential decay of recoveries with time – the longer the period since release, the fewer the proportion of recaptures. Autumnal Rustics from south Shetland behave in this way, but in the north there were consistently more moths recaptured on the second night after release than on the first. This was clearer for *f. edda* than *f. typica* because the numbers involved were greater, but it seems to be true for

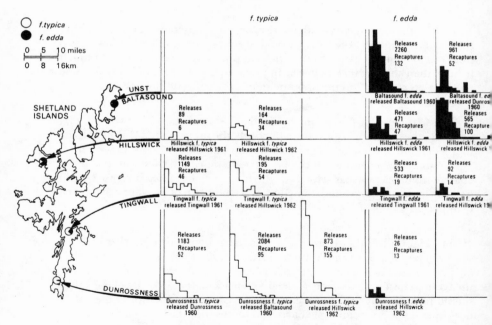

FIG 22. Histograms of marked Autumnal Rustic Moths recaptured. The horizontal axes represent days between release and recapture (from Kettlewell, Berry, Cadbury & Phillips, 1969).

both forms if they originated north of the Tingwall Valley (Fig. 22). The simplest explanation of this peculiar observation is that only a proportion of the population flies every night, which means that there will be a residue of the population surviving if catastrophe strikes on a particular night. Since a flying creature like a moth is particularly vulnerable on a small island in a high wind, this restriction of flight would obviously be advantageous. Indeed flightlessness has evolved among both bats and birds on many oceanic islands. The point in the present context is that this reduction in flight seems to occur in both *f. edda* and *f. typica*.

2. The *edda* character seems to be incompletely dominant in the Shetland Mainland, and 'dark' and 'light' *edda* can be recognized in the same proportions as those expected of homozygotes and heterozygotes. At the limit of its range on Unst, there were only a third of the expected number of light *edda*. The simplest explanation of this was that there were genes modifying the colour of the moths, so that the character was more completely dominant. Once again we have a local genetical heterogeneity.

3. Finally, measurements of a number of elements (legs, wings, antennae, etc.) in hundreds of moths from all over Shetland has shown that there was no simple distribution of these size characters such as would be expected if the only genetical variable was the *edda* allele. Moreover correlations between different measurements varied considerably between different localities.

The genetical situation in the Autumnal Rustic in Shetland is clearly not a simple story of changing advantage of the melanic morph. Ironically, we still do not know the reason for the occurrence of *f. edda* in Shetland. Attempts to find the answer to this apparently simple question have revealed a situation of considerable complexity. It is frustrating not knowing the answer to the questions which originally inspired a piece of research, but as so often, the facts that emerged may be of greater general significance.

SPIDERS

An Edinburgh University Expedition led by Drs Philip Ashmole and John Godfrey visited Shetland in 1974 specifically to study the terrestrial invertebrates. At the time of writing only the work on Spiders has been completed. The expedition collected specimens from 70 species; only 35 species had previously been recorded from the islands. Further collecting by members of an ITE Survey team and by an expedition from Leicester Polytechnic increased the number of Spider species recorded in Shetland to 90 (Table 27) and incidentally revealed how little was previously known about this group – as also virtually all other invertebrate groups.

Almost all the species found in Shetland (and in Faroes and Iceland) are also present in both Scotland and Scandinavia. However only two-thirds of the Faroe species and less than half of the Iceland species are also found in Shetland. Three hundred and eighty-four species have been recorded on the Scottish mainland. Many of those not in Shetland are undoubtedly absent because of a failure to colonize rather than an inability to survive. For example *Collinsia homgreni* and *Erigone tirolensis* are arctic-alpine species which are found high on Scottish mountains; they have been found up to 3000 ft on Ben Hope in Sutherland – but they have not been recorded in Shetland. Nevertheless, habitats that are well represented in Shetland have a higher proportion of species found in Britain than the 15% overall. For example Shetland moorland has half the species recorded from Moor House in the northern Pennines, but there are virtually no woodland species in the islands. And in the same way that plants characteristic of high mountains further south are found near sea-level in Shetland, the spiders of Ronas Hill are only found at about 3000 ft above sea-level in the Cairngorms.

The information available about other invertebrate groups indicates that the spider situation may be typical for Shetland, *i.e.* a relatively small number of species present, with no particular surprises among those that are present (*e.g.* Coleoptera: Table 26; Siphonaptera: Table 24). But the land fauna is so poorly known that further work could reveal completely unexpected situations.

References for Chapter 8
(full citations are given in the Bibliography on p. 353)

Vertebrates: Baldwin, 1978; Barrett-Hamilton, 1900; Barrett-Hamilton & Hinton, 1910–21; Beirne, 1952; Berry, 1969a, 1970, 1973, 1974; Berry, Evans & Sennitt, 1967; Berry, Jakobson & Peters, 1978; Berry & Rose, 1975; Berry & Tricker, 1969; Corbet, 1961, 1970; Corbet & Southern, 1977; Cox, 1976; Degerbøl, 1939, 1942; Delany, 1963, 1964; Delany & Davis, 1961; Evans & Buckley, 1899; Harvie-Brown, 1892, 1893; Hewer, 1974; Hinton, 1914, 1919; Jewell, Milner & Boyd, 1974; Kikkawa, 1959; Kinnear, 1906; Kruuk & Hewson, 1979; Kurten, 1959; McGillivray, 1920; Matthews, 1952; Ryder, 1968, 1971; Ryder, Land & Ditchburn, 1974; Speed & Speed, 1977; Tulloch, 1978; Venables & Venables, 1955; Watson, 1978.

Lepidoptera: Beirne, 1943, 1947, 1952; Berry, 1977; Cadbury, 1975; Ford, 1945, 1955a,b; Goater, 1969, 1973; Haldane, 1948; Hare, 1963; Kettlewell, 1961a,b, 1965, 1973; Kettlewell & Berry, 1961, 1969; Kettlewell, Berry, Cadbury & Phillips, 1969; Kettlewell & Cadbury; 1963; Lindroth, 1970; Lorimer, 1975; Manly, 1975; Mikkola, 1967; Slatkin, 1973; South, 1888; Traill, 1888; Vaughan, 1880; Weir, 1880; White, 1882; Wolff, 1971.

Arachnida: Ashmole, 1980; Bristowe, 1931; Cherrett, 1964.

Other Invertebrates: Blackburn, 1874; Bloomfield, 1904; Carpenter, 1962; Coope, 1969; Fowler, 1977; George, 1970; Grimshaw, 1905; Hall, 1954; King, 1890, 1896; McLachlan, 1884; Rothschild, 1958; Smit, 1955.

CHAPTER 9

TERRESTRIAL BIRDS

DESPITE first appearances, Shetland is one of the truly exciting areas of the world for the ornithologist; not only for the immense numbers of seabirds and breeding northern species; but for the wintering birds – Whooper Swan, Long-tailed Duck and Great Northern Diver; the migrants driven in from Iceland, Scandinavia and Siberia, precipitating onto the smaller outlying islands of Fair Isle and Out Skerries; the unique Wren and Starling; and the questions of race and adaptation to the constraints of an isolated group of islands between the North Atlantic and the North Sea. Of the 63 or so regularly breeding birds, one third occur in significant numbers in a national context, while the Rare Bird Records for 1958–72 show that Shetland has recorded over 80 species, the most for any British County.

The birds of Shetland require a book to themselves in the tradition of Saxby, the Unst doctor whose *Birds of Shetland* was published in 1874 after his death; of Evans and Buckley who collaborated to produce the *Vertebrate Fauna of Shetland* in 1899; and of the husband and wife team of Pat and Ursula Venables whose *Birds and Mammals of Shetland* was published in 1955. We have drawn heavily on these early accounts, and refer to them by the names of their authors. Our description of the bird-life of Shetland is the largest section of this book; we have tried to compress as much information as possible into this and the next two chapters – particularly in the tables of the status of the birds in the Appendix (p. 314). However our primary aim has been to summarize the important facts of the avifauna within the context of the total environment of Shetland. To make our account coherent, we have grouped our discussion into an arbitrary, although we trust, sensible manner. The major distinctions will be in life-forms, into those commonly termed 'seabirds', dependent on the sea for their presence, and 'landbirds', those constrained more by available breeding habitats and the geographical location of the islands. This chapter will deal with the landbirds and the following two with seabirds, and with Fair Isle and migrants respectively. Table 13 shows all breeding species with distribution and status and Table 14 gives breeding species in adjacent island groups. It should be noted that any indication of status change of species must be qualified by the limitations of earlier records, as Saxby's observations refer mainly to Unst, while those of the Venables are particularly relevant to the South Mainland and the Weisdale area. Nowadays there is a full time R.S.P.B. Representative and a resident Nature Conservancy Council Officer, besides a thriving Bird Club with observers located throughout Shetland.

TABLE 13.   Regular and sporadic breeding birds (including Fair Isle) in the last 50 years.
Order follows that of *Birds of the Western Palearctic* (1978)

Explanation of Symbols

Status	R or r	Resident species: the whole or most of the population remains throughout the year. R – Common; r – Scarce.
	P or p	Partial migrant: breeding species of which a substantial part of the population winters outside Shetland, the remainder remaining here throughout the year. P – Common; p – Scarce.
	S or s	Summer resident: breeding species of which the whole or most of the population winters outwith Shetland. S – Common; s – Scarce.
	M or m	Regular migrant: M – Common; m – in small numbers.
	A	Scarce migrant, usually recorded but not always.
	V or v	Vagrant. V – More than 5 occurrences; v – less than 5 occurrences.
	W or w	Winter visitor. W – Common; w – scarce.
	Sporadic	Not breeding every year, sometimes only once.
Number	Or	Order 1 1–10 If number of pairs known, indicated Order 2 11–100 Order 3 101–1000 Order 4 1001–10,000 Order 5 10,001–100,000 Order 6 100,001–1,000,000 (Auks given as birds not pairs.)
Stability		Increasing or decreasing where known.
Proportion %		Proportion of British population if known. If not known but considered important – Probably significant.
Shetland Distribution		Ubiquitous 45–49 BTO Squares Widespread 35–45 BTO Squares Moderate 25–35 BTO Squares Restricted 10–25 BTO Squares Sparse 5–10 BTO Squares Minimal 1– 5 BTO Squares

Common Name	Scientific Name	Shetland Name	Status	Shetland Distribution	British Distribution
Red-throated Diver	Gavia stellata	Raingoose	S 500 Increasing 30–50%	Widespread	N & W Scotland
Little Grebe	Tachybaptus ruficollis		w Sporadic	Sparse	Throughout
Fulmar	Fulmarus glacialis	Maalie	R 150,000 Increasing 40%	Ubiquitous	Absent only from SE coast
Manx Shearwater	Puffinus puffinus	Lyrie or Baakie craa	S Low Or 3	Circa 10 small colonies	Several large colonies West Coast
Storm Petrel	Hydrobates pelagicus	Ala mootie or Oily mootie	S Or 4	Probably widespread	West coast
Leach's Petrel	Oceanodroma leucorhoa		s m Or 1–2	1 colony	4 colonies NW Scotland
Gannet	Sula bassana	Solan	P 10,000 Increasing 8–9%	3 colonies	16 colonies N. W & E coast
Cormorant	Phalacrocorax carbo	Lorin or Big Scarf	R 500 Fluctuates	7 scattered colonies	Almost throughout
Shag	Phalacrocorax aristotelis	Scarf	R 10,000 min. 30%	Widespread	Predominantly NW Scotland
Shelduck	Tadorna tadorna		s Or 1	Sparse	Throughout
Wigeon	Anas penelope		M w Or 1 Sporadic	Sparse	Scotland
Teal	Anas crecca		r w Or 1 – Low Or 2	Sparse	Throughout
Mallard	Anas platyrhynchos	Stock Duck	R m w Or 2	Restricted	Throughout
Pintail	Anas acuta		m w Sporadic	Sparse	Scotland, N Ireland, SW England
Shoveler	Anas clypeata		m w Sporadic	Sparse	Throughout
Tufted Duck	Anthys fuligula		r W Or 2 Increasing	Sparse	Throughout

Common Name	Scientific Name	Shetland Name	Status	Shetland Distribution	British Distribution
Eider	Somateria mollissima	Dunter	R 15,000 birds 20% (including Fair Isle)	Widespread	Scotland & N Ireland
Common Scoter	Melanitta nigra		s Or 1	Sparse	N Scotland & Ireland
Red-breasted Merganser	Mergus serrator	Herald Duck	R Or 2 High	Restricted	N & W Scotland & Ireland
Merlin	Falco columbarius	Peerie Hawk/Sparrowhawk	r m 23–30	Restricted	Widespread
Peregrine	Falco peregrinus	Stock Hawk	r Or 1	Sparse	Widespread
Red Grouse	Lagopus lagopus		r Or 2 low	Sparse	Widespread
Quail	Coturnix coturnix	Deadchick	A Sporadic		Throughout
Pheasant	Phasianus colchicus		r Sporadic		Throughout
Corncrake	Crex crex		s Sporadic Decreasing		N & W Scotland, W Ireland & N England
Moorhen	Gallinula chloropus		m r 4–6 pairs Decreased	Sparse	Throughout
Coot	Fulica atra		w m r 1–2 pairs Sporadic Decreased		Throughout
Oystercatcher	Haematopus ostralegus	Shaldur	S Or 3–4 Increasing Prob. significant	Widespread	Throughout Scotland coastal Ireland & England
Ringed Plover	Charadrius hiaticula	Saandy Loo	P M 500 Increasing 10%	Widespread	Coastal throughout
Golden Plover	Pluvialis apricaria		P Or 3 5%	Moderate	Widespread except England

Lapwing	*Vanellus vanellus*	Tieves' nacket	S Or 3 Increasing	Widespread	Throughout
Dunlin	*Calidris alpina*	Plover's Page	S M Or 3 Low	Restricted	Widespread
Snipe	*Gallinago gallinago*	Snippack	R m Or 3	Restricted	Throughout
Woodcock	*Scolopax rusticola*		m Sporadic		Throughout
Black-tailed Godwit	*Limosa limosa*		s m 1–2 pairs	Minimal	Norfolk
Whimbrel	*Numenius phaeopus*	Peerie Whaup or Tang Whaup	S 200 pairs Minimum 90% Increasing	Restricted	Few pairs Scotland & W Isles
Curlew	*Numenius arquata*	Whaup	R m Or 3	Moderate	Widespread
Redshank	*Tringa totanus*	Ebb-cock	R m w Or 3 Low Increasing	Restricted	Throughout
Common Sandpiper	*Tringa hypoleucos*		S m Or 2 Low. Poss. decreasing	Sparse	Widespread
Red-necked Phalarope	*Phalaropus lobatus*		s 30 pairs. Maximum 50% Decreasing	Sparse	Very few Ireland & W Isles
Arctic Skua	*Stercorarius parasiticus*	Aalin or Skooty aalin	S 1500 pairs Increasing 75%	Moderate	N & W Scotland
Great Skua	*Stercorarius skua*	Bonxie	S 5500 pairs Increasing 95%	Moderate	N Scotland & St Kilda
Black-headed Gull	*Larus rididibundis*	Heedie Maa	P Or 3 High Possibly 1000	Restricted	Coastal throughout except SW England & Wales
Common Gull	*Larus canus*	Tina Maa or Tanyick	P m Or 4 Possibly 2000 Increasing 10–15%	Widespread	Mainly Scotland & N & W Ireland
Lesser Black-backed Gull	*Larus fuscus*	Peerie Swaabie Herring Maa	S Low Or 4 Possibly 1000	Widespread	Coastal throughout, scarce S & E England

Common Name	Scientific Name	Shetland Name	Status	Shetland Distribution	British Distribution
Herring Gull	*Larus argentatus*	Scorie or Maa	R Or 5	Ubiquitous	Coastal almost throughout
Great Black-backed Gull	*Larus marinus*	Swaabie	R Possibly 10,000 2500 pairs Increasing 13%	Widespread	Mainly N & W but coastal throughout except England
Kittiwake	*Rissa tridactyla*	Rippack Maa	P 45,000 Increasing 10%	Moderate	Coastal throughout, except SE England
Sandwich Tern	*Sterna sandvicensis*		Sporadic		Coastal to S England
Common Tern	*Sterna hirundo*	Tirrick	S Or 3, possibly 400	Restricted	Coastal throughout
Arctic Tern	*Sterna paradisea*	Tirrick	S 10,000 minimum 25%	Widespread	Coastal Scotland to NW/NE England
Guillemot	*Uria lomvia*	Loom/Longwie	P 140,000 minimum 25–30%	Restricted	Coastal throughout, except SE England
Razorbill	*Alca torda*	Sea Craa/Wilkie	P *c.* 20,000 10%	Restricted	Coastal throughout, except SE England
Black Guillemot	*Cepphus grylle*	Tystie	R Or 4 30% Possibly 4000	Widespread	Mainly in NW Scotland & Ireland
Puffin	*Fratercula arctica*	Tammy Norie	P Or 6, possibly 250,000 30–40%	Moderate	Widespread coastal
Rock Dove	*Columba livia*	Wild Doo	R Or 3 High	Moderate	Scotland/Ireland
Woodpigeon	*Columba palumbus*		S m Or 2 Increasing	Sparse	Throughout
Collared Dove	*Streptopelia decaocto*		r m Or 2 Increasing	Sparse	Throughout
Cuckoo	*Cuculus canorus*		s m Or 1	Sparse	Throughout

		Catyogie	F Sporadic		
Snowy Owl	*Nyctea scandiaca*				
Long-eared Owl	*Asio otus*		r w 1–2 pairs Now sporadic	Minimal	Throughout
Skylark	*Alauda arvensis*	Laverock/ Ladyin	S Or 4	Widespread	Throughout
Swallow	*Hirundo rustica*		s M Or 1	Sparse	Throughout
House Martin	*Delichon urbica*		s M Sporadic		Throughout
Meadow Pipit	*Anthus pratensis*	Hill Sparrow or Teetick	S M High Or 3 Low Or 4	Widespread	Throughout
Rock Pipit	*Anthus spinoletta*	Banks Sparrow	R m Poss. Low Or 4. Prob. significant	Widespread	Coastal throughout except SE England
Grey Wagtail	*Motacilla cinerea*		Sporadic (Fair Isle 1950)		Throughout
White Wagtail	*Motacilla alba alba*		s M Or 1	Sparse	Throughout
Pied Wagtail	*Motacilla alba yarelli*		s M Or 1	Sparse	Throughout
Wren	*Troglodytes troglodytes*	Stenkie/Robbie Cuddie	R m Or 3–4 Increasing	Widespread	Throughout
Stonechat	*Saxicola torquata*		m Sporadic		Throughout
Wheatear	*Oenanthe oenanthe*	Stanechakker	S M Or 4. Prob. significant	Widespread	Throughout except SE England & Midlands
Ring Ouzel	*Turdus torquatus*		M Sporadic		Fairly widespread
Blackbird	*Turdus merula*		R M Or 3 Increasing	Widespread	Throughout
Fieldfare	*Turdus pilaris*		M Sporadic		Sporadic Scotland
Song Thrush	*Turdus philomelos*		M Sporadic		Throughout
Redwing	*Turdus iliacus*		M Sporadic		N Scotland
Reed Warbler	*Acrocephalus scirpaceus scirpaceus*		m Sporadic		
Whitethroat	*Sylvia communis*		m Sporadic		Throughout

Common Name	Scientific Name	Shetland Name	Status	Shetland Distribution	British Distribution
Blackcap	Sylvia atricapilla		M w Sporadic		Throughout except N Scotland & Ireland
Willow Warbler	Phylloscopus trochilus		M Sporadic		Throughout
Goldcrest	Regulus regulus		M Sporadic		Almost throughout
Jackdaw	Corvus monedula		r m Or 2 Low	Sparse	Throughout
Rook	Corvus frugilegus	Scots Craa	R m 176 pairs 1 colony (1976)	Minimal	Throughout
Hooded crow	Corvus corone cornix	Hoodie Craa	R Or 3	Moderate	Scotland & Ireland
Raven	Corvus corax	Corbie	R Or 2 High Prob. significant	Moderate	Throughout except SE England
Starling	Sturnus vulgaris		R M Or 4	Ubiquitous	Throughout
House Sparrow	Passer domesticus		R Or 4	Widespread	Throughout
Tree Sparrow	Passer montanus		m Sporadic	Minimal	Almost throughout
Chaffinch	Fringilla coelebs		M W Sporadic		Throughout
Twite	Acanthis flavirostris	Lintie	R Or 3 Increasing	Restricted	Throughout except Midlands & S England
Reed Bunting	Emberiza schoeniclus		p M 10–20 pairs increasing	Sparse	Throughout
Corn Bunting	Emberiza calandra	Dokken Sparrow	r m 1–5 pairs Decreasing	Sparse	Throughout

Birds extinct for over 50 years and doubtful/possible breeders

Great Northern Diver	*Gavia immer*	Doubtful 19th century.
Grey Heron	*Ardea cinerea*	Bred at least twice, early 20th century.
Mute Swan	*Cygnus olor*	Introduced 1900 and 1939 and bred for several years.
Whooper Swan	*Cygnus cygnus*	Injured birds bred 1910–1918.
Long-tailed Duck	*Clangula hyemalis*	Possibly bred 1848 and 1887.
Velvet Scoter	*Melanitta fusca*	Possibly bred 1945.
White-tailed Eagle	*Haliaeetus albicilla*	Last record 1910.
Hen Harrier	*Circus cyaneus*	Bred at least once, 19th century.
Sparrowhawk	*Accipeter nisus*	Extinct before 1900.
Kestrel	*Falco tinnunculus*	Last bred 1905.
Purple Sandpiper	*Calidria maritima*	Doubtful 19th century.
Greenshank	*Tringa nebularia*	Bred 1871.
Turnstone	*Arenaria interpres*	Doubtful, 19th century.
Short-eared Owl	*Asio flammeus*	Bred once 19th century.
Sand Martin	*Riparia riparia*	Possibly 1887.
Redstart	*Phoenicurus phoenicurus*	Nested, not bred 1901.
Red-backed Shrike	*Lanius cellurio*	Bred 1870.
Snow-Bunting	*Plectrophenax nivalis*	Possibly 1861, 1881, 1907.

STATUS AND RELATIONSHIPS OF THE SHETLAND LAND BIRDS

Table 14 clearly illustrates the effect of the increasing isolation of the islands north of Britain and the decrease in species diversity with increasing latitude. Seventeen of the 37 species of regular breeders lost between the north of Scotland and Orkney are associated with woodland, a habitat which is limited and fragmentary in Orkney. Of the 29 species lost between Orkney and Shetland, 11 are either associated with woodland, parks and gardens or shrubby heath; five are associated with eutrophic lochs with ample emergent vegetation (extremely limited in Shetland); and a further five require a food supply of small mammals which are almost entirely absent in Shetland. Two factors in the loss of 16 species between Shetland and Faroe are the greater isolation of the latter, and its even more restricted range of habitats than Shetland. Iceland has only 13 species fewer than Faroe; this may be account-ed for by Iceland having a much greater land mass and variety of habitats, particularly freshwater, than Faroe (half the species occurring in Iceland and not Faroe, are waterfowl).

Table 14

BIRDS BREEDING REGULARLY CAITHNESS AND SUTHERLAND BUT NOT ORKNEY

Black-throated Diver		Wood Sandpiper		Grasshopper Warbler	
Slavonian Grebe		Little Tern		Whitethroat	x
Greylag Goose		Swift		Wood Warbler	
Common Scoter	x	Great Spotted Woodpecker		Long-tailed Tit	
Goosander		Sand Martin		Coal Tit	
Sparrowhawk	x	House Martin	x	Blue Tit	
Ptarmigan		Tree Pipit		Great Tit	
Black Grouse		Grey Wagtail		Treecreeper	
Partridge		Dipper	x	Magpie	
Dotterel		Redstart		Siskin	
Woodcock		Winchat	x	Redpoll	
Greenshank	x	Redwing		Bullfinch	

x – irregular breeders Orkney

BIRDS BREEDING REGULARLY ORKNEY BUT NOT SHETLAND

Little Grebe	x	Water Rail		Sedge Warbler	
Heron		Corncrake	x	Willow Warbler	x
Mute Swan		Coot	x	Goldcrest	x
Wigeon	x	Sandwich Tern		Spotted Flycatcher	
Pintail	x	Short-Eared Owl		Tree Sparrow	x
Shoveler	x	Dunnock		Chaffinch	x
Hen Harrier		Robin		Greenfinch	
Buzzard		Ring Ouzel	x	Linnet	
Golden Eagle		Song Thrush	x	Yellowhammer	
Kestrel		Stonechat	x		

x – irregular breeders Shetland

BIRDS BREEDING REGULARLY SHETLAND BUT NOT FAROE

Cormorant	Common Sandpiper	Rook
Shelduck	Common Tern	Twite
Tufted Duck	Cuckoo	Reed Bunting
Peregrine	Long-Eared Owl	Corn Bunting
Moorhen	Pied Wagtail	
Curlew	Jackdaw	

BIRDS BREEDING REGULARLY FAROE BUT NOT ICELAND

Mute Swan	Collared Dove	Blackbird
Red Grouse	Skylark	Starling
Lapwing	Swallow	Hooded Crow

Rock Dove   Rock Pipit   House Sparrow
Wood Pigeon

BIRDS BREEDING REGULARLY ICELAND BUT NOT FAROE

Great Northern Diver	Long-tailed Duck	Grey Phalarope
Cormorant	Common Scoter	Glaucous Gull
Whooper Swan	Barrow's Goldeneye	Brunnich's Guillemot
Gadwall	Goosander	Snowy Owl
Pintail	White-tailed Eagle	Short-eared Owl
Shoveler	Gyrfalcon	Redpoll
Scaup	Water Rail	Snow Bunting

BIRDS BREEDING REGULARLY FAROE BUT NOT SHETLAND

Slavonian Grebe	Greylag Goose	Purple Sandpiper
Mute Swan	Ptarmigan	Redwing

BIRDS BREEDING REGULARLY SHETLAND BUT NOT ORKNEY

Common Scoter	x	Whimbrel	x	White Wagtail
Black-tailed Godwit		Red-necked Phalarope		

x – irregular breeders Orkney

BIRDS BREEDING REGULARLY ORKNEY BUT NOT CAITHNESS AND
SUTHERLAND

Manx Shearwater   Leach's Petrel   Gannet

All the species breeding in the north of Scotland and absent as regular breeders in Orkney, breed further north in Europe. The two species in Orkney which are absent in the more northern islands or Europe as regular breeding species, are the Sandwich Tern and the Stonechat (although both have bred irregularly recently in Shetland). Only the Corn Bunting reaches its northern latitudinal limit as a regular breeding species in Shetland, and the small population of this bird is dwindling. The Pied Wagtail is an anomaly: the Shetland birds are from the British race which does not breed in Europe; its continental counterpart, the White Wagtail, also breeds in Shetland as well as further north in Scandinavia. The Reed Warbler and Whitethroat have both bred once in Shetland; they breed at almost the same latitude in Europe.

When northern birds are considered, of the 21 species breeding in Iceland and not Faroe, only three, Barrow's Goldeneye, the Grey Phalarope and the Glaucous Gull, do not breed further south. Of the six species breeding regularly in Faroe and not Shetland, two have been introduced and one has been a recent irregular breeder, leaving three species (Greylag, Slavonian Grebe, Purple Sandpiper) that have never been regarded as Shetland breeders. The first two of these species however, breed in Scotland, leaving only the Purple Sandpiper that does not breed in Shetland or Britain. It does however breed in southern Scandinavia, which means that there are no Faroese species at the southern limit of their breeding distribution.

Of the northern species breeding in Shetland and not Orkney, all breed further south in Britain or Europe, with the exception of the sporadically breeding Snowy Owl; while both Whimbrel and Red-necked Phalarope are limited to the north of Britain.

The three species, all seabirds, that 'officially' breed in Orkney and not Caithness and Sutherland, in fact breed on Sule Stack and Skerry and therefore could equally well be considered birds of the north of Scotland.

Moving northwards from Britain through the islands therefore, climatic factors, a restriction in the number of breeding habitats, and an increasing isolation effectively reduces the variety of breeding species, while the fact that few reach their latitudinal limit can be accounted for by the fragmented and isolated nature of the islands in contrast to the unbroken European north-south corridor further east.

It is in this context that the uniqueness of Shetland's geographical position becomes apparent (Fig. 23). The islands can be regarded as at the northern apex of a triangle drawn around the British Isles, with the south coast of Britain as base; and at the southern apex of a triangle drawn through Iceland and Scandinavia with a line from Iceland to the North Cape of Norway as base. The western and eastern boundaries of this second triangle are the migration routes which pass through Shetland with suitable weather conditions. This allows the potential for establishment in Shetland of immigrant species from Britain, from Faroe and Iceland, and from Scandinavia: Shetland is both isolated and yet sufficiently closer to Scandinavia than either Orkney or Faroe to be in a position to receive a greater variety of migrants and retain them as unique breeding species.

The position is always changing, because the islands are in some ways 'no man's land' between opposing species and races, whose hold may only be extremely tenuous. There will always be openings, and numerous species will always be sporadic breeders; therein is a good part of the excitement of Shetland's breeding birds. In fact almost 30% of Shetland's birds could be classified as sporadic breeders, while a further 15% have only a foothold status (Table 15).

Since the Boreal age there have been fluctuations in the climate, including an amelioration early this century which allowed the increase and spread of several southern species, and a deterioration since the 1950s that has permitted the expansion southwards of some northern species. Such waves of advancement and recession are a continuous feature, but the remains of birds

PLATE 9. *Above left*, Hermaness with Gannets – the northernmost point of the British Isles; *right*, the Kame on Foula – the highest cliffs in the British Isles. *Below left*, the old and the new: a Shetland croft and an oil rig; *right*, a lichen monitoring site on a gravestone at Graven, two miles from the Sullom Voe Oil Terminal. Lichens are extremely sensitive to atmospheric pollution. The lack of trees in Shetland makes it necessary to use species growing on rocks to detect any biological effects of pollution.

PLATE 10. *Top left*, spectacular cliff scenery at the Heads of Grocken near Hillswick; *right*, St Ninian's Isle with a sand tombolo connecting it to the Shetland Mainland. *Bottom left*, freshwater loch formed behind a shingle bar, Wick of Copister, Yell; *right*, a well-formed geo: Longi Geo, Whale Firth, Yell.

PLATE 11. *From top to bottom*, the largest glacial erratic in Shetland – the Stanes of Stofast on Lunna Ness; ice-moulded and striated rock surface, Stofast, Lunna Ness – the ice moved from right to left parallel to the striations; terracing on the north side of Ronas Hill; Culswick – site of special scientific interest.

PLATE 12. *Top left*, the Keen of Hamar National Nature Reserve, with orchid, plantain and Moss Campion; *right*, Arctic Mouse-ear Chickweed on the Keen of Hamar. *Centre left*, Tufted Vetch at Sumburgh; *right*, Purple Saxifrage at Fethaland. *Bottom left*, Scousburgh meadow; *right*, Shetland Campion.

PLATE 13. *Above*, meadows of Marsh Marigold at Cunningsburgh; *below*, roadside flowers at Scousburgh.

PLATE 14. *Above*, Common Seals; *below*, Grey Seal pup.

PLATE 15. Shetland birds. *Top left*, Snowy Owl; *right*, Red-necked Phala-rope; *Bottom left*, Long-tailed Duck; *right*, Great Skua or Bonxie.

PLATE 16. *Right*, Foula cliffs; *centre*, Gannets; *below*, feeding gulls.

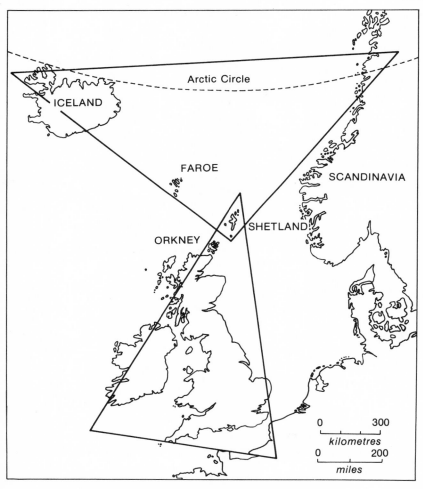

FIG 23. Shetland's relative position and migration routes.

excavated from Jarlshof indicate that for some species at least, little has changed:

Bronze Age (turn of the first millenium BC) –
Swan, Cormorant, Gannet, Great Northern Diver, Herring Gull, Razorbill.
Viking Age (turn of the first millenium AD) –
Peregrine, Shelduck, Shoveler, Velvet Scoter, Cormorant, Gannet, Leach's

TABLE 15

Sporadic breeders since 1950 at least	Species with small populations
Little Grebe	Leach's Petrel
Wigeon	Shelduck
Pintail	Teal
Shoveler	Tufted Duck
Quail	Common Scoter
Pheasant	Merlin
Corncrake	Peregrine
Coot	Pheasant
Sandwich Tern	Moorhen
Snowy Owl	Black-tailed Godwit
House Martin	Common Sandpiper
Ring Ouzel	Red-necked Phalarope
Fieldfare	Wood Pigeon
Song Thrush	Collared Dove
Redwing	Cuckoo
Stonechat	Long-eared Owl
Reed Warbler	Swallow
Whitethroat	White Wagtail
Blackcap	Pied Wagtail
Willow Warbler	Jackdaw
Goldcrest	Reed Bunting
Chaffinch	Corn Bunting
Tree Sparrow	

Petrel, Red-throated Diver, Curlew, Oystercatcher, Herring Gull (numerous), Great Black-backed Gull (numerous), Kittiwake, Guillemot, Puffin and Magpie.

It does not follow of course from this list that all these species were breeding.

BIRDS OF PLANTATION, WOODLAND AND SHRUBS

Habitats within Shetland

At the present moment there are under 100 acres of planted woodland throughout Shetland, with the largest area of eight acres at Kergord, Weisdale. Apart from areas adjacent to the house, this site has predominantly coniferous trees, as do nearby trial plots set up by the Forestry Commission in the mid-1950s. Older plantations, such as that at Halligarth, Unst, and trees planted in gardens tend to be predominantly Sycamore, Elder and Willow. In 1973 the Nature Conservancy Council planted a shelter-belt at Hillswick with a wide range of species, although mainly broad-leaved. At 2½ acres this is the largest area of woodland planted in recent years. There also exist in Shetland tiny scraps of native shrubs which at one time must have been found almost throughout Shetland. It is almost certain however, that the present situation has existed for 2–3,000 years. The wooded areas are too small to allow breeding of woodland species except very sporadically.

Yet even these few plantations attract migrants, as was noted by Saxby (1874) when speaking of the Halligarth trees which date from the mid-19th century. 'The planting of a few trees, carefully sheltered by stone walls from the sweeping gales of the Atlantic, has had a curiously marked effect in attracting birds hitherto unknown as visitors to the islands; an effect indeed, altogether disproportionate to the small scale on which the experiment has been tried.'

It is necessary to bear in mind that very few species are entirely restricted to one habitat. This is well illustrated by woodland and shrub associated species which have bred sporadically or only recently – Goldcrest, Song Thrush, Blackbird, Willow Warbler, Chaffinch, Tree Sparrow, Blackcap, Stonechat and Woodpigeon. Of these Blackbird, Wood Pigeon and Tree Sparrow appear to have become established as a result of a general expansion and immigration into Shetland from Britain and Orkney, whereas Goldcrest, Willow Warbler, Chaffinch, Blackcap and Stonechat appear to have come from Scandinavia.

The Song Thrush appears regularly as a migrant, but has gradually decreased as a breeding species from a peak in the first half of this century until the mid-1950s when it ceased to breed every year, partly due to a reduction in its small population during the severe winter of 1947. It has bred annually since 1976. The Song Thrush first bred in Shetland at the turn of the century shortly after the Blackbird became established. The latter is now fairly numerous and widespread, and has become also a regular breeder in the Torshavn plantation in Faroe.

The histories of the Song Thrush and the Stonechat illustrate the isolation of island populations. Whereas numbers of the Song Thrush in Shetland declined markedly after heavy losses from severe weather, the Stonechat rapidly recovered in Orkney from two such experiences. This was probably due entirely to the presence of a large reservoir of the species immediately adjacent on the Scottish mainland, whereas there was no such convenient source for the Shetland Song Thrush.

Besides a steady build up of an island population by regular immigration or an overall expansion of a species range, two further woodland species illustrate alternative modes of establishment. The Rook has undergone a gradual extension of its range in Britain and was a regular if not common migrant to Shetland for many years. However at the time the Kergord plantation was maturing in 1952 they were abnormally abundant in Shetland; nine nests were established in that year, averaging a success rate of three young per nest These birds then became resident and their numbers have steadily increased to 150–200 nests. It appears that if the initial immigration is high enough in one or several years and breeding attempts are successful, a species which is not normally a numerous migrant can become established.

The other woodland and farmland species which used to be virtually confined to Kergord following its introduction there is the Pheasant. It now breeds sporadically in a very few locations where there is adequate arable land and cover. It seems unlikely that it will ever be successful in Shetland.

Adaptability and the availability of prey species are two further factors in establishment. For example, a visitor familiar with the moorlands of Scotland (including those of Orkney) is surprised at the absence of Short-eared Owls in Shetland and is even more surprised to learn that the Long-eared Owl is a regular breeder (although only recently and in very small numbers). Almost certainly, the absence of the former in Shetland is due to the lack of microtine rodents (voles) as prey; conversely the relative success of the latter may be a result of its more omnivorous diet. It must be a reasonably adaptable species as like the Wood Pigeon, it has taken to nesting on open moorland in Shetland as well as in its normal woodland habitat.

This question of adaptability, which also arose with the Song Thrush, is an important one. In islands where there are finite limits to both the variety of habitats and to their physical size, immigrants may find their usual niche just not large enough, or they may find another race or species already over-lapping that niche. One of the few ways they can become established is to exploit what would normally be marginal situations.

At the close of the season as the Eiders are flocking in the voes, the Auks moving out to sea, the terns winging their way south and the Twite, Merlin and Rock Pipit moving into the croftland, the moorland seems to die with only a few Skuas, Gulls, Crows and Ravens flapping over the landscape: but then there is a sudden rush as migrant flocks descend from Iceland or Scandinavia. Fieldfare and Redwing come in October in thousands, often in tens of thousands and occasionally, as in October 1976, literally hundreds of thousands. The majority pass through, the Redwing flashing the red of its leading underwing on every upstroke, often accompanied by the heavier Fieldfare, its grey head and rump looking almost slate-blue.

In recent years the Fieldfare has been expanding its range in Europe. It bred in Shetland in 1968, and one or two pairs bred most years to 1973. The Redwing appears to have had a similar recent history in the islands; it bred on four occasions between 1953 and 1978. Saxby states, 'by merely substituting the name of the Redwing for that of the Fieldfare, my remarks upon the former scarcity and present abundance of the one would apply with equal truth to the other'. The Redwing is more confined to woodland than the Fieldfare and this is indicated by its distribution in Shetland. But more importantly, the two species show that establishment (however brief) can come from expansion in Scandinavia as well as in Scotland, and not only simply because of a previous migration pattern.

It is impossible to know how many of these species were regular breeders in the past when scrub was abundant and trees grew in sheltered ravines, but one can conjecture that the list may grow again as more woodland is established and matures. Notwithstanding, an autumn visit is still a rewarding experience for those unfamiliar with woodland species, for even the existing small patches provide focal points for woodland migrants *en route* south, such as warblers, flycatchers and thrushes. In the summer months many of the more common Shetland species can also be seen such as Starling, House Sparrow, Wren, Twite and Hooded Crow.

BIRDS OF CROFTING TOWNSHIPS AND ARABLE LAND

One of the more attractive contributions of man to the Shetland landscape are the characteristic crofting townships, scattered along the coastal strip and in the more fertile valleys. Many of the traditional elements of hilldyke, water mills and plantie-crubs are now in ruins, but the pattern of low crofthouse and byre, often accompanied by shrubs such as Rose, Flowering Currant or Fuschia, surrounded by strips of cultivated fields and edged on the low-lying, wet ground with ditched, natural hayfields, still remains. In the spring the soft yellows of the Primrose dominate the grassland; giving way in early summer to the harder yellow of the Marsh Marigolds in the ditches, and the rich red of the Shetland Campion around the houses. But by far the most luxuriant and most diverse flora occurs on the wetter margins of the croft land which remain uncut until later in the summer, bright with Red and Yellow Rattles, Ragged Robin, Iris, Eyebright, Forget-me-not, Orchids, tall grasses, sedges and horsetails.

Common breeding birds around the buildings and walls are House Sparrow, Blackbird, Wren, Wheatear and Twite; in the meadows and grassland, Meadow Pipit, Skylark, Lapwing and very occasional Corncrake; while in the wetter margins are occasional Snipe, Corn and Reed Bunting, Curlew and Redshank. In the winter months moorland and coastal species, Twite, Rock Pipit, Hoodie, Raven, gulls, Rock Dove, and even Merlin and Peregrine come seeking food. One of the few species which is virtually confined to this complex of habitats is the House Sparrow, although it does very occasionally nest on cliffs. Two further closely related species which are restricted to the area of buildings are the Swallow and House Martin. The former has been an irregular breeder in Shetland and Orkney since at least 1831, and has bred very occasionally in Faroe and Iceland. The House Martin is an even more irregular breeder in Shetland and Orkney and has bred only once in Faroe.

In the surrounding fields and moorland occurs one of those birds which has won a significant place in our literature and in our hearts, the Skylark or Laverock. There are a number of bird songs that herald the arrival of spring and the demise of winter, but the Skylark's is the first. On a quiet February day it lifts the depression of the long dark winter and the wind and the rain as it rises with its song. It is an extremely common breeding bird and correspondingly noticeable for its more or less complete absence in the winter.

Another notable absentee in the winter months apart from a small number in a few localities, is the Lapwing. Recently this species has been on the increase again after almost suffering the fate of the Song Thrush after a particularly severe winter; it now breeds in Faroe.

Like the Skylark and Wheatear, the Meadow Pipit is an ubiquitous and common breeder, although it is absent from the smaller islands. Saxby said that it was not a common breeding bird before his time and if this is true it has had a remarkable degree of success since then.

How very much part of our time we are. If we listen to the birds of the croftland today, we are aware of no discord, no absence of a particular sound and yet the generation that has grown up from the turn of the century remembers the evenings punctuated by the insistent rasping of the Corncrake, winding itself up with its rusty key. Evans & Buckley said of the Corncrake at the close of the 19th century that it could be heard in every cultivated district throughout the islands. In 1948 the Venables recorded 48 nests, but in 1976 only a few birds were heard calling and none was proved to have bred. The Shetland decline is unfortunately part of an overall decline of this species wherever agricultural practices have changed; in a few short years it may well be heard no more in the islands.

On the margins of nearly all crofts are areas of almost permanent wetland with taller vegetation and open patches of water which hide an intriguing state of flux of breeding birds. Firstly are the varying fortunes of the Corn and Reed Buntings. In the middle of the 19th century Saxby was under the impression that the former was an uncommon breeder, but Evans & Buckley point out that he was referring to Unst and they claimed it was one of the most conspicuous birds in Shetland. Since the turn of the century there has been a continuous decline throughout Britain which has been reflected in Shetland. A close relative of the Corn Bunting, the Reed Bunting is a recent colonizer. Saxby only recorded the bird on three occasions, while the Venables, who confirmed the first breeding record in 1949, described it as a scarce migrant. It now has a well established but small population scattered throughout Shetland, and there has been an associated increase in wintering. This is a species which has expanded its ecological range from a breeding dependence on nearby freshwater to a tolerance of drier habitats. Judging by its recent success one suspects that this species will rapidly increase in numbers and range in Shetland, and that its short, jerky flight will become a common sight around the townships.

The first Report of the Shetland Bird Club recorded in 1973 the first confirmed breeding record of the Reed Warbler in Shetland and Scotland. This must be a clear cut example of colonization of Shetland by a Scandinavian rather than British migrant, since in Britain this species is confined to England, where it is rare in the north. Perhaps this is a similar record to Saxby's Red-backed Shrike which bred in 1870; both birds nested in habitats not usually associated with either.

The record of the last of this group of marsh and open water associated species deserves to be clarified as the history of the two races occurring is somewhat confused. The White Wagtail breeds throughout Europe including Iceland, although uncommonly in Faroe. Its subspecies the Pied Wagtail breeds in Britain. In appearance they are very similar and the only distinctive difference is that the mature Pied has a solid black back of the same tone as the bib and the back of the head, whereas the White has a grey back of lighter tone than head or bib. Saxby was as confused about the two as many of us, and confessed that he might have overlooked the White, identifying it as Pied. The Venables stated that they had never seen the Pied in Shetland, although they accepted that it might have occurred. Possibly because of this they suggested that the hearsay records of Pied breeding, given in Evans & Buckley, may have referred to the White, which they knew firsthand sometimes bred.

The Pied however, was a not uncommon breeder in Orkney at the turn of the century and only decreased there from the late 1930s. It did in fact breed sporadically in Shetland early this century although by the time of the Venables it had become very scarce.

As far as the White Wagtail is concerned, Saxby may not have overlooked it and his first recording of the species in 1852 might have been the beginning of a more regular appearance. Evans & Buckley do not record any further occurrences until the first breeding record of 1900, and breeding has been sporadic ever since. The Pied has probably bred each year since the beginning of the 1970s. Which one, if either, will succeed in establishing itself in the face of the other deserves some attention: an island situation is an ideal place to study such interaction of species and subspecies. Indeed the two have bred with each other in Shetland!

BIRDS OF MOORLAND

Although moorland stretches from sea level to well over 1000 ft, the altitudinal zonation of plant communities in Shetland is not as clearly defined as on mainland Scotland, due to the modifying influences of latitude and climate. This has the effect that differences in habitat are of a local nature rather than an aspect of altitude, although there is some variation in otherwise generally uniform communities due to topography and underlying geology and drift. Moorland breeding bird species are therefore well distributed and only a few are restricted to either lowland or upland communities.

Wader species which *are* virtually confined to the lower lying acidic marshes on the border of moorland are the Redshank, Common Sandpiper, Black-tailed Godwit and Snipe. The first was a rare breeder in the middle of the last century but today breeds regularly in most of the islands throughout Shetland, although only sparsely. The Common Sandpiper is restricted to loch and burn sides; it is much less common as a breeding species and its status appears to have altered little in the last century. In Shetland it is reaching the northern limit of its island distribution, for although it reaches the Arctic shore in northern Europe it does not occur in Faroe or Iceland, and even in Orkney is a scarce breeder.

Of the four, the Black-tailed Godwit is the least common, probably only one pair breeding since 1949. It is also the most beautiful with its elegant neck, chestnut-red head, black bill and white tail tipped also with black. Whereas the Reed Warbler illustrates Shetland's advantageous position compared to Faroe, in being closer to Scandinavia, the Black-tailed Godwit demonstrates its advantage over the more southerly Orkneys, in being closer to Faroe and Iceland, for the species has only bred sporadically in Orkney since 1956. Elsewhere in Britain it breeds only in England which it recolonized in 1952 probably from the continent. The Shetland and Orkney birds are most probably of the Icelandic race (*Limosa limosa islandica*), although this has yet to be proved.

The Snipe, surprisingly for a shy bird, is commonly seen on the roadside, often perched on a fence post and when disturbed actually on the road surface, will frequently crouch flat on its belly as if in deep cover. Where the Grouse explodes heavily from cover or the Curlew rapidly seeks height, the Snipe emerges like an errant missile, fizzling out and dropping back out of sight as unexpectedly as it appeared. Its fast and erratic flight has always been a challenge to the gun and the autumn migrant flocks of a hundred years ago were the favourite target of Shetland's sporting gentlemen, particularly the Lairds. A glance at the bags given in *The Birds and Mammals of Shetland* gives some idea of the numbers that then occurred. Nowadays it appears to be less numerous on migration, although still fairly common.

The smaller and less numerous Dunlin is as widespread as the Snipe, although its total numbers are less. Both Saxby and the Venables give the low lying wet areas as its main breeding ground but it is also reasonably common on higher and even drier areas. Its Shetland name, the 'Plover's Page', has been earned by its habit of closely following the Golden Plover's nuptial flight.

The mellow call of the Curlew can be heard almost throughout the islands, although it has a rather curiously patchy distribution and can be found on arable, rough grazing or moorland. It appears to have a preference for damp ground and its one particular requirement which distinguishes it from the Whimbrel, is for deep cover. In Shetland it reaches the northern limit of its island distribution. It is replaced in Faroe and Iceland by the Whimbrel.

Breeding wildfowl are particularly scarce due to the predominantly acidic nature of much of the wetland and moorland. The Mallard is a reasonably common species but by no means numerous, while the Teal is very scarce. Both these species breed also in the more eutrophic wetlands with several other sporadic species, while the Mallard also breeds on the smaller islands and often feeds at the head of sheltered voes in salt water. Their status appears to have altered little in the last hundred years although there may have been some increase since the introduction of the gun-tax reduced the numbers taken for food in the last century. The Wigeon is commonly referred to as a breeding bird, but the first confirmed record was as recent as 1976.

By far the most common duck species is the Eider which breeds ubiquitously on the moorland and low lying offshore holms. The local name for this bird is the 'Dunter', which is rather evocative of its stocky appearance, although according to Jamieson's Scottish Dictionary the name comes from *dun* – down and *taer* – gnaw, from the female's habit of plucking down from her breast to line the nest. Unfortunately Eiders do not nest in sufficient density to allow an easy harvest for the making of eiderdown quilts. The female is uniformly dark brown and barred and rather uninspiring, while at first glance the male is a simple contrasting black and white. However closer inspection will reveal that his breast has a tinge of pink and the nape of the neck is an extremely soft and pale green. On a still day in spring the soft 'woo-woo' of the male carries far across the water as he throws back his head in confrontation with his competitors.

As with so many of the vulnerable and edible birds of Shetland, the Dunter may have been more numerous before the 19th century. Certainly the human population of the islands was much more dense than nowadays, and the breech-loading gun had just been introduced. Saxby deplored the efforts of many who took birds for the table, although his apology for this habit illuminates the scarcity of food and social conditions of the time – 'should . . . ornithologists . . . meditate passing a winter in the north isles, I would advise them to withold their criticism until . . . they can conscientiously aver that failing health has not driven them to a like extremity; unless, indeed, their sojourn has been with the laird, the minister, or still better with the factor'! However the introduction of the gun-tax reduced the persecution so that by the end of the century the Dunter like many other species such as the Red-throated Diver was recovering. It is worth remembering that the species is on the increase and that the past decrease may have been predominantly due to human pressure as today many in Shetland are under the impression that the Bonxie (Great Skua) and Great Black-backed Gull are taking an undue share. Once in the water creches may be formed (although not invariably) with several females acting as mother, giving additional protection. However even here the ducklings are not entirely safe: Bonxies may co-operate to distract the females while others pick off the young, and even a Great Northern Diver has been seen to snatch young.

Recent work in Shetland has shed some light on the numbers and seasonal distribution of the Eider. After mating, the males go into eclipe and gather in flocks during June; by August they are completely flightless due to the wing-moult. By September/October they move to wintering areas where they are joined by the females and young of the year and where they may remain until the spring. Flock sizes range from only a few birds up to 3000. The total Eider population of the islands (including Fair Isle and Foula) from flock counts is around 15,500, that is 20% of the British population. There is some suggestion of emigration of wintering flocks from the Shetland Mainland at least as far as Fair Isle, and there may also be immigration from further north.

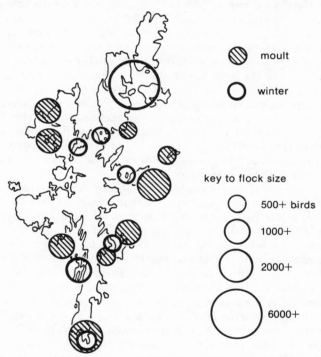

FIG 24. Eider flocks during moult (June–September) and in winter (October–February). Only concentrations of over 500 birds shown (data of P. Kinnear).

In the previous century the King Eider was extremely scarce and the first definite record only occurs in 1848. During their stay (1946–53) the Venables did not see any. However from the late 1950s a few individuals of this bird have quite regularly appeared as winter visitors, and may even summer, usually accompanying Common Eiders.

It is perhaps a slight misnomer to describe any area in Shetland as 'dry' moor, but where there are steep slopes or more permeable rocks allowing reasonably free drainage Ling gives way to Bell heather, Crowberry, Bilberry and Cowberry. The common wader of this habitat is the Golden Plover, which is widespread and quite numerous, making up perhaps 5–10% of the British population. However it does not appear to be as common as it was 100 years ago when Saxby said that it bred '. . . even on the outlying holms', which it certainly does not do today. It is the southern form which breeds in Shetland, lacking the complete dark band from the head to the back of the belly found in the northern race.

Although the Red Grouse is probably indigenous in Orkney it is not in Shetland. It occurs only in scattered groups on the Mainland, and represents the descendants of the last introduction when 600 were released at Lunna in 1901. The heather growth on which the birds depend requires sunny summer weather, and this is not plentiful in the maritime climate of Shetland. It is also the case that the density of sheep is rather high compared with Scotland, and therefore feeding is limited. Like the wildfowl population the numbers are also effectively kept below their potential by shooting.

An extremely familiar song almost anywhere in Shetland in the summer season, from the time of their return in April, is the sharp 'chak' of the Wheatear. Invariably when one looks about to find the owner he is seen flitting low across the ground, to alight on a stone or post, and bob with a loud 'chak chak' (hence his local name 'Stanechakker'). With his grey back, white rump, black eye-stripe and tail and his buff breast the male is the handsomest passerine of the moor. In their account of the Wheatear, the Venables kept a record of food carrying by the adult and found the breeding season in Shetland was at least three weeks later than that on Skokholm in Pembrokeshire. Such delayed breeding at the northern end of their range is very common for species with a wide latitudinal distribution and this includes most of Shetland's breeding birds. Plant growth begins later in the year the farther north one travels. In fact spring as such, rarely occurs in Shetland and cold weather with sleet may continue into May. The fauna, ultimately dependent on the flora for its food supply, must delay breeding until sufficient food is available to feed its young.

Possibly the most numerous passerine is the Starling and it has a characteristic Shetland form (*Sturnus vulgaris zetlandicus*). The Venables recorded it as an abundant species liable to fluctuations, although Tulloch & Hunter (1972) suggested that it might be decreasing, which is apparently the case in Fair Isle.

In the winter months Starlings are the most numerous birds around the crofting townships, wheeling round in small flocks to scatter the House Sparrows and twittering Twites from any spare food that is available. A particularly delightful memory is of returning home from line fishing in a summer dawn and hearing the chorus of Starlings issuing from high cave where they were roosting.

The Venables give an excellent description of the Shetland sub-species, and show how it fits the tendency of passerines to increase in size in higher latitudes and in pigmentation on mild islands. However the Shetland form (like its Hebridean counterpart) is intermediate between the European and Faroe subspecies and not very distinctive in its own right. Where trends in island races are continued over larger areas in this way, one can reasonably say that they are adaptations to particular environments; where they are not (as with the Shetland Field Mouse, p. 135 and Wren, p. 185) differentiation is more likely due to the founder effect (p. 2).

Two very different birds which breed occasionally on flat moorland but more often on dry banks, ravine sides, in bushes and trees and on coastal banks, are the Twite and Hooded Crow. The former is not numerous and not as abundant a migrant as it was in Saxby's day when the wintering flocks were in the 'thousands'. The Twite is a much loved bird but the Hoodie, frequently seen at the decaying body of a sheep, rabbit or hedgehog on the roadside, is an unappreciated species. Like so many birds (for example the Starling), it is only when one observes them at close quarters that the subtlety of the plumage can be seen. The ornithologist may find it surprising but a Hoodie in Shetland has been mistaken for a rather large Rose-coloured Starling! In certain lights the soft grey of the body can look pale brown and almost pink in contrast with the dark head and wings.

A species which has been regularly breeding in small numbers is the Cuckoo. The frequency of breeding has possibly increased this century, as Saxby only recorded it breeding once, while Evans & Buckley added no records. However there are more observers about today, as we have already noted.

One advantage that the ground nesting species of Shetland have over their Scottish counterparts is the relative lack of ground predators. Apart from man and dog, there are only the introduced Stoat, Hedgehog and Rat, the feral Cat, and the native Otter. None of these is numerous: Hedgehogs and Stoats are only relatively abundant around the townships, and Cats where they have been introduced to keep down Rabbits on small islands or on cliffs where there are accessible seabirds, such as Puffin or Tystie. The only relatively numerous mammalian predator is the Otter, but its main diet is fish, and few terrestrial birds are taken.

Conversely there is also an absence of small mammal prey suitable for avian predators so they must be more catholic in the diet, or be large enough, like the Snowy Owl, to take Rabbits or larger birds, such as Oystercatchers. A number of species which breed in Orkney are absent, such as the Short-eared Owl, Hen Harrier, Kestrel and Buzzard. The first two and the Sparrowhawk have bred once in Shetland in the last century; the Kestrel was once a regular breeder; there are no breeding records for the Buzzard. The only moorland avian predators breeding today are the Merlin, Long-eared Owl and Snowy Owl, the last only sporadically. One must however include as well the Skuas and larger Gulls, which may be a factor affecting the numbers and establishment of the others.

We are particularly in debt to Saxby for information on the feeding habits of Kestrel and Merlin. He noted that the Kestrel was obliged to take small birds and records Corn Bunting and Blackbird, among others, as its prey. It must therefore have come into direct competition for food with the Merlin, which itself may be rather less common today than in Saxby's time. Unhappily an investigation in 1977 into the infertility of some Merlin eggs showed they contained a high level of dieldrin, a substance known to have caused the decline of certain raptors on the mainland in the 1950s. According to Saxby the Merlin feeds almost exclusively on small birds up to the size of Rock Dove and he never found the remains of insects or small mammals in his examinations, although it will take these as prey on the Scottish mainland.

Why the Kestrel should have become extinct is something of a mystery. Its establishment must have been at a time when it was a regular summer visitor, the population being supported by a fresh supply of migrants each year, since it never wintered. Certainly at the close of the 19th century Raeburn thought it a more numerous species than the Merlin in Northmavine. Kestrels then became uncommon migrants, at least until the middle of this century. What ever the principal reason, a significant factor could have been its competition with the resident Merlin.

Many visitors have noted the resemblance of some of the heaths and sparsely vegetated areas of the North Roe plateau and summits of Colvadale and the Sobul in Unst, to the sub-arctic tundra and fellfields of Faroe, Iceland and Scandinavia; and of the sub-montane heaths, particularly on the serpentine of Unst and Fetlar, to the communities in the upper and cooler regions of the forest zone. Such sparsely vegetated areas are not common in the British Isles, being normally confined to the northern and outlying western islands and particularly to the high top of the Scottish Highlands.

Their attraction therefore to northern species and especially waders is not surprising, particularly since Shetland lies closer to the source of many of these immigrants than any other area in the British Isles. Apart from the seabirds, the waders are probably the most important group of birds numerically in Shetland in a national context. The high density and great variety of waders in Unst and Fetlar where large areas of serpentine and mettagabbro rocks occur is probably a unique situation. In Unst alone, twelve wader species regularly breed, a further two have bred once and one other has doubtfully bred. Without a doubt Shetland is one of the most important areas in Britain for waders, containing probably 90% of the Whimbrel population, 10% of the Ringed Plover and Oystercatcher, and 5–10% of the Golden Plover.

Unst is one of the most attractive of the Shetland islands for its variety of breeding birds. Besides the waders, which are particularly prolific, there breed also smaller passerines, such as Wheatear, Meadow Pipit and Twite, all the resident Gulls and Terns, plus the Great and Arctic Skuas, never mind the huge seabird colonies of the cliffs of Hermaness and Saxavord. Such is the variety of breeding birds today that it is difficult to imagine the area as devoid of bird life as it was at the turn of the century as described by Evans & Buckley – 'From Baltasound to Uyea Sound birdlife is more remarkable for its absence than its presence, and throughout the whole distance of some six miles little can be seen except a few Ringed Plover and Wheatear'!

At that time the only place where Whimbrel were seen on Unst was Hermaness, 'one or possibly two pairs' and one pair between Belmont and Uyea Sound; none was seen on Fetlar, which is their other present stronghold today; breeding birds were noted on the smaller islands between Yell and Unst where they are now absent; and reference was made to a few pairs scattered throughout the main island, where they are still thinly distributed but increasing. Earlier they had been a common species but by the time Evans & Buckley made their visits they had decreased substantially, becoming extinct for a time in Orkney (where they remain a rare species even today). The recovery in Shetland has been a very recent one: the Venables quote J. Peterson who failed to find a breeding pair on Unst in 1938, and they themselves only found 35 pairs in 1949, whereas today there are probably over 70 pairs on that island. Apart from Shetland there are only a very few other British breeding stations.

In Shetland as in Scotland, the Curlew is known as the 'Whaup', an onomatopoeic name, while the Whimbrel is known as the 'Peerie (small) Whaup' or 'Tang (seaweed) Whaup', from its comparative size and habit of feeding on the seashore. There does not appear to be any competition between the species for breeding habitat, the Whimbrel preferring its more familiar short vegetation while the Curlew seeks out a greater amount of cover.

The simplest way of distinguishing the Whimbrel from the Curlew is by its call, which is a higher and more wavering trill than the sound of the latter. It is also a smaller bird with a shorter bill, and this gives it an appearance of stockiness when compared to the more slender appearance of the Curlew. In close proximity it can be seen to have a distinctive dark and light striped crown lacking in the Curlew.

Two other extremely common waders, the Ringed Plover and the Oystercatcher nest in the same terrain, although they may both be found nesting also on shingle and gravel shores. As with many of the local names for birds, those for these two species, the 'Sandy Loo' and 'Shaldur' respectively, are much more attractive than their common name; perhaps their inclusion here will encourage their continuing use and perhaps bring back some others that have fallen into disuse. It is a pleasant fact that the local names for the Black Guillemot and Great Skua, the 'Tystie' and 'Bonxie' respectively, have now become common usage in Britain generally.

In Faroe also the Oystercatcher is very numerous and popular and has become the national emblem of those islands with almost the same local name 'Tjaldur'. If one was to make a list of the local boat names in Shetland, Shaldur would be the one in most common use with probably Tystie and Tirrick (tern) as second choices.

The Oystercatcher has been a breeding species for many years, but only in recent years have small numbers begun to over-winter. At the same time the summer population has shown a marked expansion, breeding further inland than previously. No census has been carried out, but as at least 50 pairs are known to breed on the Out Skerries alone, the total population could be of the order of 1000 pairs.

Although the Ringed Plover is a fairly common species, it has a patchy breeding distribution. In the winter months small flocks are extremely common on the sandy shores, flitting out in an arc from the shore when disturbed to alight nimbly farther along.

Often seen in the company of the Ringed Plover on sandy shores, and occurring as often on rocky foreshores is the Turnstone. This species does not nest in Britain and has doubtfully bred once in Shetland. Saxby recorded finding nest and eggs, but the discovery was slightly obscure and one must agree with the Venables that the record while 'suggestive is not conclusive'. The Turnstone is the exception that throws some doubt on the simple explanation for the presence of other breeding species. Here is a bird that is abundant as a migrant, occurs in the summer, breeds right around the coast of Scandinavia, but does not appear to have attempted, with such a wealth of suitable habitat, to breed in Shetland.

Another northern wader species which Saxby thought had bred in the 19th century is the Purple Sandpiper. Saxby states that eggs were brought to him from suitable habitats, but alas with a degree more cynicism one might suggest that they had been brought to him *via* suitable habitats. It is probably an under-recorded species because of its cryptic colouring and habit of feeding on rocky shore, particularly at the sea's edge.

At the turn of the last century Evans & Buckley's description of the absence of bird life from Baltasound to Uyeasound could well have applied also to the North Roe area, from Ronas Hill to Fethaland. This magnificent undisturbed wilderness area is bounded on the east by the main road to North Roe, on the west by six miles of high granite cliffs from Ronas Voe to Uyea Isle, on the north by three miles of ancient and eroding gneiss, and on the south by steep crags leading down to Ronas Voe. Bird life on the higher slopes and summit of Ronas Hill is as sparse as the vegetation which clings to the lee of boulders and the slopes of the periglacial terraces (Chapter 4).

Even today, looking north over the landscape from the summit, there is little movement to catch the eye – perhaps a mountain hare loping across the lower slopes, a Red-throated Diver winging in to one of the ice-scoured lochs or peaty lochans further north, or a Black-backed Gull or Bonxie drifting lazily across the sky. Now there are only sheep on the hill, but not so long ago there were crofts at Uyea and perhaps over 2000 years ago some of the ancient stone shelters by the stone axe quarries saw some regular human activity.

Apart from the view, the flora and the fascinating signs of periglacial activity, the climb of Ronas Hill is well worth the effort for the possible sight of two northern bird species which have only very recently made more regular appearances in Shetland. Since the mid 19th century the Ring Ouzel has been a regular migrant in small numbers. On a few occasions it has summered but only in the last decade has it been heard singing in suitable breeding localities, and in 1972 it bred on Ronas Hill.

The other species can be cryptic: strewn over the slopes of the hill are light coloured rocks of varying sizes which may merit more than a passing glance, particularly those of from one to two feet high. It has been known for such a rock to rise, spread broad white wings and flap away low and powerfully over the ground – the magnificent Snowy Owl or 'Catyogle' (Cat Owl)!

Until very recently the Snowy Owl was a very rare visitor to both Britain and Shetland. However in the early 1960s there was an irruption in Scandinavia and the bird began to appear regularly throughout western Europe, its first appearance in Shetland being on Fetlar in 1963 when a single male turned up to be followed in subsequent years by more birds. In 1966 two females and one male were present and finally in 1967 a pair settled and became the first 'confirmed' breeding pair in the British Isles. Confirmed, since Saxby much maligned for his credulity in accepting second-hand information, believed that the Snowy Owl had nested in Unst before his time and was supported in his belief by an earlier statement of Edmonston (1822). Certainly it was a common visitor to the northern isles throughout the year early in the 19th century, although they became uncommon again until their more recent appearances. In a long and informative account Saxby recounts one of those tales which today we commonly refuse to believe, but which was virtually duplicated recently in Fair Isle. Commenting on the Snowy Owl's habit of finding some shady spot beside a boulder to rest, he notes that normally it is difficult to approach, however '. . . a man in this island once crept up to a Snowy Owl and knocked it over with a stick'. In 1972 a sleeping Owl on Fair Isle was spotted by one of the Wardens in just such a way as Saxby described and he managed to creep up behind it, slip off his jacket, drape it neatly and smartly around the bird and carry it off for ringing and recording. Lest the reader assume it was an extremely dumb animal one should also recount a recent experience of Bobby Tulloch and Dennis Coutts, two intrepid local but internationally renowed bird photographers, who dressed up in pantomime horse outfit in an attempt to approach a Snowy Owl for close ups. The bird was not taken in by the sight of a very crippled horse stumbling over the rough ground, probably being particularly suspicious of the back legs which could not see where they were going. . . .

Although the bird appears large even from a distance, it is only when close that one realizes it stands two feet tall when adult. Like many birds of prey the male, which is almost pure white, is slightly smaller than the more mottled brown female. The writer was once taken into a room on a croft in Fetlar where a sick bird was being taken care of. She was sitting docilely in the grate of an empty fireplace and the first impression was of an outsize 'Wally-dog'.

The feeding habits of Snowy Owls in Shetland appear to be rather catholic; in 1968 the nesting birds took rabbits, Oystercatchers and Arctic Skuas in that order of abundance. However they also feed on other waders, Rock Doves, Terns, and in the early 1970s when myxomatosis occurred on Fetlar, took a number of Hooded Crows, much to the locals delight. The present status of the Snowy Owl is well documented in the Shetland Bird Reports. Although several females have been present, there have been no males for several years; the last successful breeding was in 1975. On the positive side there are now a number of maturing females in the islands in the summer months and it may be only a matter of time before one or more find a mate and breed; on the pessimistic side they may disappear from Shetland as suddenly as they appeared.

BIRDS OF MOORLAND LOCHS

As discussed in Chapter 7, the acid moorland lochs make up over 75% of all Shetland waterbodies. These can be further divided into the 'dystrophic' peaty lochs and the clear hard-edged, often ice-scoured 'oligotrophic' lochs. The distinctions are important as only one of Shetland's breeding birds has a preference for the soft-edged peaty loch and lochan, and that is the Red-throated Diver, which because of its build can manoeuvre only clumsily on land and seeks sites where it can easily slip from its nest on the bank into the relative protection of the water. Divers also breed (often more than one pair) on the larger peaty lochs and on some of the slightly harder-edged serpentine and mettagabbro lochs. Shetland is in an ideal situation to support an increasing breeding population of this species as it has numerous suitable sites and the fretted nature of Shetland's coast with its frequent intrusions of voes and sounds, ensures that no point of land is more than three miles from the sea where the Divers feed.

No sound is more evocative of the wilds of Shetland than its melancholy wail or rapid and high 'kwick'. They are notes set clear of the background and continuous chorus of Gulls, Waders and Passerines, as if deliberately included in the score to re-awaken the sense of the listener. The Red-throated Diver is an elegantly streamlined bird adapted for preying on free-swimming fish, with narrow wings and large powerful legs set well back in the body. On the water it floats in a more submerged position than a duck, with its head and neck held forward and upward. Those not familiar with it can confuse it on the sea with a Shag, but its habit of slipping under the surface of the water, rather than plunging with the propulsive dive of the latter sets them apart. The flight to and from the sea is high and direct, and on its homeward flight it can be seen circling and calling over its breeding site, suddenly to descend in a rapid glide with its wings in an almost 60 degree 'V', finally scoring the water in a flurry of braking. Besides its call, its shape in flight is also very distinctive, the body slung under the wings, the back smoothly humped with the long neck and head drooping at one end and the feet at the other.

This is another species worth a close inspection to see the definition of the red throat patch, which gives the bird its name, and the grey head and white velvest cord striping of the back of the head. The Shetland name is 'Raingoose', as the bird is supposed to foretell the coming of rain, not a hard task in Shetland! In the *Birds and Mammals of Shetland* the Venables say that the cry is interpreted 'We're a' weet, we're a' weet . . . Waur wadder, waur wadder' ('We're all wet, worse weather'), which is a much more evocative description of its call than the 'rapid quacking' given in some handbooks.

Death of young Red-throats can be caused by flooding or drought, or by predation by Crows or Gulls. It is also caused by over zealous birdwatchers continually disturbing the adults. Studies on Hermaness, Fetlar and Foula, where there are considerable Skua colonies have indicated that even where Divers breed in the heart of a Bonxie colony there have been remarkably few instances of the latter taking eggs, young or adult.

The status of the Raingoose in Shetland is that of a common and wide spread species which is still increasing. In the 19th century it was not a numerous species as Saxby described its status as being a 'constant resident . . .' but 'not very common in the breeding season'. At the close of the century Evans & Buckley rightly pointed out that Saxby was referring to Unst, but went on to say 'a considerable number may be found breeding in Yell, commonly on the Mainland north of Lerwick, (but) no trace of a single nest has ever been discovered in the south of that island, in Foula and Fetlar', adding that a single pair probably bred on Whalsay. At the same time Raeburn found only four pairs in North Roe and two or three pairs in the West Mainland. Today approximately 50 pairs breed on Unst, 170 on Yell, 20 on Fetlar, 10 on Whalsay, 60 in North Roe, 16 in the South Mainland, and 10 on Foula; which leaves a substantial area of suitable breeding sites on the mainland which could easily support a further 200 pairs. The total is therefore of the order of 500 pairs which would be 40 per cent of the British total.

Before its slump in the 19th century, partially due to egg collecting and predation by man for food, it must have been a widespread and common breeder. The Shetland name for a Diver lochan is 'loomieshun' deriving from the old Norse 'loomr' and 'tjorn' or tarn, and there are 'Loomieshuns' as far apart as Foula, Saxavord, Girlsta, Swinnester and Voxter, to name but a few.

Other changes in the Raingoose's occurrence in Shetland, probably associated with its increase as a breeding species, are its earlier return in Spring – widely reported in January in recent years, compared to mid-April given by the Venables; also its growing habit of wintering in the voes and sounds, previously unrecorded.

Before leaving the Divers, mention must be made of the Great Northern Diver, which is almost as famous and mythical to the Shetland ornithologist as the Great Auk is to the rest of humanity. To understand this one must return to the discussions as to whether or not it bred in Shetland in the old texts of Edmonston, Saxby and Evans & Buckley, concluding with that of the Venables who summarize that 'the data presented are extremely suggestive'. Today the situation is unchanged and the Great Northern Diver is still often seen in the summer months in breeding plumage although rarely on freshwater. In the winter months it is a reasonably common species around the coast: probably between 200 and 400 birds winter around Shetland. The Great Northern Diver has bred once in Wester Ross, but the Shetland saga must continue – the data continue to be suggestive but by no means conclusive!

The other bird of the moorland loch is the Red-breasted Merganser, but it generally prefers clear oligotrophic lochs to peaty ones. The Shetland population is probably less than 300.

A similar aura of legend to the one which clouds the history of the Great Northern Diver obscures the record of the Long-tailed Duck or 'Calloo' and there is not a Shetland ornithologist who would not throw away his binoculars to be the first this century to confirm the Calloo as a breeding bird. Evans & Buckley noted two records of fresh eggs purchased in Lerwick, which must have been a thriving market for eggs in those days. Of these the Venables have said '. . . that if subsequent investigations prove that the bird breeds in Shetland, they may fairly be taken as genuine'. But how subsequent is 'subsequent' for no proof of breeding has appeared for 75 years! Certainly the species is more common in recent years as a summer resident and it has bred in Orkney and in the Western Isles this century. One therefore feels compelled to accept that it has bred at some time in Shetland and may yet do so again.

As far as wintering numbers are concerned, a conservative estimate is from 1500 to 2000. The flocks are usually small, up to 30 birds, but occasionally flocks of 100 or more are observed. To see a flock of these birds running before the wind in a crisp sea with their long tails curling over their backs and to hear their soft yodelling chorus, is one of the magic moments of the islands in winter.

The last of the regular moorland loch breeding birds, apart from the ubiquitous Mallard, is the Common Scoter. This bird has only been recorded breeding in the 20th century, with neither Saxby nor Evans & Buckley recording many wintering or summering birds. It has probably been an irregular breeder since 1911 with no more than ten pairs breeding in any year. Its close relative the Velvet Scoter has possibly bred, but this is unconfirmed.

The mesotrophic lochs lying on more soluble rocks or within their catchment area, have a greater diversity of flora and fauna than the commoner acid lochs, and cover and feeding for several other duck species. A recent breeder, probably as a result of its general expansion in the British Isles, is the Tufted

Duck. In the last century it was an irregular visitor, but by the 1950s was a common wintering species, particularly in the South Mainland and it bred there for the first time. Today there are possibly 20 pairs breeding throughout the islands.

A number of Shetland birds can be described as 'magnificent' or 'attractive' but only the Red-necked Phalarope can truly be said to be 'charming' and 'intriguing': charming, because so small and tame; intriguing, because the female is the handsome one of the pair and it is the male who incubates and feeds the young. Without being accused of too much anthropomorphism how can one convey the courage of such a tiny bird, under a hand-span in size, which spends almost ten months of the year in the open sea off South America, West Africa, and south-east Asia, and only two ashore among the stalks of sedge and bogbean?

The Phalarope's main breeding preference is for shallow water with plenty of cover – in a marsh on the margin of a reasonably productive or brackish loch, or in old cuttings in sedge-peat. Of all the migratory breeding birds they are the last to return, usually towards the end of May but sometimes not until the first week of June; they depart from their breeding sites often before the close of July.

Although they have little fear of man, probably because they have such little knowledge of him, they are often difficult to spot as they are always active, either darting with quick movements through the emergent vegetation or bobbing and spinning on the water as they pick off disturbed insects from the surface.

The status of the species has fluctuated somewhat over the last century, but accurate information is not available. Certainly the Unst population has dwindled from 10–20 pairs in the last century to only a few pairs today; the Fetlar population appears to have decreased since the mid-fifties; and most of the Mainland sites are now empty. There must have been some decrease overall to the present estimate of 30 pairs. However even this represents 90% of the British population.

Good examples of productive eutrophic lochs are the Lochs of Hillwell and Spiggie in the South Mainland. There are extremely few of this type and it is therefore hardly surprising that the breeding birds associated with them (so common in Orkney immediately to the south) are absent or only irregular breeders. The Loch of Hillwell has been the main breeding site for species such as the Coot, and the only site for Little Grebe and Shoveler. Spiggie Loch is the chief site for Pintail, and the marsh between it and Brow Loch is the principal site for Moorhen.

However only the Coot and Moorhen have bred regularly, and only since the latter half of the 19th century. The former nested in small numbers with a stable population sometime into the 20th century, but by 1977 only a couple of pairs remained. Similarly, Moorhens appear to have a small but relatively stable population scattered throughout the islands, although fewer birds are wintering than 20 years ago. Since the preferred sites for these species are widely scattered it is impossible to be sure of any status change, although there are certainly fewer of both species now in the South Mainland than there were 20 years ago. The Coot has been decreasing in Orkney and the Western Isles since the beginning of the century, while the Moorhen has been decreasing generally in Scotland.

The Shelduck is another species of the eutrophic lochs, although it may also breed on sheltered soft sea shores. The South Mainland has been its stronghold for two centuries at least. There probably has been little change in its status over the past 50 years or so, with several pairs at Hillwell and Boddam and up to seven pairs at Virkie. Unfortunately developments at Sumburgh Airport adjacent to the Virkie site in 1975 caused too much disturbance for the birds and they did not breed there for several years. Occasionally birds breed elsewhere, such as Papa Stour and Unst, but the total number of breeding birds in any year is probably less than ten pairs. The birds return to Shetland in mid-winter, pair in April and nest in old rabbit burrows or holes close to the shore.

Of the other freshwater wildfowl Mallard are widespread though not particularly numerous, while Teal are fairly uncommon and Wigeon are only sporadic breeders (see Table 29).

WINTERING WILDFOWL

The scarcity of productive freshwater lochs means that relatively small numbers of wildfowl occur in the winter, although some species, such as Goldeneye, Mallard, Teal and Whooper Swan are regularly found in brackish and marine situations, while others (such as Slavonian Grebe, Great Northern Diver and Long-tailed Duck) are almost exclusively on the sea. The virtual absence of large cultivated fields and Eel grass *(Zostera)* means there is little feeding for Geese.

To estimate the present status of wintering wildfowl is a difficult task as widespread counts have only taken place over the last few years and these do not cover a multitude of minor sites on the main islands never mind the outlying holms where Geese and Wigeon graze and some species, such as Mallard, roost. To estimate change in status is even more difficult as Saxby's estimates refer only to Unst, Evans & Buckley were not present for long periods in the winter, and the Venables could not adequately cover the whole Mainland. There is a general movement of nearly all species between lochs in late winter and early spring as the limited food supplies on the important lochs become exhausted, and this very often includes a dispersal to more marginal sites.

However a degree of credence can be given to the conclusions that follow, assuming there have been no major changes in the importance of the South

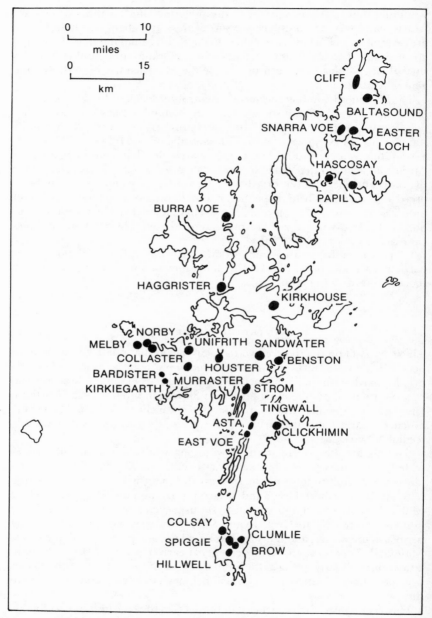

FIG 25. Major wintering sites of wild-fowl (Whooper Swans; Tufted, Pochard, Mallard, Wigeon, Golden-eye Ducks).

Mainland lochs relative to the others since the Venables carried out their counts in the early 1950s. The major sites are shown in Fig. 25.

Whooper Swans appear to have been birds of passage from at least the middle of the 19th century, and Saxby states that none showed any dis position to winter. Early in this century they began regularly wintering in small numbers on Spiggie Loch and by the later 1940s and early 1950s the November and October peaks were regularly just under 100 with a maximum of 122 in the winter of 1950–51. More recently peaks have consistently been nearer 200 for the same area. There has clearly been a considerable increase in the population. The Venables stated that the other important areas for wintering Whoopers were Easter and Wester Lochs in Unst. The peak numbers they give for Easter Loch are 54 in the winter of 1948–49 whereas peak counts in recent years have been regularly over 80 and 114 were recorded in November 1976. Very few however are recorded today from Wester Loch. These are still the most important early wintering sites, but there are others on Fetlar, Clickhimin and the West Mainland which all regularly have over 10 birds, and to which other birds may disperse later in the winter.

The only reasonably accurate overall count carried out to date was on 6th November 1977; this gave a total of 390 birds, around 5–10% of the overall British wintering population. It is possible that the number of Shetland wintering Whooper Swans has nearly doubled in the last 30 years. As with most wildfowl, departure commences in March, although stragglers may still be present into May. On several occasions individuals have summered in recent years.

Mallard have been a common wintering species for at least 200 years. Thirty years ago up to 250 passed through the South Mainland in early September, but such numbers have not been seen in the last decade. Wintering numbers of approximately 100 for this area may not have changed however, allowing for yearly fluctuations. Since the early 1970s, with more observers, several flocks of up to 70 have been seen in various areas, which suggests a total wintering population from 300 to 500. Normally the birds are only in small flocks of less than 30 and very widely dispersed.

In the early 1950s the Venables considered that although wintering Tufted Duck were quite common throughout Shetland, their main concentrations were on the South Mainland lochs with a peak of 80 birds. The peak count in recent years in this area has been 210 in October 1975. Peak counts elsewhere at the same time of year at such places as Tingwall, Snarravoe (Unst) and Clickhimin, have been well over 100 and occasionally over 200, with lesser sites on Yell, Fetlar and the West Mainland. The highest count anywhere was at Snarravoe with 310 birds in December 1976. It is obvious that there has been a great increase in the last few decades with wintering peak totals of well over 300 birds and a possible maximum of 500. Most of these birds depart in mid-March.

The situation regarding Goldeneye is less clear. Previous estimates by Saxby '. . . common in winter'; Evans & Buckley '. . . large number, some times of great size, usually 30'; Venables '. . . Common in Shetland from autumn to spring, with peak numbers of just over 100 in the Dunrossness area'; compare reasonably with the picture today. The highest counts in October and November 1976 gave 140 at Spiggie and 110 at Easter Loch. Other fresh and salt water sites might add a further 100 to give a peak wintering total of 350. It appears that there may have been a small increase in numbers recently, but it is hard to be certain on the existing data.

The situation with Teal is very similar, with small flocks of the order 20–30 being seen most years on both fresh and salt water. The total wintering number is probably less than 150. With Wigeon the numbers are most probably unchanged in the last 30 years with the Spiggie-Brow area remaining the most important with usually around 100 birds at peak, and flocks of 20–30 or occasionally more at other sites, giving an overall wintering total of 200–300 birds. In 1977, 150 were recorded on 3rd December at Sullom in the heart of the developing oil terminal.

Pochard may have wintered in the South Mainland for 200 years at least, but they became scarce towards the end of the 19th century although by the 1950s the number in Shetland had increased again to between 30–40 birds, mainly on Brow Loch. In recent years the numbers for Brow have consistently been over 100 with the highest number of 180 recorded there in January 1975. The Venables were not aware of Pochard elsewhere in Shetland, but it appears on recent evidence that the Brow population often frequents Tingwall Loch, while numbers from 40–100 may be seen at other sites such as Benston, Clickhimin and Snarravoe. Wintering totals for the whole of Shetland are probably around 200, which is a substantial increase over the past few decades.

No other freshwater ducks winter in significant numbers. For example, there is a small passage of Scaup in the autumn, but rarely more than half a dozen winter; few individuals of such species as Pintail and Shoveler regularly winter; Great Crested Grebe, Little Grebe, Green-winged Teal, Gadwall, Garganey, Goosander and Smew all occur occasionally as passage or winter visitors.

As far as Geese are concerned the most common is the Greylag, but only in small autumn and winter flocks of 20–30 birds with very occasionally large passage flocks of over 100. Barnacles have wintered on offshore islands in parties of 40 or more, while individuals of other species (White-fronted, Pink-footed, Brent and Canada) may winter, but they are most commonly seen in very small numbers in passage. On the sea, wintering Eider are joined by Long-tailed Duck, Great Northern Divers and perhaps 100 Slavonian Grebes in a few specific localities.

A number of species which normally breed inland, such as the Oystercatcher and Ringed Plover on sparsely vegetated ground, and the Starling, Wren and occasionally House Sparrow among the buildings and dykes of the townships, may also be found on the coast. The Wren however is the only one that occurs on high cliffs. Even in the strongest updraught one comes across these tiny birds, cocking their tails nervously and whirring from one crevice to another with an amazingly loud 'tit-tit-tit'. The Venables even recorded a nest at the top of the Kame of Foula, 1200 feet above the sea. Like the other Shetland subspecies of bird (the Starling *Sturnus vulgaris zetlandicus*), the Wren *Troglodytes troglodytes zetlandicus*, illustrates the tendency to increasing size in northerly latitudes. The Wrens of the Scottish islands, St Kilda, Fair Isle and Shetland all have differences of behaviour and song, while the Shetland and Hebridean forms show a tendency to lighter rather than darker plumage, whereas local races found in mild wet climates are usually darker than normal. The reason for this is unknown.

The other small passerine of the coast is the Rock Pipit which rarely strays from there except in winter when it may feed in the townships.

The Rock Dove, which has a curiously discontinuous distribution in Europe, with its nearest population to Britain in the Mediterranean, is a fast disappearing species due to interbreeding with feral populations. The feral forms have come from commensal and Racing Pigeons which themselves were originally bred from the Rock Dove. Until fairly recently Shetland had few feral birds in its large and widespread population and was therefore a fairly pure breed, but Racing Pigeons have been released traditionally from remote areas like Shetland and such birds are now appearing in the Rock Dove population.

When the Viking navigator, Flokki, was *en route* from Shetland to Iceland 1000 years ago he released a Raven to show him the way. Ravens are not regarded with such value today in Shetland, and their only accepted contribution are their wings to adorn the make-believe Viking helmets of Up-Helly-Aa. Like the Bonxie, the larger Gulls and the Hoodie, the Raven has long been persecuted by man because of its carrion association, and nest, eggs, young and adults are all destroyed. Although Ravens will attack sick or helpless sheep and lambs, there is little evidence that they will harm healthy animals. A recent investigation into the predation of sheep by birds in Shetland, suggested that the problem had become more acute recently because of the changes taking place in crofting, with less attention being given to hill-lambing than in the past, rather than because of an increase in predators. When the Skuas and Gulls are absent from the moorland in the winter months the Raven is the only large bird one may meet, drifting along lazily like a great scrap of black paper. It is a fairly common bird throughout the coast and occasionally also found nesting inland.

In the 17th century the King's Falconer used to visit Shetland to collect young Peregrines for hunting. Today he would be hard put to find a choice of young. There are approximately 8 sites at present with some activity associated with them, but in 1977 none was proved to have bred.

There are no good figures for the past level of the Peregrine population. Saxby said there were several pairs in Unst in the mid 19th century; Evans thought there were two pairs on Foula, 2–3 pairs in Fair Isle; Dunn quoted two pairs on Noss; there was believed to be one pair on Fetlar; Evans & Buckley cited T. Henderson of Spiggie for several sites on Fitful; other sites included Papa Stour, Fethaland, Ronas Hill and Foraness; recently there have been sites on the east coast, at least two in the West Mainland and one in the North Mainland. This could give a past total of between 20–30 pairs, but it must be a conservative estimate. With a wealth of suitable cliff and ample summer feeding of smaller seabirds and Rock Doves, and taking account that falconers came specifically to Shetland from Scotland, one would hazard a guess that the total number of sites in the past must have been nearer 50. The Venables give an impression of around 30 pairs as a minimum, but just at the time they wrote the population crashed on the mainland of Britain as a result of toxic agricultural chemicals, especially dieldrin in sheep dips. This decline has since been reversed.

How is it that the Shetland Peregrine, which is mainly resident, has continued to decline, and how is that the Merlin is still picking up dieldrin? There are two possible factors. Firstly the Peregrine in Shetland is seldom seen taking kills on land, except perhaps in the winter months when the bulk of the small seabirds are absent. One is drawn to the conclusion therefore that in coastal areas Peregrines are accumulating toxic chemicals from their seabird prey. It is interesting that, in a recent paper, Bourne & Bogan noted high levels of PCBs (polychlorinated biphenyls), industrial derivatives, and DDE (a breakdown product of DDT) in pelagic feeding seabirds, notably Fulmars and Kittiwakes; while the highest organochlorine levels were found in the Gulls and Skuas feeding around isolated seabird colonies. No examination has been made of coastal nesting Peregrines like those of Shetland, but when it is, one suspects that they will be found to be still suffering indirectly from man's by-products.

Secondly, is it mere coincidence that the decline of the Peregrine has been paralleled by the substantial increase in the Fulmar? When four Sea Eagles were introduced to Fair Isle a decade ago, one was subsequently found liberally coated with Fulmar oil and died, and Shetland Peregrines have occasionally been seen in a similar state.

The answer may lie with either or both of these factors and if it is the second there is probably little that we can do about it. It will be a sad loss for Shetland though if nowhere we can see the swift stoop or hear the piercing screams of the Peregrine Falcon.

References for Chapter 9
(full citations are given in the Bibliography on p. 353)

Armstrong, 1952, 1953; Balfour, 1968, 1972; Baxter & Rintoul, 1928; Berry, 1974; Bogan & Bourne, 1972; Bourne, 1974; Drosier, 1830–31; Dunn, 1837, 1848; Evans & Buckley, 1899; Groundwater, 1974; Hamilton, 1974; Harvie-Brown, 1895; Jackson, 1966; Joenson, 1966; Johnston, 1974; Lack, 1942; Lea & Bourne, 1975; Parslow, 1973; Salomonsen, 1935; Saxby, 1874; *Shetland Bird Reports*, 1969 on; Spence, 1974; Stewart, 1962; Tulloch, 1967, 1968; Tulloch & Hunter, 1972; Venables & Venables, 1948, 1950*a,b*, 1952, 1955; Williamson, 1951*a,b*, 1958, 1965.

CHAPTER 10

SEABIRDS

VIRTUALLY everywhere in Shetland one is aware of the variety and number of the seabirds which crowd the islands in the summer months. Two of the best places for getting a sense of the vast numbers of individuals involved are the Nature Reserves of Hermaness and Noss. From the relatively peaceful landing on Noss, or the Reserve entrance at Hermaness, it is a very short distance into the territories of Great and Arctic Skuas, where every step is challenged by a rush of wings and the air appears full of birds. But even this is no preparation for the spectacle hidden over the cliffs: here the observer is assaulted and engulfed by noise, smell, and seemingly incessant movement. The cliff faces are packed with jostling, squabbling forms landing and leaving in a continuous stream; while the water below is dotted with birds apparently resting from their struggles.

At these larger colonies, the seabirds are mainly Auks and Kittiwakes, although at Hermaness and Noss they include also the very much larger Gannet. Many colonies however are much smaller, and may be composed of only one species – Gull, Tern, Shag, or Cormorant. These smaller colonies occur on moorland and offshore holms as well as on the cliffs. Black Guillemots and Fulmars are not strictly colonial, but spread out thinly along the shore.

Only the Roseate and Little Terns of the regularly breeding British seabirds do not nest in Shetland, although the Sandwich Tern has only bred irregularly recently. A large proportion of the United Kingdom population of several of the others occurs in the islands, especially the Great and Arctic Skuas, Fulmar, Shag, Arctic Tern, and Black Guillemot (Fig 26, Table 16). It is estimated that around 900,000 seabirds nest in Shetland; Orkney supports about 400,000, while Faroe has several million (mainly Puffins and Common Guillemots).

The attraction for these birds is the position of the islands in the path of the North Atlantic Drift near the edge of the continental shelf and at an exit point of the North Sea. Here warm and salty waters from the Atlantic meet the enriched water from continental Europe, and provide nutrients for phytoplankton, and hence the zooplankton, fish, seals, cetaceans, and birds which feed on it (Chapter 5). The islands are convenient and relatively undisturbed breeding stations close to the feeding grounds.

The variety and distribution of marine life is reflected by the feeding adaptations of the seabirds. For example, the Petrels skim the water surface and feed mainly on zooplankton; they share the open sea with the Auks which dive for the smaller shoaling fish, and the Kittiwake which picks plankton

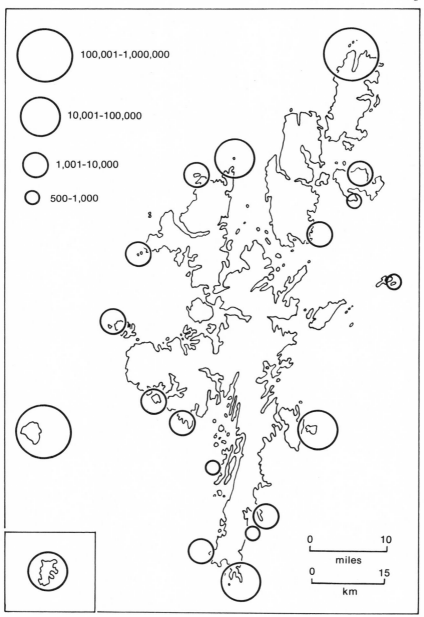

FIG 26. Main seabird breeding colonies.

TABLE 16: Composition and approximate breeding numbers of larger seabird colonies 1978

	Fulmar	Manx Shear-water	Storm Petrel	Leach's Petrel	Gannet	Cormorant	Shag	Arctic Skua	Great Skua	Black-headed Gull
UNST	20,000	?			5500		3000	200	1000	50
FOULA	40,000	10–100	1000+	20			3000	264	3000	
NOSS	5500				4500		150	44	260	
FAIR ISLE	25,000		100		30+		1500	116	25	
SUMBURGH	3000+						500			
FETLAR	15,000	50–100	200+				1000	200	250	25
FITFUL	9000+						50+		30	
RAMNA STACKS						40				
SHETLAND TOTAL	150,000	150+	2500+	20	10,000+	500	11,000	1500	5500	1000
% OF BRITISH TOTAL (if over 1%)	30–40				7	6	30	65–70	90	

	Common Gull	Lesser Black-backed Gull	Herring Gull	Great Black-backed Gull	Kittiwake	Common Tern	Arctic Tern	Razorbill	Guillemot	Black Guillemot	Puffin
UNST	550	350	250	120	5000	50+	1000	2000	20,000	100+	100,000+
FOULA		1	23	20	6000		3000	10,000	60,000	120	70,000
NOSS	15	2	500	400	10,600		60+	2000	29,000	100	5000
FAIR ISLE		50	300	50	12,000			2500	20,000	160	30,000
SUMBURGH	3	200	500	140	1800		13	1000	7000	25+	5000
FETLAR	200	75	275	400	770	20+	3000	200	400	150	5000
FITFUL		5	700	70	800			60	600	35	5000
RAMNA STACKS				200	2–3000			+	10,000		1000
SHETLAND TOTAL	2000	1000	10,000	2500	45,000	500+	10–12,000	20,000	150,000	4000	250,000
% OF BRITISH TOTAL (if over 1%)	10–15	2	3	10–15	10	3	25	5–10	15	30	25

Circa 1,000,000 breeding birds.

Note: Razorbill, Guillemot, Black Guillemot and Puffin = *individuals*; others = *pairs*

from the surface and dives superficially for fish. The Gannet dives spectacularly from up to 100 ft to catch larger fish such as Mackerel or Herring. Inshore waters are fished mainly by plunging Terns and the surface diving Shag, Cormorant and Black Guillemot. Almost everywhere the Arctic and Great Skuas harry the other birds as pirates or predators.

The pelagic seabirds (Petrels, Gannet, Auks and Kittiwake) are so highly adapted to marine life, either with long wings for effortless gliding over larger distances (Fulmar and Gannet) or small, narrow wings and strong legs placed well to the rear for powerful swimming (the Auks) that they are ill-suited for manoeuvring on land. They therefore seek nesting sites inaccessible to predators, such as cliff-faces and stacks, crevices and burrows. Even the near-shore seabirds, such as the Shag, Cormorant, Terns and Gulls prefer isolated breeding sites such as small islands in either sea or fresh water, remote moorland, or the base of cliffs. Such sites are abundant in Shetland, and where the rocks form tiers on high cliffs (as at Noss, Hermaness, Foula, Sumburgh and Fair Isle), they are packed with nesting birds.

STATUS OF SHETLAND SEABIRDS

The history of seabirds in Shetland is a very long one, and before man arrived, the population of many species must have been much greater than in recent times (some, notably the Gannet, Fulmar, Great Skua and Greater Black-backed Gull have greatly increased in the past few decades). In the days before terrestrial predators arrived the seabird colonies could have spread over the islands in places where they could not possibly be undisturbed today. With the coming of man, eggs would have been farmed from the more accessible species such as Gulls, Guillemots and Eider, while the young of many species and even the adults of species such as Gannets, Puffins and Guillemots could have been caught (as they are in Faroe today). In fact it is likely that any accessible nest was plundered until comparatively recently.

In the 19th century the human population of Shetland grew to over 30,000 (Chapter 3) and many outlying islands were inhabited. This would have disturbed many of the remote seabird colonies and there is no doubt birds were plundered for food. Some species must have suffered severe losses. With the introduction of the gun, the taking of birds became relatively easy and fowling reigned uncontrolled for decades. Several species also had a price on their head, such as the Sea Eagle which was exterminated in Shetland by 1910.

Somewhat ironically the lairds and merchants who ruled supreme and often despotically in the 18th and early 19th centuries, acted as bird pre-servers, since they regarded fowling by crofters as unproductive labour and attempted to discourage it. An extract from Saxby illustrates the view of fowling in the middle of the 19th century, 'Fowling is now very little practised except by some of the old hands, (although) considerable quantities of eggs are taken annually, either for home consumption or for local dealers. The cause of this decline has not been any failure in the supply, but the steady manner in which the proprietors have endeavoured to persuade the men to turn their time to a better account. A somewhat ludicrous occurrence took place some years ago when a well-known landowner who was shooting from a boat was suddenly interrupted in his aim at a row of guillemots by one of the crew, who exclaimed that there was a man up there; and so there was – one of his tenants, lying flat upon the ledge, perhaps not in a very tranquil state of mind, but for all that more willing to risk the reception of a charge of shot than to incur the inevitable anger of the Laird'. With the introduction of the gun-tax and the first Bird Protection Acts in the 1880s shooting became still less common.

During the harder years of this century, eggs have been taken for food, but generally only of Gulls and Eiders, and there has been little if no fowling. Notwithstanding Shags were shot in some numbers after the 1939–45 war and exported to the restaurants of London as 'Highland Duck'. A few eggs are still harvested from Gulls and Eiders, but adults or young are rarely eaten.

Saxby in the mid-19th century said of the Fulmar (or Maalie, as it is known locally) that 'it never breeds in Shetland' and that to make its acquaintance one had to go offshore with the haaf fishermen. Few adult bones of the species have been recovered from 10th century deposits at Jarlshof, and its status may have been similar at that time.

The Fulmar is a very widespread species occurring in both the Pacific and Atlantic. It varies in colour, in the eastern North Atlantic from mainly light birds in the southern part of the range to a high proportion of dark grey or 'blue' in the northern parts (Fig 27). On Bear Island in the Arctic the latter make up about 60 per cent of the population, while in Shetland only very few regularly occur and breed with the lighter form. In their book the Venables quote a curious passage from Saxby concerning the Fulmar of his day – 'Adult birds in full plumage – that is, with the pure white head and underparts – are comparatively scarce at all time'. Saxby seems to have been unaware that the fledged young have the same plumage as the adult. To suggest that these birds were comparatively rare possibly indicates that the more common birds were the blue form.

Although the Fulmar bred on St Kilda from at least the 17th century, the first confirmed breeding elsewhere in the British Isles was on Foula in 1878. Thereafter the Fulmar spread rapidly around Shetland, nesting on Herma-ness in 1897 and their expansion there, which was reflected elsewhere in Shetland is illustrated in Fig 28. It is incredible that a bird known only offshore less than 100 years ago should now number around 150,000 pairs, breeding from high cliffs to low shores, from peat banks to stone walls and derelict buildings. Next to the Puffin this is now the most abundant Shetland

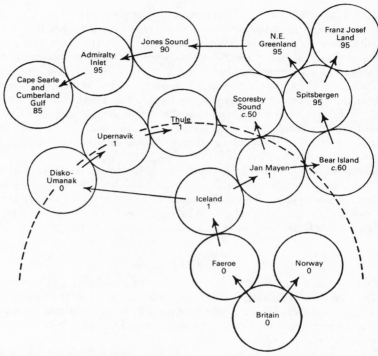

FIG 27. Percentages of dark ('blue') birds in breeding populations of the Atlantic Fulmar. The broken line represents the approximate boundary of the 'high arctic'. The arrows indicate the most likely movement of birds between colonies (from Fisher, 1952).

seabird and if its rate of increase of 6% per annum at Hermaness is maintained, it will outnumber even the Puffin before very long.

The reason for the sudden expansion of the Fulmar has never been satisfactorily explained although a host of suggestions have been put forward, ranging from Fisher's theory that there has been an increase of available food from human activity, beginning in the early Greenland fishing days; through behavioural changes associated with genetical changes, proposed by Wynne-Edwards; to the recent warming of the eastern North Atlantic providing further areas for expansion (Salmonsen). The natural food of the Fulmar is zooplankton, but it has an ability to thrive on fish remains and garbage and to drive off even the Bonxie (Great Skua) and the large Gulls, and this must have considerably helped its expansion round the coasts of Britain.

With such a vast increase in the population of one species, fears naturally arise that others might be influenced, particularly since Fulmars may affect

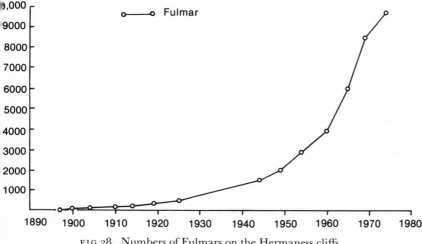

FIG 28. Numbers of Fulmars on the Hermaness cliffs.

other birds directly – they produce an oily secretion which can clog up the feathers of birds who receive it, even to the extent of hindering flight. Most species affected are sufficiently numerous for the odd fatality not to matter, but the Peregrine and young Sea Eagles introduced to Fair Isle in the early 1970s may have been afflicted much more seriously. However Fulmars often nest close to Guillemots and Kittiwakes, without apparently harming them. Nevertheless they sometimes take over nests of other species, even though their own nest is a mere scrape. I have seen fulmars take over both Oystercatcher and Herring Gull nests, complete with the eggs of the former occupant. Moreover the Fulmar is the only seabird species that will happily nest in dense vegetation and this is threatening some of the shrubby sites left on sheltered coasts in Shetland, by over enrichment from the nitrogenous guano of the birds. This is particularly effective as Fulmars spend more time at their nests than any other species: apart from an absence in October and November just after moult, they are only away from the breeding sites for a couple of weeks in May prior to egg-laying. However much one respects the success of this highly adaptable species, there is also an aesthetic attraction in the beauty of its controlled gliding as it manoeuvres stiff-winged across the updraughts of waves, cliffs and even drystone dykes.

The other Petrel with long, narrow wings designed for gliding which breeds in Shetland is the Manx Shearwater. There are only two proven colonies (on Foula and Fetlar), although at least one other site is suspected. The race which breeds in the islands is confined to the eastern side of the North Atlantic from the Westmann Islands to Madeira. It nests in burrows usually on soft sloping cliffs and it is entirely nocturnal, like its close relatives the Storm and

Leach's Petrels. On late summer evenings Shearwaters can be seen sitting in 'rafts' on the sea just offshore from their breeding colony. There never appear to have been a very large population in Shetland, and even this seems to have declined since the last century.

The Storm Petrel has a similar breeding distribution to the Manx Shearwater. It is the smallest of our seabirds and is very much like a sand martin in size and appearance; in flight it moves in bursts of fluttering and gliding. The tarsii are very long relative to the body, and when feeding on surface plankton and fish the birds patter along the surface. On land the Storm Petrel is very awkward and is able only to shuffle short distances from its landing place to its nest in a burrow or crevice. Favoured breeding sites are small uninhabited islands and probably the most famous Shetland colony is within the massive walls of the Broch of Mousa. During the long summer daytime anyone admiring this ancient structure is likely to be completely unaware that the walls are literally alive. It is only in the depth of summer nights when mates change shift that the shadowy movements of birds and sustained chattering and purring reveal the extent of the occupation.

In the haaf fishing days last century, Storm Petrels were familiar birds to Shetlanders in their boats away from land but today they are merely ghosts in the night at their breeding sites for most of us. Besides Mousa, the Storm Petrel breeds on Foula, Fair Isle, Fetlar, Unst, and on the islands off Scalloway and those between Unst and Fetlar. It probably nests on several other islands and where recordings of their voice have been used to attract them they appear in surprisingly large numbers almost anywhere round the Shetland coast. Although rarely seen there are probably several thousand pairs breeding in Shetland.

A near relative of the Storm Petrel is Leach's Petrel, which has only very recently been proved to breed in Shetland (in 1973 on Foula), although suspected for a number of years. It is a rather uncommon bird in the eastern North Atlantic, and is restricted to oceanic islands from the Westmanns to Faroe (where it was proved to breed in 1934), Foula, St Kilda, the Flannans, Sula Sgeir and North Rona.

GANNETS

The Gannet or Solan Goose, is the largest of our British seabirds. It has been present in Shetland waters for a great many years: as far back as the Bronze Age its bones were fairly numerous in the Jarlshof middens. That it bred at that time cannot be assumed since they were taken for food as late as the mid-19th century when they were certainly not breeding in Shetland. Saxby noted that in windless conditions with a flat sea '. . . these birds may not unfrequently be knocked down with an oar'. At that time they were seen throughout the year, and in the breeding season on the North Stack of Muckle Flugga and the Outstack – but even today they have never been known to breed on either, although they now breed in large numbers in adjacent areas.

Bones have also been found in 9th- and 10th-century dwellings and if Gannets were not breeding before the 20th century, there must have been a steady immigration from elsewhere. In general the Gannet may have been widely distributed, but from at least the time of man's settlement in remote parts it has been effectively prevented from colonizing accessible sites because it had been steadily culled for human food.

When fowling ceased as a tradition around the end of the 19th century, the species began to expand and sites such as Hermaness and Noss were safely founded. Expansion at these sites (Figs 29) and other British sites probably led

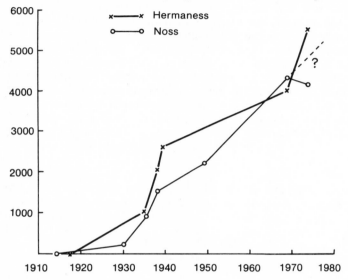

FIG 29. Increase in Gannet numbers at the two large Shetland colonies.

to the founding of the Norwegian colonies as recently as 1946; in more local waters Gannets have been roosting in several new situations in recent years (for example, Copinsay in Orkney, Foula and Fair Isle). In fact they bred on Fair Isle in 1975, and by 1978 had a small colony there of some 30 nests. The only site in the eastern North Atlantic where there has been a decline this century is at Faroe where young are still taken at the only colony on Mykines. There has been an increase on the western side of the North Atlantic in Newfoundland and the Gulf of the St Lawrence, which are the only sites for the Gannet on the American side of the Atlantic.

The brilliant white plumage, black wing tips, six-foot wing span and yellow head of the adult Gannet makes it a beautiful and a conspicuous bird. It can be seen around the coasts throughout the year, although the mottled brown first-year birds tend to migrate further afield in the winter months. Anywhere

where shoals of Mackerel, Herring, Piltock or Haddock occur, Gannets can be seen plummeting with half-closed wings into the sea. Their velocity gained from diving is obviously the main factor in the capture of fish, but they may use their wings under water as well to give some extra propulsion. Except in high winds they require a run to gain enough momentum to take off from the sea and at this point are prone to attack from Bonxies who will repeatedly knock a Gannet back into the water until it gives up its catch, the latter will also tip them up on the wing.

At Hermaness and Noss the colonies continue to increase at a tremendous rate. The Neap and Neapna Stack at Hermaness were colonized in 1932, and expansion has been particularly rapid in the last decade. In this area they are breeding mainly on a vegetated cliff face; at the boundaries of the expanding colony they actively throw off the vegetation so that they can build their nests on bare rock. Disturbance rather than open aggression has allowed Gannets to extend possibly at the expense of Guillemots at Noss, and Kittiwakes at Hermaness, but there are no accurate counts over the relevant period. There appears to be nothing, apart from the possible lack of food, to prevent the continued expansion of the existing Gannet colonies and a colonization of Foula and possibly other sites.

SKUAS

The only seabird that breeds in both the North Atlantic and Antarctic is the Great Skua (or Bonxie). The history of this species in Shetland does not appear to be very old: there are no remains from Jarlshof and no site names

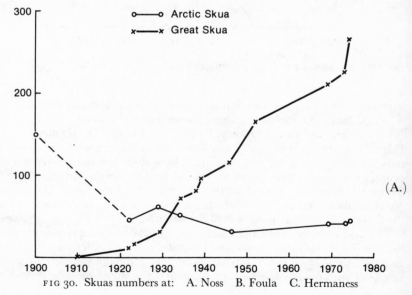

FIG 30. Skuas numbers at: A. Noss   B. Foula   C. Hermaness

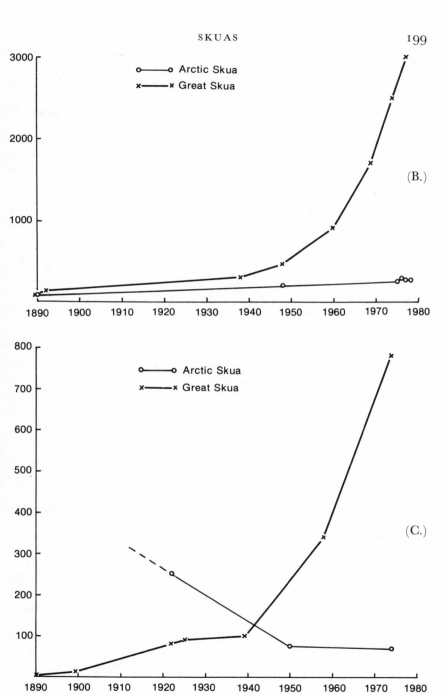

based on the old Norse root name 'sku' as there are in Faroe. The first record of 1774 may in fact be the time the species first settled in Shetland. The term Bonxie itself is also not very old; it was used to describe a thick-set person and therefore is aptly applied to a bird like the Great Skua which is like a short and heavy gull. The Arctic Skua (Aalin or Skooty Aalin) is an older inhabitant, and there is at least one site in Yell (Aalin Knowes) which may be named after it.

In the 19th century the Bonxie was heavily persecuted and it was only through the active protection of Dr L. Edmonston at Hermaness and John Scott of Foula, and its inclusion later in the Wild Birds' Protection Act of 1880 that it recovered – though not a few Shetlanders would have been glad if it had been exterminated! The increase in the population of three sites can be seen in Fig. 30 to have been accompanied by a partial decline of the Arctic Skua in the same areas. This led to fears that growth of the Bonxie population at these sites would eventually drive out the smaller Skua, but it is now clear that the latter's status has been steady in recent years and that at least on Hermaness and possibly on Noss the Bonxie has now colonized nearly all its optimum habitat: it appears to prefer a deeper cover than the Arctic Skua and slightly drier situations. Besides the increase at these sites the Bonxie is also actively expanding throughout the Shetland mainland (Fig. 31).

The increase in Shetland has been accompanied by a decrease in Faroe and Iceland, where the species has been resident much longer. At one time on Skuvøy in Faroe (named after the Bonxie), up to 6000 young were taken annually. Today there are only about 500 pairs in the whole of Faroe; while in Iceland the population has decreased from approximately 6000 pairs in 1954 to under a quarter of this today. Apart from Bear Island, colonized in 1970, the north of Scotland and Orkney are the Bonxies' only other breeding sites and only about 200 pairs breed there (mainly in Orkney). The total Shetland population is now thought to be of the order of 5500 pairs of which half are on Foula and one fifth on Unst. The islands therefore support over 95% of the British population and over 60% of those breeding in the northern hemisphere. It is an ironic situation for Shetland conservationists that probably the most disliked species occurring in the islands is also the most important in both the national and international contexts.

The Bonxie is disliked because it is a kleptoparasite on most seabird species and also a predator of almost any bird species from the size of Dunlin upwards; it has been blamed for falls in the populations of species from Eiders to Arctic Skuas. Even if one did not know that it might dine off an attractive Puffin or Kittiwake fledgling its aggressive attacks on any intruder at its nesting territory make it difficult for many people to love it. It has a nasty habit too of making sheep driving within a colony extremely difficult, since it may drive off dogs as well as sheep. Notwithstanding there is no actual evidence that this bird has been severely detrimental for either seabird or terrestrial bird populations within the period of its expansion; indeed many of

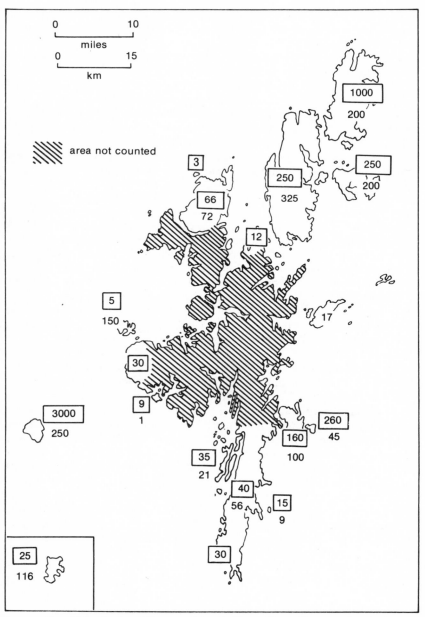

FIG 31. Numbers of pairs of Great and Arctic Skuas (Great Skua numbers in boxes).

its prey species (Kittiwake, Guillemot, Arctic Skua and Whimbrel) have actually increased in numbers over recent years. It appears that the Bonxie is very much of an opportunist feeder, taking whatever is immediately available, from Puffin to Storm Petrel and Snipe to Rabbit, different individuals having different preferences.

Bonxies and Arctic Skuas both establish a much larger territory around their nest sites than any of the other kleptoparasitic gulls. When the off-duty bird is present, it appears to favour a particular point from which to keep watch, very often a slight hummock which has become green with grass due to constant enrichment, and which stands out from the otherwise darker background of heather or wood rush in which it scrapes its nest. Another feature of Bonxie colonies are the 'clubs', which are the meeting areas for immature birds. These areas are green with grass and long lasting like the territory vantage points and also like the nearest lochan shore where the birds gather to wash.

Bonxies have a habit of rubbing in, or rather 'knocking in' their dislike of intruders into their breeding territory, by diving on any passer by and often striking him on the head. The secret of avoiding this is to carry a stick above the head – or to make sure one's companion is taller than oneself! The birds swoop in at about 30 degrees to the horizontal, often from the side or behind. Occasionally they approach from the front at about head height. It is a magnificent spectacle and a beautiful demonstration of the Bonxie's sprinting power which it otherwise uses only to catch up with its prey. Outwith the breeding season Bonxies disperse throughout the southern Atlantic.

Where the Bonxie uses sheer weight and strength and some reputation in obtaining food, the Arctic Skua relies on speed, manoeuvrability and a sharper aggression. This produces very different emotional responses from visitor and local alike. The two species are similar in overall length, but the Arctic Skua is considerably lighter and has slimmer pointed wings and characteristically pointed tail feathers. Although they take young birds and may even strike adult prey to the ground so as to devour them, the Arctic Skua is mainly a kleptoparasite on Kittiwakes and Terns and it is in the pursuit of these birds that it demonstrates its magnificent flight and tenacity, pursuer and pursued drawing increasingly tight circles around one another.

Although there is a lot of variation in the plumage of the Bonxie it does not show polymorphic forms as does the Arctic Skua which can vary from almost completely dark chocolate with the only light feathers in the wing flash to very light almost creamy underparts, usually with a dark breast-band and a more intermediate dark back with the dark head cap separated by a buff collar. It has been described as 'the most strikingly dimorphic' species on the British (bird) breeding list. Due to the labours of successive Wardens of Fair Isle Bird Observatory, a considerable knowledge of the biology of the species has been amassed. There is a colony of the bird near the Observatory and over a 15-year period every chick and adult was recorded – their times of laying, hatching, fledging, their territory and survival, but most important – their colour. As a result it has been possible to show that the colour phases are determined by two alleles at a single locus. True dark and pale birds are homozygous, and intermediates can be recognized as birds with dark tips to the feathers hiding all ventral white colouration. Most intermediates are heterozygotes, but there is a wide range in the variation, and a substantial proportion of birds classified as dark are heterozygous.

The Fair Isle Skua colony was extinct from about 1906 to the early 1920s. From 1935 to 1947 eight to 12 pairs bred each year, and then in the period of intensive study it increased from 40 breeding pairs in 1949 to 142 in 1962. Throughout the time the bird was studied, pale birds comprised 21% of the total.

What is the reason for the pale-dark dimorphism? The frequency of pales increases in a northerly direction, and northernmost colonies have few or no darks. It has been suggested that the pales may be at an advantage in hunting lemmings over a snowy tundra, whilst dark and dark-intermediate might be more cryptic over the ocean where they parasitize Terns and smaller Gulls. There is no evidence for either idea. However a close study of the Fair Isle birds has given the probable answer.

In Arctic Skuas, mating behaviour is initiated by the female approaching the male, who reacts angrily against her. This approach-rejection cycle goes on for some time until the male weakens and finally accepts the female. Mating then takes place.

The significant point is that dark birds are less aggressive than light ones: a dark male does not react as vigorously as a pale against an importunate female, and matings involving a dark male are set up earlier than those with a pale one (the colour of the female does not matter). Pairs with a dark male hatch their eggs three days before ones with a pale male. For first pairings this difference increases to 11 days, and this is biologically important because Arctic Skuas pair more or less for life. (They change partners readily if a pair fails to rear young.) This means that dark males will have a higher fitness than pale ones, and indeed the frequency of the pale allele in the Fair Isle colony is 43% in breeding males but 51% in females. In matings between phases, 60% involve pairs where the male is darker than the female. Presumably this difference would be greater if the colony had not been increasing so rapidly during the period of study, making it easy for birds to find a mate whatever their phenotype.

Now the frequency of pale birds increases in a northerly direction (Fig 32). Pale birds have an advantage over darks because they begin breeding at a younger age than darks. This may be another consequence of their importunate aggressiveness. It means that a pale bird has a higher chance of surviving to breed than a dark. However another factor comes in. The higher the proportion of pales in a colony, the later will be the breeding season. In the north of its range, Arctic Skuas feed largely on lemmings and voles which

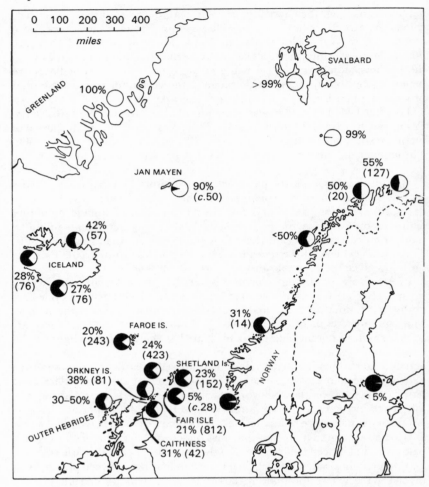

FIG 32. Proportions of dark and light phases in the Arctic Skua. For each sample the proportion of pale birds is represented by the white portion of the circle. The same size (where known) is indicated alongside the circle (from Berry & Davis, 1970).

become common late in the summer; further south it has to adjust its time of breeding to that of the Gulls and Terns on which it preys, and they in turn will breed at a time when food and climate are best for raising their own broods. The dark/light segregation is really a mechanism for varying the time of peak breeding which happens to produce a colour difference of no apparent importance to the birds themselves.

The Arctic Skua has a holarctic breeding distribution extending in the British Isles only as far south as the Inner and Outer Hebrides. A few breed on the north mainland of Scotland, and between 200–300 pairs in Orkney. There are about 1500 pairs in Shetland and this is some 80% of the British population, although only a very small proportion of the world total. In a British context therefore it is an important species. Although numbers have fallen in several colonies where Arctic Skuas are adjacent to Bonxies, these colonies now appear to be stable while it continues to expand over the rest of Shetland (Fig. 31).

Outside the breeding season the Arctic Skua follows the migrating Arctic Terns south down the coasts of Africa and South America, wintering in the region of 40 degrees South. The return is usually about two weeks later than the Bonxie, from about the middle of April.

KITTIWAKES

Both the Fulmar and the Kittiwake are often spoken of as Gulls. In fact the former with its torpedo-shaped body, long, narrow wings and stiff, gliding flight, apart from general colour and size, bears little resemblance to a gull. On the other hand the Kittiwake is technically a Gull, but its way of life and form of movement is very unlike the other British Gulls. It is one of the most oceanic of birds, spending nearly all of its time outside the breeding season over the North Atlantic, delicately picking plankton or small fish from the surface of the sea, or plunging to take larger fish. The other Gulls feed immediately offshore or on land, the larger species scavenging and robbing, and the smaller feeding on terrestrial and estuarine invertebrates. The Kittiwake is also the only Gull that is adapted for breeding on vertical cliffs.

The Kittiwake is more lightly built than the Common Gull (which is the same size), and it has a distinctive buoyant flight, intermediate between that of the Gulls and the Terns. If one imagines that a Gull has a regular downstroke in flight, the Kittiwake appears to miss one stroke out of every three, while the Tern misses two out of three in an distinctly erratic flight. There are several other distinctions – the wings are narrower than Gulls and are usually held in a half-jack-knife position; while the body appears torpedo-like in flight, as in the Fulmar, and in contrast to the neck constriction evident in Gulls.

The Kittiwake is an oceanic species with colonies on open coasts, on the eastern side of the North Atlantic. Its breeding range stretches from the north coasts of Russia to Brittany. In Shetland the largest colonies are on Fair Isle, Noss, Foula and Hermaness with several other small colonies scattered around the coast (Fig. 33). All the colonies have favourite freshwater lochs or lochans for bathing, and keep a particular flight line between these and their

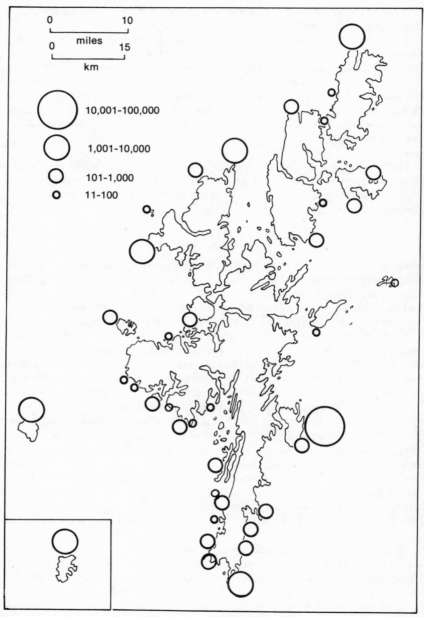

FIG 33. Kittiwake colonies and numbers.

nests. From the west side of Hermaness they stream across the headland, following the line of burns, to the Loch of Cliff, while from Noss they fly across the Sound to the Bressay lochs (there being only one small lochan on Noss which is dominated by Skuas and other Gulls). The contrast between the noisy Kittiwake colonies and these seemingly endless streams of silent white birds is striking and somewhat eerie.

The species has been increasing in Britain since the turn of the century at an incredible rate of 50% every ten years. In Shetland there have been insufficient counts over the years to understand the whole picture but several new colonies have formed during the last 30 years at Bressay, Yell, Out Skerries and Wats Ness. At the first two of these expansion has continued; there has also been an increase at Sumburgh, Fair Isle and Fetlar, but decreases at Papa Stour and Eshaness. At present it is difficult to know what is happening in the large colonies of Hermaness, Noss and Foula as, unlike Fair Isle, there have not been enough accurate counts. There is a suggestion from recent work on Hermaness that there has been a decline in Kittiwakes, possibly at the expense of the increasing Guillemots. At Noss there has been a decline in the past, but present trends are unknown. The Kittiwake provides a large proportion of the diet of the local Bonxie populations at all those sites. A study on Foula in 1974 showed that of 574 corpses of birds identified as Bonxie prey, 158 were Kittiwakes.

AUKS

The other pelagic seabirds of Shetland are the Razorbill, Guillemot and Puffin, all belonging to the Auk family. Of this group the Puffin (or Tammy Norie) is the most oceanic, the most numerous and the best known. With its dumpy body, disproportionately large red, blue and yellow bill, shuffling gait and endless quarrels with neighbours it is the Pierrot of the great cliff circus. It is the most difficult seabird of those active in the daytime to put an accurate number to, for attendance at the burrows in the breeding season can vary by a factor of as much as a thousand in a day. The populations are certainly a great deal larger than was thought only a few years ago: the north Unst colonies from Hermaness to Saxavord are probably of the order of 100,000 plus – the same magnitude as the famous St Kilda colonies. Other large colonies are on Foula, Fair Isle, Fitful, Sumburgh and Fetlar with numbers in the thousands, and there are many smaller colonies (Fig. 34).

Like the Kittiwake, the Puffin provides a substantial share of the Bonxie diet. At Hermaness they are regularly waylaid on their return from long fishing trips when they are carrying Sand Eel and Sprat. They appear to feed much farther offshore than the Guillemot and Razorbill, perhaps right up to the edge of the continental shelf. Their return from the open sea after winter is later than the other Auks, not until early April, when they gather offshore in rafts for a few days before tentatively setting foot on dry land. Although in the

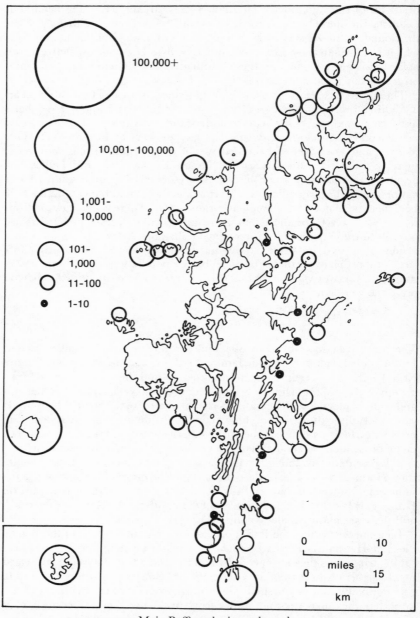

FIG 34. Main Puffin colonies and numbers.

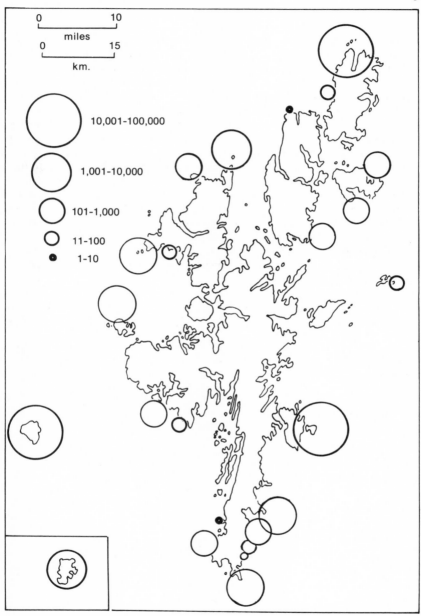

FIG 35. Guillemot colonies and numbers.

south and west of Britain there has been a decline of the Puffin, there is no evidence for this occurring in Shetland.

The Guillemot is the third most numerous seabird in Shetland and the most social in that it breeds in dense and usually large colonies, shoulder to shoulder on narrow ledges or broad shelves on the cliff face, or deep within caves. The largest colonies in Shetland are at Foula and Noss, with colonies of several thousand also at Fair Isle, Hermaness, Sumburgh and Ramna Stacks. Although there has been a decline of the more southerly subspecies *Uria aalge albionis* in the south of Britain, the more northerly *U. a. aalge* which breeds in Shetland appears to be increasing. At Fair Isle, which is the only site where there has been consistent counting over a number of years the population has increased more than fivefold since 1966. At Hermaness they appear to have increased by 15% since 1969, while Harris in 1974 estimated numbers in other colonies that had been counted five years previously during the Seafarer seabird survey of 1969, and noted an overall increase in all accurately countable colonies. This increase is of course, a partial recovery from the decline that took place in the 19th century.

The variant 'bridled' Guillemot is more common in Shetland than on the Scottish mainland. Bridled birds have a white ring and tail around the eye; this is inherited as a recessive trait.

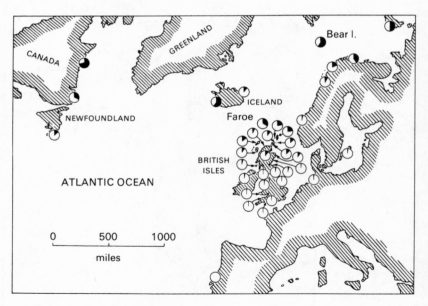

FIG 36. Frequencies of bridling (shown in black) in the Common Guillemot.

In 1938 and 1939 members of the British Trust for Ornithology were enlisted by H. N. Southern to count the numbers of bridled and non-bridled Guillemots in as many colonies as possible. With a few irregularities, the frequency of bridled birds increased with latitude: at the southern end of the range in Portugal not a single bridled bird was seen, but northward the proportion of bridled birds increased until it reached over 50% in southern Iceland. Bridling does not occur in Pacific populations of the species. In Iceland, the Common Guillemot is replaced by Brunnich's Guillemot *(Uria lomvia)*, and the frequency of bridling apparently falls with the species density, so that only 10% of Guillemots are bridled on the island of Grimsey, north of Iceland. The counts were repeated in 1948–50 and the proportions of bridled Guillemots were found to have fallen by up to 10% in quite a few colonies (although it was the same as before in over half); but in a third count ten years later (in 1959–60) the frequencies were the same as in the first count.

Now it is difficult to collect information about the population structure and amount of movement of individuals between colonies of Guillemots, never mind about the relative fertility and survival of bridled and non-bridled birds. An intensive study with colour-ringed birds of a Guillemot colony near Aberdeen showed that the generation time was about nine years, and the rate of population turnover normally very low. This meant that the change in bridling frequencies in the two ten-year periods between surveys could not be due to natural selection, and must be due to either a mass movement of birds (which has sometimes been recorded for Guillemots) or that the counts were inaccurate because of the patchy distribution of bridled birds.

Whatever the true explanation for the frequency changes in time, the reasons for the cline in space is completely unknown. Southern showed that bridling frequencies increase as water temperature falls, and there is some slight evidence that bridled brids had a higher basic metabolic rate than non-bridled ones. If so, this could be the explanation for the northern extension of the species (mainly bridled birds) in this century. Certainly, the increase in proportion of bridled birds with latitude is so consistent that it must have some causal explanation in the same way as the Arctic Skua. It is easy to speculate about bridled Guillemots, but very difficult to find out why they occur.

The Common Guillemot and its two close relatives, Brunnich's Guillemot and the Razorbill, are the only seabirds that do not make a nest or even a scrape. The large pyriform egg is laid on a ledge and held there by body and feet. As incubation proceeds the air sac at the broader end becomes larger, shifting the centre of gravity to the narrow end. However the egg must always be in a precarious position on narrow and sloping ledges among crowds of jostling birds and disturbance to the parent may easily dislodge it. Not long ago it used to be the habit of the North Isles steamer to pass round Noss in the summer months on its way from Lerwick to show passengers the huge colonies, and for their amusement induce a mass departure from the cliffs by sounding the ship's whistle. No one seemed to be aware at that time what a catastrophic effect this could be having on breeding success.

Like the other Auks (except the Black Guillemot), the Common Guillemot feeds mainly on free swimming fish such as Sand Eels, Sprats and Herring, sometimes diving to considerable depths. These fish occur in shoals and the Auks very often prey on them in well distributed flocks, travelling to and from the fishing grounds in long low strings with Puffins, Guillemots and often Razorbills mixed together. Where they must pass around headlands or through sounds there is often a massive stream of traffic which includes also the other pelagic colonial species such as the Gannet and Kittiwake. One of the best known of these maritime highways in the winter months is through Bluemull Sound between Yell and Unst, while at the headlands of Lamba Ness in Unst, the north west tip of Yell and at Uyea Isle in North Roe, there is always a constant stream of traffic. This seems greater on the return journey to the colony; the birds disperse rapidly on their outward journey to feed, but on the return use these headlands as focal points. Another spectacular site is at Sumburgh in the South Mainland where the Noss and local birds pass on their way to and from the feeding grounds of the Sumburgh roost.

The return from wintering in the North Sea takes place over many weeks. Indeed in good weather Guillemots can be seen offshore and even on the cliffs, especially in the morning, from October onwards. Their attachment at this time is not very strong and they are easily disturbed. Numbers and strength of attachment gradually build up through the early spring until they settle on the cliffs for breeding in April. The breeding season ends suddenly and spectacularly in late evenings during late June and early July when the flightless young descend under the safe net of darkness from the ledges to the sea. Here they join up with their parents and paddle rapidly offshore. Shortly after this the adult commences its moult and becomes flightless and vulnerable. Puffins on the other hand disperse well offshore before they begin their moult.

In Shetland Razorbills almost invariably breed adjacent to Guillemots, although they prefer crannies and corners to open ledges. They are many fewer in number and much less pelagic, especially during the breeding season when most feeding seems to be well inshore. Like the Guillemot they feed on Sand Eels and Sprats as well as on molluscs and crustaceans, but how much their bulkier shape and transversely flattened bill are indications of a different feeding method is not known. Departure from the breeding cliffs occurs at a similar time to the Guillemot, but the return slightly later, and they are usually not seen offshore until after the New Year, finally settling on the cliffs in April. At present there is no indication locally of any changes in the population. Perry (1948) thought they were decreasing on Noss, estimating that there were probably fewer than 1000 pairs between Hovie Geo and Punds Geo. A count in 1970 in the same area however found 1800 individuals, which does not suggest any progressive change.

The remaining seabirds, the Black Guillemot, Gulls and Terns, Shag and Cormorant are coastal birds and only the Arctic Tern is pelagic outwith the breeding season, making an incredible double journey of 10,000 miles each year and enjoying the long summer days in the high latitudes of both hemispheres. The Arctic Tern (or Tirrick) is a well loved bird in Shetland because of its buoyant flight and lightsome nature, but also because its return in mid-May heralds the end of the somewhat rumbustious spring of the north and the arrival of the more peaceful summer.

The Shetland population of Arctic Terns is probably of the order of 12,000 pairs, made up of a few large colonies of over 1000 pairs and numerous smaller colonies of over 100. Any figure however must be tentative as Terns are notoriously fickle in their attachment to breeding sites and overall numbers may rise or fall by several thousand in one year. The recent figures for Foula well illustrate these fluctuations.

	Number of pairs
1960–62	100–300
1969	400
1971	900
1973	750
1974	1800
1975	6000
1976	5650
1977	3000

During the period of dramatic increase from 1974, the huge Orkney colonies on Westray fell by some 12,000 pairs and it seems likely that some moved north. Similarly the population in Papa Stour rose from less than 500 pairs in 1969 to 1000 in 1974 and 3000 in 1977, suggesting perhaps that some of the Foula Terns deserted in 1977 in favour of Papa Stour. It is of interest that the Actic Skua population on Papa Stour showed a presumably associated increase – from 30 pairs in 1974 to 150 in 1977. Similarly other fluctuations, though not of the same magnitude, have been recorded for other terneries in the islands. With such widespread fluctuations it is difficult to discern any overall trend in the population.

Generally the Arctic Tern prefers short vegetation or shingle for nesting and this can be found both on the shore or on moor not far from the shore. Almost invariably a few Common Terns occur with the Arctic Terns and there are a few small colonies, mostly on low holms, of almost purely Common Terns. Like the Fulmar and the Bonxie the Common Tern is a comparative newcomer to Shetland, with the first proven breeding record in 1901. It was not recorded by Saxby but was noted by Evans & Buckley in 1890. An even more recent Tern immigrant to Shetland has been the Sandwich Tern. The first doubtful record is of an egg from Out Skerries in 1924 but subsequently none was recorded until 1949 when the Venables saw one in the South Mainland. Then in 1955 two pairs bred off Whalsay and by 1960 six pairs were breeding. But from 1961 they did not return there. In the last decade 1–8 birds have put in a regular appearance, usually in the North Isles. At the present moment the Sandwich Tern is increasing in Britain with its most northerly regular breeding station in Orkney – the farthest north it breeds anywhere in its range, which extends from the east coast of North America to the Caspian Sea. In Shetland therefore it is at its extreme northern limit and unless there is a further expansion it is unlikely to breed more than sporadically.

Whereas the Terns feed on small fish by plunge-diving, the Black Guillemot, Shag and Cormorant are diving birds. The Black Guillemot (or Tystie) is one of the small Auks, 'black' since unlike the others it is uniformly sooty black ventrally as well as dorsally, apart from conspicuous white wing flashes. It is also distinguished by its brilliant red legs and feet, by its habit of squatting rather than standing upright and by the fact that it is a solitary rather than a colonial breeder spread out thinly along almost the whole Shetland coast apart from the heads of the sheltered voes. Unlike the other British Auks it also lays two eggs rather than one.

Although it is not a social breeder except in a very loose sense it indulges in communal displays early in the season and has a curious habit of lining up on the sea in evenly spaced single file. Moult flocks collect at several sites in the winter where presumably feeding is good – over 1000 birds have been recorded off Hascosay in mid-winter. During the 1969 Seafarer census 2400 birds were recorded. This is almost certainly a low estimate and the actual population could well be much higher. The species habit of nesting well within the shelter of boulders or caves makes them extremely difficult to count. Black Guillemots are only found in the extreme north and west of the British Isles; Shetland has at least 30% of the total population.

The call of the Tystie is a plaintive and high pitched whistle; there is little music about the calls of the Shag and the Cormorant. Normally they are extremely quiet birds but when confronted on the nest make a sound like a croak through a rubber tube. Locally the Shag is known as the Scarf and the Cormorant as the Big Scarf or Lorin, the last because of its white thigh patch. Outwith Shetland the Cormorant's diet is said to be flatfish or demersal species and as there is little sheltered, sandy and shallow water to support such fish in Shetland it is not surprising that their numbers are restricted to about 450–500 pairs. No one knows if the size of the population has changed over the years. Cormorants were present at Sumburgh from at least the Bronze Age and they were recorded at the Heads of Grocken and Brae Wick in the 18th century. However there is a great deal of movement of whole colonies and of adults from one site to another. All the present breeding sites are on the west coast of Shetland (Fig. 37); the last east coast site was Bard Head, Bressay

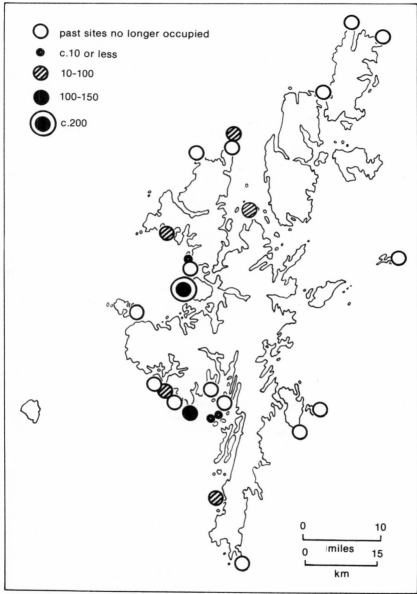

FIG 37. Cormorant colonies totalling 480–500 pairs in 1977. (There has never been a complete count of all sites in a single year: the last full count on Muckle Roe gave 237 pairs in 1952).

which was deserted after 1966 (there were small colonies at Out Skerries and Noss in the 19th century).

Feeding dispersal during the breeding season appears to be quite widespread: there is a regular flight line over Spiggie and Brow Lochs to Boddam Voe which is presumably from the St Ninian's colony, and one across Mavis Grind to Sullom Voe from the Muckle Roe colonies. Outwith the breeding season Cormorants are dispersed in small numbers within the sheltered voes and sounds and also on the freshwater lochs.

In contrast to the low number of Cormorants, Shags are very numerous and widespread, the Shetland population being some 30% of the British total. They feed on Sand-eels and the more pelagic fish species, and have therefore an abundant food supply throughout the more exposed Shetland coastline. Similarly they are a common breeding species further north in Faroe where the Cormorant is now extinct. Whereas the recent Cormorant census is fairly accurate, since that species breeds on fairly open ledges and stacks, it is likely that Shag censuses are usually underestimates because most breed almost hidden under boulders or completely obscured on ledges within caves. There appears to have been little change in population in recent years.

Both these birds belong to the family Phalacrocoracidae which is the only web-footed family that does not waterproof its feathers, hence their habit of standing on rocks or sitting up in the water with their wings outstretched to dry. With their large broad tail they often resemble their primitive ancestor *Archaeopteryx*.

GULLS

The largest family of seabirds breeding in Shetland is undoubtedly the Laridae which includes the Terns, Kittiwake and Gulls. The larger Gulls – the Greater Black-backed, Lesser Black-backed and Herring (known locally as Swaabie, Peerie Swaabie and Scorie respectively), all appear to have had changing fortunes over the years. In the last century a degree of control was exercised on all Gull species by harvesting eggs. For example there was a colony of Greater Black-backs on the Holm of Noss in the 18th century, but in the early 19th century a cradle connecting the Holm to Noss was erected and the colony dwindled due to egg collecting. In 1864 the cradle went out of use and the Gulls returned. Up to 200 pairs have nested there ever since. Although the Venables were not aware of any change in this species during their time it has undoubtedly increased quite substantially in the last 30 years, now breeding on moorland very widely where the Venables did not record it (*e.g.* in North Roe and on Unst). Another very large Greater Black-backed colony on Gruney with some 200 pairs may be relatively recent as it is also not referred to by them. Harris found his 1974 counts significantly higher than the 1969 counts.

The Lesser Black-backed has apparently suffered a huge reduction all over

Shetland since the last century, but its present status is rather confused. Thirty years ago it had a similar breeding preference to the other large Gulls – sloping, grassy banks above the sea, and holms on both freshwater and the sea. Today it breeds also on open moorland like the other two. In the 19th century Saxby described Lesser Black-backs as nesting 'in countless numbers' in Unst; Evans & Buckley found them 'nearly, if not quite as numerous as the Herring Gull'; and while the Venables suggested 'this is very far from the case now', Bundy in 1974 found approximately 300 pairs of Lesser Black-backed and 170 pairs of Herring Gull on the moorland of the southern half of Unst. Similarly Raeburn considered the Lesser Black-backed the most numerous gull on Papa Stour in 1890, including about 300 pairs on Lyra Skerry; but the Venables found only 'a few pairs'. In 1969 there were 180 pairs. It is obvious that this species has abandoned many of its former breeding sites and is not as numerous as it was a hundred years ago, but whether or not this decrease is continuing, must await a series of systematic annual counts.

The Herring Gull remains the most numerous of the larger Gulls and is probably more conspicuous because of its relatively sedentary nature. As with the other two large Gulls it is difficult to know what changes in its overall population are taking place at the moment. It has certainly increased on the Lerwick roof-tops where there are now 20 pairs nesting regularly.

In the winter months second- and third-year Herring and Greater Black-backed Gulls are absent from Shetland while all the Lesser Black-backs migrate and are away from September to April. The last species is much less of a scavenger than the others, feeding more on arable land and shore. There is no doubt that the Shetland population of the Greater Black-backed and Herring Gulls are sustained in winter by the availability of fish offal from boats and factories and other food stuffs found on the large rubbish tips.

The smaller Common Gull (Peerie Maa or Tina Maa) has increased in numbers this century and the population may possibly still be growing. It has become almost an ubiquitous breeder – from sloping banks above the sea, to freshwater and marine holms, and even dry moorland sites in short vegetation. However the majority of sites are inland and this accounts for the poor showing they made in the Seafarer census. As it is the only Gull, apart from the Black-headed Gull, that regularly nests within crofting areas (on the margins of the wet hayfields, in eutrophic marshes and on islands in the more eutrophic lochs), it is subjected to more egg collecting than any other species and it may be that numbers are still controlled by this harvest in some localities. Egg harvesting is, however, very much less common than it used to be even a few years ago.

The smallest of the Gulls breeding in Shetland is the Black-headed Gull (or Heedie Maa). Its English name is a slight misnomer as the head is chocolate-brown rather than black. In contrast to further south, it is the least numerous of the Gulls in Shetland, and is virtually confined in its breeding sites to islands in freshwater or saltmarsh, often where these islands are no more than a dense stand of grass or sedge. As with the Terns it often changes its breeding sites which are liable to flooding and disturbance. For example the Venables recorded 100 pairs in a colony in Unst in 1949; in 1958 there were 30; in 1969 300; 1973 120; and in 1974 only 40. The 1973 season yielded only 3 juveniles because of flooding. Unfortunately a number of other previously well-known colonies, such as that on the marsh between Spiggie and Brow, have been extinct now for several years, although there are probably several small unrecorded colonies scattered through the Mainland.

The overall picture for seabirds in Shetland appears on the surface to be very rosy, with nine seabird species known to be increasing, and only one or two decreasing. However several species, particularly those with large populations, rely on commercial fish for their survival. As the fish come under pressure from man, especially from industrial fishing in the last few years, the seabird populations may be affected. Subtle industrial pollutants are also known to be having their effect and oil is bound to take its toll. The years ahead are going to be a critical time for seabirds in Shetland, possibly even more critical than the hard times of the 19th century.

References for Chapter 10
(full citations are given in the Bibliography on p. 353)

Balfour, 1968, 1972; Berry & Davis, 1970; Bourne, 1974; Brathay, 1969–76; Cramp, Bourne & Saunders, 1974; Dott, 1967; Dyck & Meltofte, 1975; Fisher & Lockley, 1954; Fisher, Stewart & Venables, 1938; Fisher & Venables, 1938; Furness, 1977, 1978; Groundwater, 1974; Harris, 1976; Jefferies & Parslow, 1976; Kay, 1947, 1948; Kinnear, 1976; Lea & Bourne, 1975; Lloyd, 1975; Lockie, 1952; Perry, 1948; Salomonsen, 1935; Southern, 1939, 1943, 1962; Tulloch & Hunter, 1972; Venables & Venables, 1955; Williamson, 1948.

BIRDS OF FAIR ISLE

HALFWAY between the main island groups of Orkney and Shetland lies Fair Isle. There can be few birdwatchers who have not heard the name. For them, it conjures up visions of huge 'falls' of migrant birds, exotic rarities from Siberia or Central Asia, and teeming seabird colonies set against a background of stark cliffs and (sometimes) a sparkling blue sea.

Fair Isle is the southernmost of the Shetland group, lying 22 miles south of Sumburgh Head and a similar distance north of North Ronaldsay in Orkney. It is a small island, only three miles long by one and a half miles wide, a mere 2000 acres, yet on this speck of land over 320 different species of bird have been recorded, over half the species ever seen in the British Isles.

The island is divided into two by a 'hill dyke' separating mainly fertile, agricultural land to the south where the crofts are situated, from moorland rising to a height of 712 feet at Ward Hill to the north. This is the common grazing of the crofters – a mixture of heather, short turf and bog. The coastline is heavily indented and almost entirely cliff-bound, those on the west side reaching over 500 feet. The numerous geos and inlets are the nesting place of large numbers of seabirds. On the east side the landscape is dominated by the bulk of Sheep Rock, a block of sandstone rising to over 400 feet, joined to the main isle by a knife-edge of crumbling stone. Until recently sheep were kept on the eleven acres of rabbit-free grazing at the top, but now only Herring and Greater Black-backed Gulls live there.

There are over 80 people resident on the island and despite being the most isolated community in Britain (a claim Fair Isle disputes with Foula), the future seems assured with an ever growing number of pupils at the school. The island's sea link with the rest of Shetland is the mail boat *Good Shepherd III*, based at North Haven; nearby is the Bird Observatory situated well away from the rest of the island dwellings. This community shares the island with thousands of birds, and at least two endemic races – the Fair Isle Wren, *Troglodytes troglodytes fridariensis*, and the Fair Isle Field Mouse, *Apodemus sylvaticus fridariensis*. Besides Field Mice the only other mammals are House Mice, Rabbits and Grey Seals, though Common Seals and various cetaceans are seen regularly.

Fair Isle is internationally famous for the study of bird migration. In the early years of the century Dr William Eagle Clarke visited the island and immediately realized its potential for studies of migration. He enlisted the help of an islander, Jerome Wilson, to collect specimens of unusual birds for him. Another visitor in those early years was Mary, Duchess of Bedford, who used to come by yacht and stay at the small croft of Pund to observe the migrants. In the 1920s Rear Admiral James Stenhouse became the successor to Eagle Clarke, and he received the assistance of islander George Stout of Field Croft. During these years many interesting birds were obtained including a number new to Britain. In 1935 George Waterston made his first visit to the isle, returning annually till 1939 and developing an ambition to found a Bird Observatory, similar to the one he had helped to start on the Isle of May in the Firth of Forth. Then war years intervened and George Waterston became a P.O.W. in Germany. There he and a fellow prisoner, Ian Pitman planned their proposed Observatory. After the war George Waterston bought Fair Isle and with the help of grants and support from ornithologists acquired some ex-Naval huts at North Haven. These were converted and equipped as a hostel and laboratory and in 1948 Kenneth Williamson was appointed Director of a Fair Isle Bird Observatory. With regular daily observations the true worth of Fair Isle as a site for studying migration became apparent and more and more rare birds were recorded.

In the 1950s the island population dropped to a dangerously low level, and there were fears of an evacuation, like that of St Kilda 25 years earlier. However the National Trust for Scotland were able to acquire the isle with the help of a grant from the Dulverton Trust and they have invested heavily in improvements to the pier, slipway and the croft houses. By the late 1960s the Observatory huts were becoming dilapidated and an appeal was launched to build a new Observatory. The appeal met with a tremendous response and in 1969 a new, purpose-built Observatory was opened. Here the bird studies continue in the luxury of a modern, spacious building commanding superb views of the cliffs and sea.

PATTERNS OF MIGRATION

The work of the Observatory varies throughout the year. One of the most important tasks is the daily count of all migrant species on the island. On days when there has been a big fall it can take a couple of hours to sort out all the different totals, with birds being seen at every corner. Another job is the trapping of birds for ringing. Most of the migrants are caught in Heligoland Traps. These are large wire netting structures, based on a type of trap developed on the island of Heligoland in the German Bight. They have a large entrance which narrows down to a funnel, and ends in a glass-fronted catching box. The traps are driven regularly throughout the day and all captures brought back to the Observatory where they are weighed, measured and a small metal ring placed on the leg before release. Since 1948, over 130,000 birds have been ringed and about 1300 of these recovered elsewhere, providing much useful information on migration.

When migration ceases during the summer months work turns to the breeding birds, particularly seabirds. The Observatory staff climb into the geos and visit less accessible sites by boat to ring both chicks and adult birds.

As a result of this work we have learned a great deal about the movement and winter quarters of our seabirds, as well as information on their biology. Some species have been the subject of intensive study, particularly Fulmar, Tystie (Black Guillemot) and Arctic Skua. The Arctic Skua colony has been worked for many years and now most of the adult birds wear colour rings which enable the identification of individuals in the field. This means that the life history of each bird, changes in mates due to death or divorce, faithfullness to nest site, and genetical differences between the colour phases of this polymorphic species can be studied (see pp. 202–5).

The seabird population is regularly censussed, and certain species are monitored each year at special sites in order to detect changes in the population. On summer nights Storm Petrels visit the island, some to breed but many more just passing through. The birds are caught in mist-nets set up on the cliffs, supplemented by tape recordings of the species call. Many of the birds trapped have been ringed previously at sites as far apart as Southern Ireland, St Kilda and Faroe.

Besides the ornithological work the Observatory keeps records of most aspects of Natural History including the flora, mammals and insects of the island.

The vast amount of data collected over the years has been used to extend our knowledge of migration, distribution, population and general biology of birds. Fair Isle Bird Observatory, though completely independent and self-supporting, collaborates with about a dozen or so other observatories around the coasts of Britain and Ireland. The work carried out at each Observatory is similar and by pooling the results a comprehensive picture of migration or population levels throughout the country can be obtained. The information obtained from ringing is collated by the British Trust for Ornithology who run the bird ringing scheme in Britain.

It is perhaps difficult to understand why a tiny island should attract such a large and varied number of birds. The answer lies in the fact that Fair Isle lies at a crossroads for many migrant species (Fig. 38). The geographical isolation of the island means that it is a haven for tired migrants needing to rest and feed before the next stage of their journey. The rest of Shetland attracts migrants for the same reasons but they are scattered over the length and breadth of the county and consequently much more difficult to observe. On Fair Isle they are concentrated into a small area where they can be recorded with comparative ease. Some of the smaller islands in Shetland (notably Out Skerries) are almost as good as Fair Isle for migrants, but they lack its isolation and many birds pass right over them to the richer and more varied habitats of Mainland Shetland. Notwithstanding, it is the regular observations by generations of ornithologists on Fair Isle that account for the greater variety of migrant species recorded there; keen birdwatchers elsewhere in Shetland have begun in recent years to find species that were previously thought to be 'Fair Isle specialities'. An additional factor is that the trapping of birds for ringing has

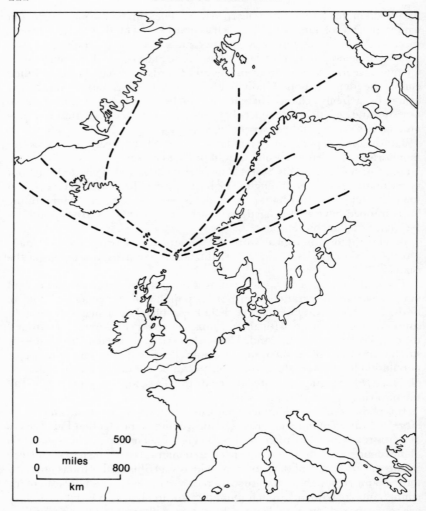

FIG 38. Approximate routes followed by migrating birds which use Fair Isle and Shetland as 'stepping stones'.

advanced the identification of many of the rarer and more difficult species, and made it more likely for them to be recognized in other places.

The majority of birds which occur in Shetland as migrants are using the islands as stepping stones. They can be divided into two groups: those that breed in Iceland, Greenland, Faroe and even North America; and those that breed to the north east, in Scandinavia, Russia, Spitsbergen and the Arctic. Shetland is a natural stop on their flight to or from their southern winter quarters. Some species (like the Thrushes, and especially Blackbirds) regularly pass through Shetland on their way from their breeding areas in Scandinavia to their wintering place in Ireland or the west coast of Britain; others such as Pied Flycatchers, Redstarts, and Willow Warblers also breed in Scandinavia, but winter in Africa. Their route is less obviously through Shetland and the vagaries of the wind play their part here. When birds are crossing the open sea they are particularly prone to being drifted off course by cross winds. Typically, a south easterly wind over the North Sea will deflect birds off their normal course and bring them to Shetland, often resulting in huge falls (Fig 39). The birds are not lost however, and after a few days resume migration, correcting their course to counter-act the effect of the wind. For many the islands are their salvation, for otherwise they would be swept out into the Atlantic to inevitable death.

Birds which breed to the north west of Shetland may make a non-stop flight from Greenland to the west coast of Scotland, or use a route *via* Iceland, Faroe and Shetland. Sometimes a westerly wind will affect the 'long-hop' migrants such as Barnacle Geese or Greenland Wheatears and they will be swept to Shetland instead of directly to the Scottish mainland.

The pattern of migration is constantly changing, and the daily counts of migrants at Fair Isle have been used to detect and study the variations. For example, Stonechats were once a very scarce migrant on Fair Isle but from 1973 they have appeared in increasing numbers every spring. This period has seen the species colonizing western Norway and a few breeding records for Shetland. However the trend may now be reverting, since after a hard winter in 1977–78 the numbers in the following spring were very low. Scarlet Rosefinch is another species which has increased considerably from being a vagrant almost confined to Fair Isle, to occurring in spring as well as autumn with increasing frequency. There is evidence that the species has expanded its range in Scandinavia, and it may well be that a small proportion of the population now winters in western Europe or Africa instead of India. Species such as Woodlark and Rook have declined, perhaps due to a contracting breeding range in Scandinavia or a shift in winter quarters.

Even the falls which occur as a result of unusual winds can have an effect on population and distribution. In 1969 and 1970 abnormally large numbers of Wrynecks occurred on Fair Isle in Spring (up to 45 in a day, the previous record total being only 12). Though many of these birds made a landfall in Shetland, some appeared also on the east coast of Scotland, and a few of these moved inland and bred in the old Caledonian Pine Forest. Now there is a small population of Wrynecks in the Highlands of Scandinavian origin, which chooses a different habitat and food to the now almost extinct population in southern England.

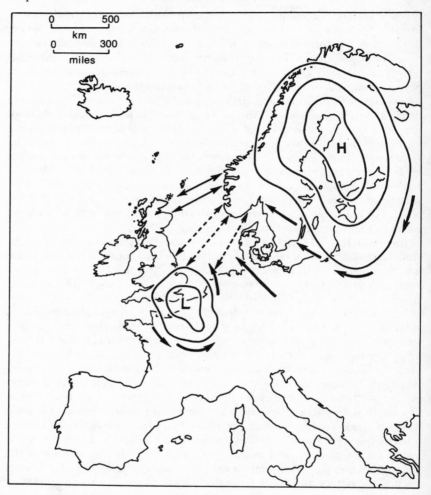

FIG 39. High pressure over Scandinavia and low over the Low Countries combine to produce South East winds over the North Sea, and deflect normal migration (dotted lines) to bring birds to Shetland.

These changing patterns make bird migration a fascinating subject. No two seasons are the same, and after each migration one is left with more questions – perhaps to be answered in a few years time when yet another change becomes apparent.

PLATE 17. *Above left*, Red-throated Diver and chick; *right*, Red-throated Diver on nest. *Below left*, Oyster-catcher; *right*, Ringed Plover.

PLATE 18. *Left*, Whimbrel on nest, Unst; *centre*, Curlew; *below*, Cormorant.

PLATE 19. *Top*, feeding Fulmars; *centre*, Arctic Skua. *Below left*, Great Skua or Bonxie; *right*, Gannet with chick.

PLATE 20. *Top*, Arctic Tern; *centre*, Common Gull. *Below left*, Eider with chicks; *right*, Eider.

PLATE 22. *Above*, Sullom Voe Oil Terminal: aerial view looking north-east, after completion of major earthworks (October 1977). *Left*, the Ninian pipeline after backfilling and land reshaping. Looking northeastwards towards Grutwick, Lunna Ness (February 1977).

PLATE 23. *Above*, newly widened road with wide verge to discourage straying sheep; *below*, crofts in snow.

PLATE 24. *Above left*, Shetlander and croft; *right*, fishing boats in Scalloway Harbour, with castle in the background. *Below*, herring station in the 1930s.

SPRING AND AUTUMN MIGRATIONS

The Spring migration starts in February or March with the return of local breeding birds such as Skylark, Oystercatcher and Lapwing. Numbers slowly increase during March when the first Puffins and Lesser Black-backed Gulls appear. In April numbers are swollen by the first of the Scandinavian migrants passing through: Blackbirds, Thrushes, and Goldcrests, with perhaps the odd Great Grey Shrike or Long-eared Owl. Towards the end of April the first of the long-distance migrants on their way from Africa to Scandinavia arrive (Redstarts, Whinchats, Pied Flycatchers), but May is the month for the large numbers of these birds, often with overshooting rarities. Bird watchers anxiously peer at the weather maps, looking for signs of the systems that will bring south easterly winds over the North Sea to sweep the migrants north westwards to Fair Isle. Often the weather in Shetland will be fine and warm whilst in southern England rain and gales urge the birds northwards. Occasionally the resulting falls are truly amazing in both variety and sheer numbers. A single day in 1970 brought 1000 Willow Warblers, 350 Tree Pipits, 140 Reed Buntings, 300 Redstarts and more than 2000 Wheatears. Even rarities may arrive in force, with totals of 31 Bluethroats and 32 Ortolan Buntings on record. The majority of these birds are males, as they move slightly earlier than the females. Spring migration is a rather hurried affair however, since the birds are pressing to the breeding areas in order to raise their young in the few short months of the northern summer. This means the birds do not stay long on the island, and after a day or so they will be on the move again, heading for Scandinavia. At this time of year all the birds are in splendid plumage and often males will sing on fine mornings. There can be few places in Britain where the birdwatcher can be woken up by the combined songs of Redwings and Bluethroats on a May morning!

In late May or early June more migrants arrive: Red-backed Shrikes, Spotted Flycatchers, a few Reed and Marsh Warblers, and usually one or two stragglers from southern Europe, such as Golden Orioles, or Great Reed Warblers. There are always a few late migrants, either those that started late or ones delayed by unfavourable weather and needing to spend a week or so resting and feeding. Such appear right through June, and may even breed if they find a mate and a suitable nesting site. On Fair Isle, Redwings, White Wagtails and Swallows have done this, whilst in Shetland proper, Reed Warblers, Whitethroats and Fieldfares have bred.

The last stragglers have barely left when the first returning birds appear. Usually by mid-July there are a few Turnstones and Purple Sandpipers on the rocks, just back from their incredibly short breeding season in the Arctic. Most pass through quickly; others, like the Purple Sandpiper, stay on the island for some weeks to complete their moult before moving on. By the end of July there are many waders on the move, and the first passerines appear – White Wagtails from Iceland, Willow and Sedge Warblers from Scandinavia.

Migrant numbers then remain low till mid-August when the main return movements begin. The Autumn migration is rather protracted without the urgency of Spring, and birds often remain on the island for a week or two feeding and gathering strength. Moreover many will be making their first migratory flight, and choose to do so in easy stages rather than one or two long hops. Migrant numbers are always higher in Autumn than in Spring, as there are large numbers of juvenile birds on the move, as well as adults, but the mortality will be high: many die due to bad weather, such as rain or fog over the North Sea, others are exhausted by the long hot crossing of the Sahara, while some will find that climatic changes or drought have ruined their wintering area and destroyed their food. By the following Spring only the fittest will be left to start the cycle all over again.

September is the month when the greatest variety of species occur, when the ranks of the small summer visitors are swelled by thrushes and finches pouring out of Scandinavia to winter in Britain, and when ducks and geese are

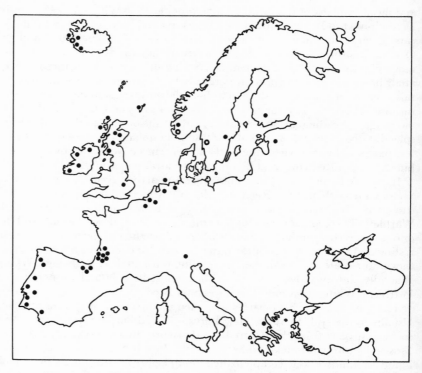

FIG 40. Recoveries of Redwings (*Turdus iliacus*) ringed on Fair Isle (solid circles) or ringed elsewhere and recaptured on Fair Isle (open circles).

also on the move. At this season, bird watchers scour the crofting area, looking in every patch of crop, in the ditches, and down the deep geos in the hope of spotting some new and exciting bird. However the weather at this time of year is very unpredictable and a spell of westerly gales may halt all migration for a week or more, except perhaps for a few Greenland Wheatears or Geese; then as another weather system comes through bringing a touch of east in the wind, the birds start to arrive again.

October is the month for large thrush movements, with up to 20,000 Redwings liable to arrive one morning. With them come predators, Long-eared Owls, Sparrowhawks, Merlins, Great Grey Shrikes, all on the look-out for an easy meal amongst the tired migrants. Large flocks of Snow Buntings appear from Scandinavia, Greenland or even arctic Canada and make an impressive sight, their white wings flashing in the autumn sunlight. Towards the end of the month winter sets in and migrants become scarce, confined to a few arctic visitors arriving for the winter – Glaucous and Iceland Gulls, a few Little Auks.

OCCASIONAL VISITORS

Some species which visit the isle are not true migrants, in that they do not have separate breeding and wintering areas. These are the 'invasion' species like Crossbills, Waxwings and Great Spotted Woodpeckers. The invasions may involve thousands of birds or only a few hundred. They usually occur after a good breeding season increasing their numbers, followed by a cold winter bringing hard weather when food is difficult to find. In the case of Crossbills it is usually a failure of the seeds of conifers which is their main food, that triggers off their emigration. The birds then move rapidly in search of better conditions, generally passing quickly through Shetland and on to the more productive habitat of the forests of Scotland or eastern England. Most return to breed in Scandinavia the following season and may not 'invade' again for many years. Some Crossbills however, are less faithful to their homeland and remain to breed in suitable forests elsewhere.

The occurrence of rarities is by definition unpredictable, but the weather plays its part here as well. Species which breed in Southern Europe or the south of Britain may overshoot their breeding grounds on their return in Spring from wintering in Africa. This usually happens when anti-cyclonic conditions are prevalent over Europe bringing fine weather and light winds. The birds fly high, without hindrance from rain or fog, and pass right over their normal destination. Some, such as the British race of the Yellow Wagtail only overshoot by a few hundred miles and are probably able to correct their mistake in time to get back for that season, while others may travel much further and find themselves well out of range. The Subalpine Warbler is a good example of the latter, normally breeding along the Mediterranean coasts yet occurring fairly often in Shetland, although almost always in spring. The Shetland records of this species account for over half the British sightings, showing how the North Sea acts as a funnel for these overshooting birds.

Of the vagrants which occur in autumn some come from eastern Europe, Siberia and even as far as Manchuria in Central Asia. An example of this is the Yellow-browed Warbler, hardly bigger than a Goldcrest, which may be found flitting about on the cliffs after a journey of perhaps 3000 miles. Most such birds normally migrate on a south east course to take them to their wintering grounds in India, or South east Asia. The reason for their occurrence in Shetland is still a matter for conjecture, but one of the more likely theories is that of 'reverse-migration'. This assumes that the birds, invariably birds of the year on their first migratory flight, somehow take the opposite bearing to normal and fly steadily north west. Two species in particular are good examples of this: the Barred Warbler and the Red-breasted Flycatcher breed in eastern Europe and should migrate south east, but they are recorded frequently on Fair Isle and in Shetland in the autumn. In fact the Barred Warbler is recorded in the northern isles more regularly than anywhere else in Britain. It is exciting to find such vagrants from the east, but always with a touch of sadness at seeing them so irretrievably lost.

Little could Eagle Clarke have realized, as he stalked round the Fair Isle crofts, gun at the ready, that his observations would lead to a permanent centre for studying migration; and that after 30 years of recording new species would continue to be added almost every year to the already impressive Fair Isle list (Table 17). Yet there is every indication that the work will continue for many years to come and that with each year that passes more light will be shed on the mysteries of bird migration.

TABLE 17. Status of birds breeding or seen in Fair Isle.

Key to symbols

Status: P   Passage migrant
            p   Passage migrant in small numbers or irregularly
            V   Vagrant, or irregular visitor
            V (A)   Vagrant, recorded annually
            W   Winter visitor
            w   Winter visitor in small numbers or irregularly

Breeding Order 1   1–10 pairs
                  2   11–100 pairs
                  3   101–1000 pairs
                  4   1001–10,000 pairs
                  5   10,001–100,000 pairs

Where more than one symbol occurs, symbols are in order of priority

Red-throated Diver *Gavia stellata* P
Black-throated Diver *Gavia arctica* V
Great Northern Diver *Gavia immer* P
White-billed Diver *Gavia adamsii* V
Little Grebe *Tachybaptus ruficollis* V
Great Crested Grebe *Podiceps cristatus* V
Red-necked Grebe *Podiceps grisegena* V
Slavonian Grebe *Podiceps auritus* p
Fulmar *Fulmarus glacialis*
    Breeds order 5
Cory's Shearwater *Calonectris diomedia* V
Great Shearwater *Puffinus gravis* V
Sooty Shearwater *Puffinus griseus* P
Manx Shearwater *Puffinus puffinus* p
Storm Petrel *Hydrobates pelagicus*
    Breeds order 2?
Leach's Petrel *Oceanodroma leucorrhoa* V
Gannet *Sula bassana* Breeds, order 2. P
Cormorant *Phalacrocorax carbo* P
Shag *Phalacrocorax aristotelis*
    Breeds order 4
Little Bittern *Ixobrychus minutus* V
Grey Heron *Ardea cinerea* P
Purple Heron *Ardea purpurea* V
White Stork *Ciconia ciconia* V
Mute Swan *Cygnus olor* V
Bewick's Swan *Cygnus columbianus* V
Whooper Swan *Cygnus cygnus* P
Bean Goose *Anser fabialis* V
Pink-footed Goose *Anser brachyrhynchus* P
White-fronted Goose *Anser albifrons* V
Greylag Goose *Anser anser* P
Canada Goose *Branta canadensis* V
Barnacle Goose *Branta leucopsis* P
Brent Goose *Branta bernicla* V
Shelduck *Tadorna tadorna* P
Wigeon *Anas penelope* P
Gadwall *Anas strepera* V
Teal *Anas crecca* P
Mallard *Anas platyrhynchos* P
Pintail *Anas acuta* p
Gargany *Anas querquedula* V
Shoveler *Anas clypeata* p
Pochard *Aythya ferina* V
Tufted Duck *Aythya fuligula* p
Scaup *Aythya marila* p
Eider *Somateria mollisima*
    Breeds order 3
King Eider *Somateria spectabilis* V
Steller's Eider *Polysticta stelleri* V
Harlequin Duck *Histrionicus histrionicus* V
Long-tailed Duck *Clangula hyemalis* P
Common Scoter *Melanitta nigra* P

Velvet Scoter *Melanitta fusca* p
Goldeneye *Bucephala clangula* p
Smew *Mergus albellus* V
Red-breasted Merganser
    Mergus serrator P
Goosander *Mergus merganser* p
Honey Buzzard *Pernis apivorus* p
White-tailed Eagle *Haliaeetus albicilla*
    Formerly bred. V
Marsh Harrier *Circus aeruginosus* V
Hen Harrier *Circus cyaneus* p
Pallid Harrier *Circus macrourus* V
Montagu's Harrier *Circus pygargus* V
Goshawk *Accipiter gentilis* V
Sparrowhawk *Accipiter nisus* P
Buzzard *Buteo buteo* V
Rough-legged Buzzard *Buteo lagopus* V
Golden Eagle *Aquila chrysaetos* V
Osprey *Pandion haliaetus* p
Kestrel *Falco tinnunculus* P
American Kestrel *Falco sparverius* V
Red-footed Falcon *Falco vespertinus* V
Merlin *Falco columbarius* P
Hobby *Falco subbuteo* V
Gyrfalcon *Falco rusticolus* V
Peregrine *Falco peregrinus* P
    Bred order 1
Quail *Coturnix coturnix* P Has bred
Water Rail *Rallus aquaticus* P
Spotted Crake *Porzana porzana* V
Little Crake *Porzana parva* V
Baillon's Crake *Porzana pusilla* V
Corncrake *Crex crex* P Formerly bred order 1
Moorhen *Gallinula chloropus* p Has bred
Coot *Fulica atra* p
Crane *Grus grus* V
Great Bustard *Otis tarda* V
Oystercatcher *Haematopus ostralegus*
    Breeds order 2
Stone Curlew *Burhinus oedicnemus* V
Collared Pratincole *Glareola pratincola* V
Black-winged Pratincole
    Glareola nordmanni V
Little Ringed Plover *Charadrius dubius* V
Kentish Plover *Charadrius alexandrinus* V
Ringed Plover *Charadrius hiatacula*
    P Breeds order 1
Dotterel *Charadrius morinellus* V
Lesser Golden Plover *Pluvialis dominica* V
Golden Plover *Pluvialis apricaria*
    P Breeds occ. order 1
Grey Plover *Pluvialis squaterola* p
Lapwing *Vanellus vanellus* P

Breeds order 1
Knot *Calidris canutus* P
Sanderling *Calidris alba* P
Western Sandpiper *Calidris mauri* V
Little Stint *Calidris minuta* P
Temminck's Stint *Calidris temminckii* V
White-rumped Sandpiper
　Calidris fuscicollis V
Pectoral Sandpiper *Calidris melanotus* V
Curlew Sandpiper *Calidris ferruginea* V
Purple Sandpiper *Calidris maritima* P w
Dunlin *Calidris alpina* P
Buff-breasted Sandpiper
　Trygnites subruficollis V
Ruff *Philomachus pugnax* P
Jack Snipe *Lymnocryptes minimus* P
Snipe *Gallinago gallinago* P
　Breeds order 1
Great Snipe *Gallinago media* V
Dowitcher sp. *Limnodromus* sp V
Woodcock *Scolopax rusticola* P
Black-tailed Godwit *Limosa limosa* p
Bar-tailed Godwit *Limosa lapponica* P
Whimbrel *Numenius phaeopus*
　P Has bred, order 1
Curlew *Numenius arquata* P
　Breeds order 1
Upland Sandpiper
　Bartramia longicauda V
Spotted Redshank *Tringa erythropus* p
Redshank *Tringa totanus* P
Greenshank *Tringa nebularia* P
Lesser Yellowlegs *Tringa flavipes* V
Green Sandpiper *Tringa ochropus* P
Wood Sandpipers *Tringa glareola* p
Common Sandpiper *Tringa hypoleucos* P
Turnstones *Arenaria interpres* P w
Red-necked Phalarope *Phalaropus lobatus* V
Grey Phalarope *Phalaropus fulicarius* V
Pomarine Skua *Stercorarius pomarinus* V
Arctic Skua *Stercorarius parasiticus*
　Breeds order 3, P
Long-tailed Skua *Stercorarius longicaudus* V
Great Skua *Stercorarius skua* Breeds order 2, P
Mediterranean Gull *Larus melanocephalus* V
Laughing Gull *Larus atricilla* V
Little Gull *Larus minutus* V
Sabine's Gull *Larus sabini* V
Black-headed Gull *Larus ridibundus* P
Common Gull *Larus canus* P Breeds order 1
Lesser Black-backed Gull *Larus fuscus*
　Breeds order 2
Herring Gull *Larus argentatus*

Breeds order 3 W
Iceland Gull *Larus glaucoides* p w
Glaucous Gull *Larus hyperboreus* p W
Great Black-backed Gull *Larus marinus*
　Breeds order 3 W
Kittiwake *Rissa tridactyla* Breeds order 5
Ivory Gull *Pagophila eburnea* V
Gull-billed Tern *Gelochelidon nilocta* V
Caspian Tern *Sterna caspia* V
Sandwich Tern *Sterna sandicansis* V
Common Tern *Sterna hirundo*
　P Breeds order 2
Arctic Tern *Sterna paradisaea* P
Black Tern *Chlidonias niger* V
White-winged Black Tern
　Chlidonias leucopterus V
Guillemot *Uria aalge* Breeds order 4
Razorbill *Alca torda* Breeds order 3–4
Black Guillemot *Cepphus grylle*
　Breeds order 3
Little Auk *Alle alle* W
Puffin *Fratercula arctica* Breeds order 5
Pallas's Sandgrouse *Syrrhaptes paradoxus* V
Rock Dove *Columba livia* Breeds order 1–2, P
Stock Dove *Columba oenas* p
Woodpigeon *Columba palumbus* P
Collared Dove *Streptopelia decaocto* P
Rufous Turtle Dove *Streptopelia orientalis* V
Cuckoo *Cuculus canorus* P
Barn Owl *Tyto alba* V
Snowy Owl *Nyctea scandiaca* V
Long-eared Owl *Asio otus* P
Short-eared Owl *Asio flammeus* P
Nightjar *Caprimulgus europaeus* V
Needle-tailed Swift *Hirundapus caudacutus* V
Swift *Apus apus* P
Alpine Swift *Apus melba* V
Bee-eater *Merops apiaster* V
Hoopoe *Upupa epops* V
Wryneck *Jynx torquilla* P
Great Spotted Woodpecker
　Dendrocopus major P
Calandra Lark *Melanocorypha calandra* V
Bimaculated Lark *Melanocorypha
　bimaculata* V
Short-toed Lark *Calandrella cinerea* V
Crested Lark *Galerida cristata* V
Woodlark *Lullula arborea* V (once p)
Skylark *Alauda arvensis* Breeds order 2–3, P
Shore Lark *Eremophila alpestris* p
Sand Martin *Riparia riparia* P
Swallow *Hirundo rustica* P; has bred, order 1
Red-rumped Swallow *Hirundo daurica* V

House Martin *Delichon urbica* P; has bred, order 1
Richard's Pipit *Anthus novaeseelandiae* V (A)
Tawny Pipit *Anthus campestris* V
Olive-backed Pipit *Anthus hodgsoni* V
Tree Pipit *Anthus trivialis* P
Pechora Pipit *Anthus gustavi* V
Meadow Pipit *Anthus pratensis*
  P Breeds, order 2–3
Red-throated Pipit *Anthus cervinus* V
Rock Pipit *Anthus spinoletta*
  Breeds order 2, p
Yellow Wagtail *Motacilla flava flavissima* p
  M. f. flava P
  M. f. thunbergi p
  M. f. feldegg V
Citrine Wagtail *Motacilla citreola* V
Grey Wagtail *Motacilla cinerea* p
Pied Wagtail *Motacilla alba yarrellii* p
  Has bred order 1
  Motacilla alba alba P Has bred order 1
Waxwing *Bombycilla garrulus* P
Dipper *Cinclus cinclus* V
Wren *Troglodytes troglodytes* Breeds order 2
Dunnock *Prunella modularis* P
Alpine Accentor *Prunella collaris* V
Robin *Erithacus rubecula* P
Thrush Nightingale *Luscinia luscinia* V
Nightingale *Luscinia megarhynchos* V
Siberian Rubythroat *Luscinia calliope* V
Bluethroat *Luscinia svecica* p
Black Redstart *Phoenicurus ochruros* p
Redstart *Phoenicurus phoenicurus* P
Whinchat *Saxicola rubetra* P
Stonechat *Saxicola torquata* p
Wheatear *Oenanthe oenanthe* P Breeds order 3
Black-eared Wheatear *Oenanthe hispanica* V
Desert Wheatear *Oenanthe deserti* V
Black Wheatear *Oenanthe leucura* V
Rock Thrush *Monticola saxatilis* V
White's Thrush *Zoothera dauma* V
Hermit Thrush *Catharus guttatus* V
Grey-cheeked Thrush *Catharus minimus* V
Ring Ousel *Turdus torquatus* P
Blackbird *Turdus merula* P Has bred, order 1
Dusky Thrush *Turdus naumanni* V
Black-throated Thrush *Turdus ruficollis* V
Fieldfare *Turdus pilaris* P
Song Thrush *Turdus philomelus* P Has bred, order 1
Redwing *Turdus iliacus* P Has bred, order 1
Mistle Thrush *Turdus viscivorus* p

Pallas's Grasshopper Warbler
  Locustella certhiola V
Lanceolated Warbler *Locustella lanceolata* V
Grasshopper Warbler *Locustella naevia* p
River Warbler *Locustella fluviatilis* V
Savi's Warbler *Locustella luscinioides* V
Aquatic Warbler *Acrocephalus paludicola* V
Sedge Warbler *Acrocephalus schoenobaenus* p
Paddyfield Warbler *Acrocephalus agricola* V
Blyth's Reed Warbler *Acrocephalus dumetorum* V
Marsh Warbler *Acrocephalus palustris* p
Reed Warbler *Acrocephalus scirpaceus* p
Great Reed Warbler *Acrocephalus arundinaceus* V
Thick-billed Warbler *Acrocephalus aedon* V
Booted Warbler *Hippolais caligata* V
Icterine Warbler *Hippolais icterina* p
Melodious Warbler *Hippolais polyglotta* V
Subalpine Warbler *Sylvia cantillans* V
Sardinian Warbler *Sylvia melanocephala* V
Barred Warbler *Sylvia nisoria* P
Lesser Whitethroat *Sylvia curruca* P
Whitethroat *Sylvia communis* P
Garden Warbler *Sylvia borin* P
Blackcap *Sylvia atricapilla* P
Greenish Warbler *Phylloscopus trochiloides* V
Arctic Warbler *Phylloscopus borealis* V
Pallas's Warbler *Phylloscopus proregulus* V
Yellow-browed Warbler
  Phylloscopus inornatus V (A)
Dusky Warbler *Phylloscopus fuscatus* V
Bonelli's Warbler *Phylloscopus bonelli* V
Wood Warbler *Phylloscopus sibilatrix* p
Chiffchaff *Phylloscopus collybita* P
Willow Warbler *Phylloscopus trochilus* P
Goldcrest *Regulus regulus* P
Spotted Flycatcher *Muscicapa striata* p
Red-breasted Flycatcher *Ficedula parva* V (A)
Pied Flycatcher *Ficedula hypoleuca* P
Willow Tit *Parus montanus* V
Coal Tit *Parus ater* V
Blue Tit *Parus caerulus* V
Great Tit *Parus major* V
Treecreeper *Certhia familiaris* V
Golden Oriole *Oriolus oriolus* V
Isabelline Shrike *Lanius isabellinus* V
Red-backed Shrike *Lanius collurio* p
Lesser Grey Shrike *Lanius minor* V
Great Grey Shrike *Lanius excubitor* p
Woodchat Shrike *Lanius senator* V
Jackdaw *Corvus monedula* P

Rook *Corvus frugilegus* P
Carrion Crow *Corvus corone cornix*
   Breeds order *1*
Raven *Corvus corax* Breeds order 1, p
Starling *Sturnus vulgaris* P Breeds order 2–3
Rose-coloured Starling *Sturnus roseus* V
House Sparrow *Passer domesticus*
   Breeds order 2
Tree Sparrow *Passer montanus* p Has
   bred order 1
Chaffinch *Fringilla coelebs* P
Brambling *Fringilla montifringilla* P
Serin *Serinus serinus* V
Greenfinch *Carduelis chloris* p
Goldfinch *Carduelis carduelis* V
Siskin *Carduelis spinus* P
Linnet *Carduelis cannabina* p
Twite *Carduelis flavirostris* Breeds order 2, P
Redpoll *Carduelis flammea* P
Arctic Redpoll *Carduelis hornemanni* V
Two-barred Crossbill *Loxia leucoptera* V
Crossbill *Loxia curvirostra* P
Parrot Crossbill *Loxia pytyopsittacus* V
Scarlet Rosefinch *Carpodacus erythrinus* p
Bullfinch *Pyrrhula pyrrhula* p
Hawfinch *Coccothraustes coccothraustes* V

Tennessee Warbler *Vermivora peregrina* V
Yellow-rumped Warbler *Dendroica coronata* V
Song Sparrow *Zonotrichia melodia* V
White-crowned Sparrow *Zonotrichia leucophrys*
   V
White-throated Sparrow
   Zonotrichia albicollia
Lapland Bunting *Calcarius lapponicus* P
Snow Bunting *Plectrophenax nivalis* P
Pine Bunting *Emberiza leucocephalos* V
Yellowhammer *Emberiza citrinella* p
Ortolan Bunting *Emberiza hortulana* p
Cretzschmar's Bunting *Emberiza caesia* V
Rustic Bunting *Emberiza rustica* V
Little Bunting *Emberiza pusilla* V
Yellow-breasted Bunting *Emberiza aureola* V
Reed Bunting *Emberiza schoeniclus* P
Pallas's Reed Bunting *Emberiza pallasi* V
Black-headed Bunting *Emberiza melanocephala*
   V
Corn Bunting *Miliaria calandra* V

Category 'D'

Baikal Teal *Anas formosa* V
Red-headed Bunting *Emberiza bruniceps* V
Indigo Bunting *Passerina cyanea* V

References for Chapter 11
(full citations are given in the Bibliography on p. 353)

Berry & Davis, 1970; Davis, 1965; Davis & Dennis, 1959; Lack, 1960; Reinikainen, 1937; Svardson, 1957; Svensson, 1954; Venables & Venables, 1955; Waterston, 1946; Williamson, 1958, 1965; Williamson & Spencer, 1960.

CHAPTER 12

SHETLAND NATURALISTS

EARLY naturalists in Shetland were visiting a foreign land, and their comments are important, but have to be read critically. The earliest accounts are those of ministers who, generally speaking, were more interested in antiquities than natural history. Around 1800 medically trained men began to write about the islands and they have left us more information about natural history. Then in Victorian times, rarity seekers braved the journey north, and laid the basis for our modern understanding of the islands' fauna and flora. Since 1945, natural historians in the modern sense have flocked to the islands – recording the species present and more recently interpreting the interactions and adaptations of local forms. But apart from visitors from the south, many Shetlanders have become expert naturalists by any standards: names such as Bruce, Kay, Henderson and particularly Edmonston and Saxby have recorded the Shetland scene and provided the base upon which 'scientific' natural history can build.

EARLY TRAVELLERS

In 1700 the General Assembly of the Church of Scotland sent seven ministers and one ruling elder 'to settle the ecclesiastical affairs of the islands on a presbyterian basis'. One of the ministers was John Brand, who published *A Brief Description of Orkney, Zetland, Pightland Firth and Caithness* in 1701. He was a wondermonger whose comments are always interesting even when gloriously wrong. For example he recorded at length how shell fish in Shetland are often found buried alive in the ground a mile or more from the sea without realizing that this was a fishermen's habit so that bait was ready to hand. But he is worth reading: his account of Arctic Skua (Scuti-allan in Shetland) habits is far more entertaining than modern ornithological pomposity: 'There is a fowl called the Scutiallan, of a black colour and as big as a Wild Duck, which doth live upon the vomit and Excrements of other Fowls whom they pursue and having apprehended them, they cause them to Vomit up what they have lately taken and not yet digested: The Lord's Work both of Nature and Grace are wonderful, all speaking forth His Glorious Goodness, Wisdom and Power'.

However the first real naturalist to leave a record of Shetland was George Low, minister of Birsay in Orkney, who made tours of the northern group in 1774 and 1778 on the instigation of Pennant, who published some of the results in his *Arctic Zoology* of 1784. Low's own account was not published in Kirkwall until 1879 as *A Tour through the Islands of Orkney and Schetland*.

At much the same time Sir John Sinclair of Ulbster, Caithness was collecting answers to 166 questions which he sent to every parish in Scotland, and which were published as *The Statistical Account of Scotland* between 1791 and 1799. (This is known as the 'Old Account' in distinction to the 'New Account' which appeared in 1845.) Answers to the natural history questions varied enormously. The minister of Northmavine deals with migratory birds simply: 'The Kettywakes and Thomas Norie (puffin) birds nestle in great numbers, and come here in May and return in August'. Other ministers are more informative. But in general they were more interested in archaeology than natural history.

However the most important Shetland naturalists also emerged at this time. The first was Dr Arthur Edmonston of Hascosay (1776–1841). His two volume work of *A View of the Ancient and Present State of the Zetland Isles* (1809) was the most comprehensive account of Shetland so far, and included a complete list of the Shetland fauna as known at that time. His younger brother Laurence (1793–1879) became doctor in Unst, and planted a small plantation round his home of Halligarth outside Baltasound, the northernmost wood in the British Isles. He was responsible for adding the Glaucous, Icelandic and Ivory Gulls, and the Snowy Owl to the British list.

Laurence Edmonston's youngest daughter Jessie married Henry Saxby in 1859, who later took over from his father-in-law as Unst doctor. He died in 1871, but his book *The Birds of Shetland* was published in 1874. Laurence's eldest son, Tom, had meanwhile become a botanist, and was appointed Professor of Botany at Glasgow in 1845 at the age of 20. He was accidentally shot on an expedition to Peru the next year. He was responsible for the first *Flora of Shetland* (1845). Saxbys still live on Unst and still contribute to the natural history of the islands.

GEOLOGISTS

The first account of the geology of Shetland was published in 1798 by Robert Jameson. Before this only a few mineralogical notes in travellers' accounts of Shetland had been published.

Robert Jameson, who descended from a Shetland family, was interested in natural history from childhood. His interests led his father to apprentice him to an Edinburgh surgeon. Among the lectures he attended at the university were those of the first active Professor of Natural History there, John Walker, a noted geologist. Soon he was a favourite student, was given charge of the museum and taken on field excursions. His chief interest became geology and in 1794 at the age of 20, he gave up his medical career before graduation and spent three months in Shetland during the summer studying geology and natural history. In 1797 he visited Arran and his *Outline of the mineralogy of the Shetland Islands and of the Island of Arran* appeared in the next year. In 1799 he made a six week survey of Orkney and declared it the most uninteresting journey he ever made. In 1800 an account appeared in his book *An outline of the mineralogy of Scottish Isles*. In modern terms both are geology books.

In 1804 he became Professor of Natural History at Edinburgh and remained in this post until his death 50 years later. Jameson was extraordinarily successful in producing geologists and for many years most of the geologists working in Shetland were his students. He was a poor lecturer, but students were attracted by his subject matter, his field excursions, his genial nature, and his ability to befriend them. Charles Darwin, his most famous student, declared that Jameson's lectures were so dull that they made him determined never to read a book on geology. However, Darwin found virtually all lecture courses dull.

One of Jameson's earliest students was an Orcadian, T. S. Traill, who went on to have an eminent career in medicine but whose lifelong interest was chemistry, mineralogy and mineral collecting. He also made an important collection of fossil fish from Orkney. He qualified in 1803 and immediately visited Shetland. His account of the geology was published in 1806 in Patrick Neill's *A tour through the islands of Orkney and Shetland*. Some of the minerals he collected may be seen in the Lerwick Museum. Later in life he became Professor of Medical Jurisprudence at Edinburgh and on a number of occasions gave Jameson's course of lectures.

In 1805 John Fleming graduated at Edinburgh. He was an ordinand but in 1802 had attended chemistry classes as well as his theological ones and gained a love for chemical analysis which he concluded was the only true basis for mineralogy. This sentiment is so close to Jameson's views that it is almost certain that he was also a student of Jameson. In 1807 he embarked on a tour of Orkney and Shetland and, finding the Bressay ministry vacant, became minister there. He immediately began to publish geological and zoological papers. He was engaged to carry out an economic mineralogical survey in Shetland in 1809 for the sum of £20. The report was published in Shirreff's book *A general view of the Agriculture of the Shetland Islands* (1814). Soon afterwards he moved to mainland Scotland and by 1815 was regarded as Scotland's foremost zoologist. Eventually he became a professor of natural history at Edinburgh and at the end of a long life was still publishing both zoological and geological papers. As a minister, a geologist and a zoologist he was active in the controversies over the Book of Genesis and evolution. After his death he was remembered as a tall rather grim figure, full of personal kindness and gifted with a keen critical power. He seemed never happier than when he had an opportunity of exercising that power in sarcastically demolishing the arguments of those to whom he was opposed.

In 1817 two of Jameson's medical students qualified and became geologists. One was Ami Boué who returned to the Continent and wrote the book *Essai geologique sur l'Écosse* (1820) which contained the first geological map of Scotland and the first attempt at correlation between the rocks of Scotland and Shetland. He became one of France's more eminent geologists.

The knowledge of Shetland Boué exhibited in his book and map was drawn largely from Samuel Hibbert, who graduated the same year. On qualifying at the age of 35, 'sick of grinding', Hibbert departed for Shetland. He spent three months in 1817 and six months in 1818 surveying the islands. He had long been keen on 'pedestrian tours' and now scoured the hills and coasts of Shetland, a tall slightly stooped figure in a battered hat, a disreputable coat with capacious leather pockets stuffed with specimens, wearing leather gaiters and followed by his dog Silly. He spent his nights wherever was most convenient, sometimes on the straw covered floor of a smoke filled crofter's cottage, at others in a laird's house. His vagabond appearance seems to have been no disadvantage to him in Shetland but in England it once got him imprisoned on suspicion of poisoning a race horse! His wife wrote to him urging him to return home from Shetland but not to bring his 'mineralogical dress' – 'for fear of lively company'. In six months he collected 4000 specimens, a prodigious number to collect in that length of time even today. His greatest difficulty lay in the lack of a good base map on which to record his observations. This involved him in much laborious topographical survey work. By 1820 he had published a detailed interpretation of the geology of Shetland, far more advanced than any previous account and, more important, the first geological map of Shetland, which was one of the earliest geological maps of any part of Scotland. His account was considerably expanded to include the antiquities of Shetland and published as *A Description of the Shetland Islands* (1822).

Hibbert discovered chromite in Unst in 1817 and this enabled Thomas Edmonston of Buness (elder brother of Arthur and Laurence Edmonston) to start a chromite mining industry there. He endeavoured to start a kaolin mining industry by sending samples of kaolin from Fetlar *via* his friend W. Henry (discoverer of Henry's law) to Josiah Wedgwood in England.

In 1817 Thomas Edmonston was visited by another scientist, the great French astronomer and physicist J. B. Biot, who stayed with him for two months while determining the gravitational field with a pendulum, part of a project to determine the shape of the earth. In 1818 H. Kater, the English surveyor arrived to repeat the experiment. This was the first geophysical work done in Shetland. More than 100 years were to elapse before any further geophysical work was done there.

These two visitors were followed in 1820 by John MacCulloch who had been a student with Jameson and who was then employed as a geologist by the Ordnance Survey of the time. He was sent to Shetland to determine what allowances should be made in the gravity determinations for local gravitational anomalies, and to add the geology of Shetland to the geological map of Scotland which he was making. He is a much neglected and under valued geologist. He was probably the world's first government employed geological surveyor and for a time constituted a national (Scottish) geological survey;

his map published in 1836 is the first official geological map of a country. R. J. H. Cunningham attended chemistry classes at Edinburgh in 1833–36 including almost certainly Jameson's classes; even within that time he was already reading papers on his own geological survey work. In 1838 he read a paper on the geology of the southern Mainland of Shetland, based on a survey made in 1837, which was unfortunately never published. Five years later he died having already surveyed six Scottish counties and six islands and published five papers.

Another of Jameson's students was W. F. Heddle, an Orcadian. He was a medical student qualifying in 1851. As a child he was already a fanatical collector. A prize-winning herbarium of his was dropped into a stream by a fellow pupil and destroyed. Heddle immediately resolved to collect only indestructible objects and became a mineral collector. He spent some of his undergraduate years in Germany studying mineralogy and chemistry and his graduation thesis was entirely mineralogical. Nevertheless on graduation he became a doctor in Edinburgh, but gave up after 5 years and departed to Faroe to collect minerals. He spent the next 20 years teaching in St Andrews University. He was one of the most dedicated, ruthless and successful mineral collectors who ever lived. He attacked the rocks with 28 lb hammers, wedges and explosives and when possible, travelled in yachts to save time. His detailed mineralogical survey of the cliffs of Shetland was carried out in company with Patrick Dudgeon of Cargen in the latter's yacht and his geological map contains the navigational instructions needed to repeat the operation. His description of Shetland minerals published first in 1878 in *The County Geognosy and Mineralogy of Scotland, Orkney and Shetland* remained unimproved for about 80 years. His collection of Scottish minerals grew to be the greatest collection of any single country made by one man. However, he was much more than a collector, analysing his minerals both chemically and crystallographically, describing them in detail, and publishing the results.

The next major contribution to Shetland geology was made by very different men. B. N. Peach and J. Horne were career Geological Survey officers trained in London and Glasgow. Peach's father, C. W. Peach, a customs officer, was a very talented amateur geologist. In 1858 he visited Orkney and Shetland on the annual cruise of the ship belonging to the Commissioners of Northern Lights in company with Stevenson, the lighthouse engineer who constructed the Bound Skerry and Muckle Flugga lighthouses. Later (1865) he published the first paper to attribute the effects of glaciation visible in Shetland to ice action.

In 1876 B. N. Peach, as part of his duties, accompanied his chief A. Geikie, another great geologist, later to become the first Professor of Geology at Edinburgh University and still later Director General of the Geological Survey, on a tour of Shetland. Disillusioned by having the results of his researches published by his superiors, Peach proposed to Horne in 1878 that they spend their summer holidays together carrying out work they could publish in their own names. Glaciation by major ice sheets was then just becoming accepted, and in 1870 Croll had proposed that the Scottish and Norwegian ice sheets had filled the North Sea and flowed to the west across Orkney and Shetland. They resolved to test this hypothesis by field work and to start work that summer in Shetland.

In 1879 they published an improved geological map of Shetland, an updated account of the geology and at the same time confirmed that Shetland had been glaciated by an ice sheet from Norway. In the following years they went on to survey Orkney and Caithness in the same way and completely vindicated Croll's hypotheses. They worked together for the rest of their lives. Their names became inseparable and famous in the geological world as they solved major problems in the Highlands of Scotland. Nevertheless their work in Shetland was partly wrong: much of the evidence they cited for the glaciation of the central and northern parts of Shetland by Scandinavian ice was in fact produced by ice moving eastwards towards Scandinavia as indeed, C. W. Peach had originally suggested. The Dalsetter erratic which confirms the presence of Scandinavian ice in the southern part of Shetland in an earlier glaciation was discovered in the 1900s by a Bressay schoolmaster, T. Mainland.

In the 1930s the Geological Survey of Scotland returned to survey Shetland officially. A team of geologists devoted several summers to the project. Unfortunately, a backlog of work in the economically more important coal field areas of Scotland interfered with the publication of the results. Consequently the first official geological map of Shetland did not appear until 1963. That map was on the scale of ¼ inch to one mile, about the same as Hibbert's map. The Survey returned again to Shetland in the 1960s to update the work. One inch to the mile maps appeared in 1968 and 1971 and the first Memoir, *The Geology of Western Shetland*, by W. Mykura and J. Phemister was published in 1976.

It is interesting to compare Hibbert's map of 1822, Peach & Horne's somewhat smaller map of 1879 and the survey map of 1963. If Hibbert's boundaries are transferred to a modern base map and his archaic nomenclature is translated into modern terms his map is seen to be very similar to the more recent maps. It is obvious that Peach and Horne based their work on his map, copying some of his boundaries and correcting others. The survey map differs from Peach and Horne's chiefly in the addition of more details. Taking into account the inaccuracy of the base map Hibbert had to use, the rudimentary state of geology in his time and the complexity of Shetland geology, his map is extraordinarily accurate. There can have been few maps made at that time that were as good.

Several members of the original Geological Survey team, in particular J. Phemister and H. H. Read produced very accurate maps of parts of Shetland which were published at the time of the survey or soon after. H. H.

Read became a professor and in 1934 published the first paper on the geology of Shetland which interpreted the rocks in terms of their history of development rather than merely describing and identifying them. This interpretative work inspired one of his students, Derek Flinn, to start a survey of Shetland which has so far lasted 30 years and which has provided the basis for chapter 2.

BIOLOGISTS

Steamship transport between Shetland and the Scottish mainland was introduced in the 1830s, and a weekly service was instituted in 1838. This was a spur for many naturalists to visit the islands. One of these was John R. Tudor, who wrote a series of *Rambling and Angling Notes from Shetland* for the *Field* between 1878 and 1880. In 1883 he produced his *Orkneys and Shetland: their Past and Present State*, a book of considerable achievement. It contains many observations on birds and mammals as well as chapters on botany and geology (the last by Peach and Horne).

But the closing decades of the 19th century were dominated by record and specimen collectors. For example, Harold Raeburn an Edinburgh ornithologist trudged vast distances on four visits between 1885 and 1895, recording his exploits in a journal now in the Royal Scottish Museum. The Duchess of Bedford cruised the northern seas in her yacht, making many useful observations. Rich entomologists from the south sent professional collectors to the islands where the unique local varieties were being discovered – and proving highly marketable in London.

During the same period J. A. Harvie-Brown and his colleagues were making a gallant attempt to cover the whole of Scotland in a series of *Vertebrate Faunas*. Harvie-Brown himself circumnavigated Shetland in his yacht in 1890 with Eagle Clarke of the Royal Scottish Museum, who was to more or less found modern bird migration studies with his work on Fair Isle around the turn of the century (despite having been originally trained as a civil engineer),* and Heddle the geologist. At Uyeasound they met and were joined by two ornithologists, A. H. Evans and T. E. Buckley, and together visited many of the outlying stacks and holms. From this partnership came Evans' and Buckley's *Vertebrate Fauna of Shetland* (1899) which was the standard work of Shetland natural history (albeit with limited coverage) until the publication of the Venables's *Birds and Mammals of Shetland* in 1955. The former authors covered the islands very thoroughly and arranged for local naturalists to send them further observations. The result was one of the best volumes of the *Vertebrate Fauna* series.

*David Lack has commented that 'Eagle Clarke's work on migration was not seriously followed up in these islands for 45 years, being regrettably side-tracked by his incidental discovery that on Fair Isle and similar places there was a big chance of collecting rarities'.

In 1900, 1902 and 1913 a poor Suffolk barrister, Edmund Selous, visited Shetland and the modern biological era can be said to have dawned. He did not add greatly to our knowledge of Shetland birds in themselves, but he observed carefully and accurately, and laid a much firmer basis for future ornithological studies than is apparent from reading his rambling descriptions. For this reason, Lack has argued that he has had a more profound influence on ornithology than any other British pioneer.

Since then regular flocks of bird-watchers have invaded Shetland, many of them producing much sought-after books – Frances Pitt with *Shetland Pirates* (1923) of the earlier generation; Niall Rankin *Haunts of British Divers* (1947), G. K. Yeates *Bird Haunts in Northern Britain* (1948) and Richard Perry *Shetland Sanctuary* (1948) wrote books in the immediate post-war period; and finally Pat and Ursula Venables who had lived in Shetland since 1947 produced their *Birds and Mammals of Shetland* in 1955 which magisterially reviewed and summarised much information.

Two other ornithological developments must be mentioned. Eagle Clarke repeatedly returned to Fair Isle in the early years of the century. He interested and trained an islander, Jerome Wilson, in his work, and in 1908 appointed Wilson as a paid recorder on a day-to-day basis. A Fair Isle man thus became probably the first-ever professional bird-watcher. What is more, he was in fact the resident warden of what Eagle Clarke claimed to be 'the most famous bird-observatory in our islands' – in the process establishing this as a new term in the language.

By 1921 Eagle Clarke decided he was getting too old for island-hopping, and made his last visit to Fair Isle in the company of Rear-Admiral James Stenhouse. They bothied in the Duchess of Bedford's old cottage, and 'lived on bad food and good whisky for a fortnight'. During the next decade Stenhouse may be said to have wardened Fair Isle, with the help of another islander, George Stout.

Stenhouse handed on his mantle to a young Edinburgh man, George Waterston, who eventually bought the island in 1948, and set up a 'proper' bird observatory in old naval huts. Kenneth Williamson, Peter Davies, Roy Dennis, Roger Broad and Ian Robertson have since been a continuing and distinguished series of professional wardens. The Observatory moved into new, purpose-built accommodation in 1970.

Jerome Wilson and George Stout can be regarded as part of an indigenous Shetland naturalist tradition. To them must be added G. T. Kay and G. W. Russell of Lerwick, S. Bruce and J. Simpson of Whalsay, Tom Henderson of Dunrossness, Bobbie Tulloch of Mid Yell (who discovered the Snowy Owls nesting on Fetlar in 1967) and many others. But undoubtedly Shetland natural history took a major step forward with the formation of a Bird Club in 1973 – and this must be regarded as a major development paralleling the establishment of the Observatory on Fair Isle.

To the outsider Shetland is probably best known for its birds. However the islands also have considerable botanical interest. As already noted, Tom Edmonston produced the first Shetland flora in 1845. His work was enlarged by W. H. Beeby in the 1890s and capped by G. C. Druce who visited Shetland three times between 1920 and 1924, and published his *Flora Zetlandica* in 1922. Druce was an amateur who took over the professionals. Born in Northampton, he moved to Oxford and opened a chemist's shop. He became Secretary of the Botanic Exchange Club, and by a mixture of charm, audacity, industry and deviousness transformed it into the Botanical Society of the British Isles. Blessed with a venerable appearance he died in 1932 possessed of two honorary degrees and a fellowship of the Royal Society.

Shetland botany is still in the hands of an amateur – but this time he is a Shetland man, Walter Scott. And another son of Shetland is Professor of Botany at St Andrews and author of chapter 4.

References for Chapter 12
(full citations are given in the Bibliography on p. 353)

Boué, 1820; Brand, 1701; Clarke, 1912; Donaldson, 1966; Drosier, 1830–31; Druce, 1922; Edmonston, 1809; Edmonston & Saxby, 1889; Edmonston, 1845; Evans & Buckley, 1899; Fresson, 1967; Gibson, 1877; Gifford, 1786; Heddle, 1878; Hibbert, 1822; Jameson, 1798; Low, 1774; Mykura & Pheimster, 1976; Peach, 1865; Peach, & Horne, 1879, 1884; Pennant, 1784–85; Perry, 1948; Pitt, 1923; Raeburn, 1888, 1891; Rankin, 1947; Read, 1934; Saxby, 1874; Selous, 1905; Shirreff, 1814; Sinclair, 1795; Smith, 1661; Spence, 1979; Tait, 1925; Traill, 1806; Tudor, 1883; Venables & Venables, 1955; Waterston, 1946; Williamson, 1965; Yeates, 1948.

CHAPTER 13

OIL AND THE NATURAL HISTORY
OF SHETLAND

OIL development is, like it or not, a major influence on the present and forseeable environment of Shetland. Already there have been oil spills, damage to wild-life, and recriminations against the oil industry (p. 258). Notwithstanding, the possible effects of oil have been the subject of considerable discussions between the oil industry, the local authority, and conservation bodies ever since the implications of the oil finds in Shetland waters were realized, and the search for solutions to minimize the damage produced by spillage is continually pursued – whatever the more cynical environmentalists may decide to believe.

The first consequence of oil exploration in the northern North Sea was the need for service and supply bases in Shetland. Generally speaking, the impact of these was small and was concentrated in, or close to, already developed areas at Lerwick and Sandwick. The increase in air traffic movement as a result of oil rig crew changes led to the extension of Sumburgh Airport,

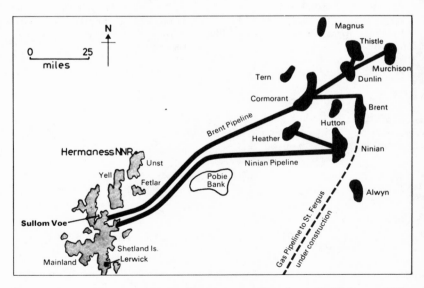

FIG 41. Routes of the two 36 inch diameter pope lines from the Ninian and Brent group of oil fields.

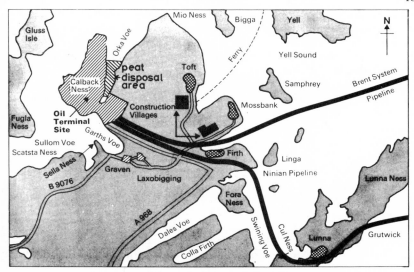

FIG 42. Oil terminal site at Sullom Voe.

including the building of a new runway which intruded, in part, into the Pool of Virkie, a Site of Special Scientific Interest for its wildfowl and wading birds. More recent extensions to the airport have led to the cutting of a new road through the sand dunes near Jarlshof.

With the discovery of the large Brent field in 1971, and later finds, including Ninian, it soon became clear that oil would be piped to the nearest land mass, Shetland (Fig. 4). Zetland County Council were quick to realize the importance of such a decision and promoted a bill through Parliament which subsequently became the Zetland County Council Act, 1974. This gave the Council considerable powers over subsequent oil developments. In 1972, at the same time as their promotion of the parliamentary bill, Z.C.C. (now the Shetland Islands Council) appointed consultants to identify sites that would be suitable for a major oil terminal. This led to the selection of Calback Ness, a small headland within Sullom Voe, as the site for development of the oil terminal, and the oil industry was directed to that area (Fig. 42).

The council also prepared an area development plan which identified the infrastructure necessary for the region of Shetland closest to the oil developments. In 1975, construction of the terminal began.

The oil fields of the East Shetland Basin are approximately 125 miles north-east of Shetland. They are now connected to Shetland by two 36 in diameter pipelines which terminate at Calback Ness, where the terminal is built. The oil arriving at the terminal contains gases dissolved under pressure and these require separation so that the oil can be stored safely and shipped out by tankers. When the terminal is fully operational it is envisaged that ship arrivals will average two oil tankers and one liquified petroleum gas (LPG) tanker per day. The tankers will be arriving at Sullom Voe with up to 40% ballast water on board and comprehensive ballast water treatment facilities are being built at the terminal.

The lighter gases from the separation process will be used to fuel gas turbine generators. The power station will be capable of providing 125 megawatts of electricity, some four times that generated by the Lerwick power station which supplies the rest of Shetland.

ENVIRONMENTAL CONSIDERATIONS

In 1974, before construction of the terminal began, a Sullom Voe Environmental Advisory Group (SVEAG) was formed as the result of a joint initiative of the then Zetland County Council and the oil industry. SVEAG included not only County Council and oil industry representatives, but also members from the Nature Conservancy Council, the Natural Environment Research Council and the Countryside Commission for Scotland, as well as two professors from Scottish universities both with special interests in Shetland. The group was essentially independent but was, of course, linked through its membership to both the Shetland Islands Council (SIC) and the oil industry who between them formed the Sullom Voe Associated Limited (a non-profit making organization comprising Shetland Islands Council on the one hand and the Brent and Ninian Pipeline Groups, representing 32 oil companies, on the other).

It was not the group's responsibility to advise on the siting of the terminal, but how best to achieve minimum environmental disruption in an area chosen primarily on engineering and operating grounds, albeit with some environmental considerations. The group's terms of reference reflected this:

'The SVEAG will advise on environmental aspects of the developments associated with the oil terminal at Sullom Voe, Shetland, including the onshore sealine (out to the SIC limit), landfalls, terrestrial pipeline corridors, storage and other related installations and the tanker jetties and ship handling facilities. The aim is to ensure that environmental considerations are taken into account in the planning, development and operation stages of the project. Responsibility for environmental aspects offshore (exploration, production and undersea pipelines) will remain with the individual operators. The SVEAG will liaise with those operators on environmental aspects of the pipelines carrying oil offshore to the terminal site at Sullom Voe.

The role of the group will be advisory. It may set up subgroups for specific tasks as required and call upon or co-opt expert assistance as deemed necessary'.

One of the group's main aims was to assess the environmental impact of the terminal development, not on a once-and-for-all basis before construction began, but while it was in progress. While the impact assessment was being

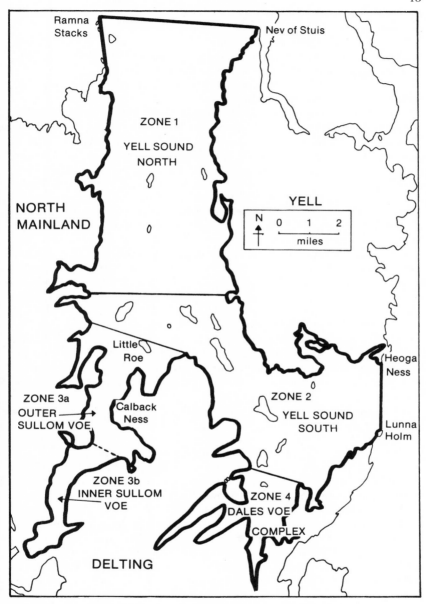

FIG 43. The control area for oil spills around the Sullom Voe terminal.

drawn up, the group was fulfilling its other main aim, that of giving advice to the Council and constructors.

The formation of SVEAG and the way it operated, therefore, represented a unique step in conservation and environmental consideration for such a major development.

In June 1976 the group published a substantial report, *Oil Terminal at Sullom Voe: Environmental Impact Assessment.* This was presented to an international audience at a public seminar in Shetland. Briefly SVEAG identified two phases of potential environmental effects: the first would be during construction of the terminal, when the biggest impact would be felt on the land. There was the disposal of large quantities of peat and sub-standard rock and moraine to be considered. The group recognized the difficulties in handling this material – the peat in particular – and endorsed a proposal that it should be put in Orka Voe behind an armoured bund (Fig. 43). There it could neither escape to the sea nor could it flow and endanger livestock. Four million cubic yards of peat and 9 million cubic yards of rock debris have now been placed behind the bund. Eventually this area and the wayleaves of the two pipelines will more than offset the grazing land lost as a result of construction work. It was recognized also that once the terminal was built the area generally would require 'landscaping' and the buildings, tanks and units painted in such a way as to blend into the background against which they are set. Again SVEAG was able to advise.

The second phase would come with the operation of the Terminal. Here the greatest impact falls in the marine environment. Recognizing the potential for oil spills from the handling of oil at the terminal and from tanker traffic in Yell Sound, SVEAG formed a working group to make recommendations on the type and extent of oil spill clean-up equipment which should be used in Sullom Voe.

Tankers will arrive at Sullom Voe in ballast. SVEAG recommended that final oil levels in the treated ballast water should average 10–15 ppm, should not exceed 25 ppm and should be discharged through a diffuser to ensure a one-hundred fold dilution within 50 m of the discharge point. By commissioning hydrographic studies of the area the group was able to identify a suitable area for a diffuser that would ensure mixing with the surrounding water body. That area lies between Calback Ness and the island of Little Roe, where there is water movement at all states of the tide. The currents in this area are an offshoot of the main Yell Sound tidal stream. The local currents give a dilution capability in excess of 2000:1 – a figure which assumes full throughput of the two pipelines and a 40% ballast loading factor – thus ensuring adequate dispersion. The treated ballast water will at all times be taken away by the tide from Sullom Voe into Yell Sound, where the dilution capacity will be far greater.

Having published its impact assessment, SVEAG stood down. Since 1977, ongoing environmental advice has come from a second, independently chaired group, the Shetland Oil Terminal Environmental Advisory Group (SOTEAG) which has a sub-group to deal with monitoring. In comparison with SVEAG, SOTEAG has a wider range of environmental scientists, a greater Shetland representation, and local conservation bodies have a significant input to it. The group's main function is to provide advice during the operating phase of the terminal and to interpret data obtained from the continuing biological and chemical monitoring programme.

PLANNING FOR OIL SPILL CLEAN-UP

Two parallel oil spill advisory committees, the Sullom Voe Oil Spill Advisory Committee (SVOSAC), dealing with the harbour area, and the Industry Oil Spill Advisory Committee (INOSAC), dealing with landward aspects have been constituted. SOTEAG does not deal formally with oil pollution contingency planning, but has examined the ecological advice which has gone into the plan and upon which oil spill clean up strategy is based. SVOSAC has taken SVEAG's original advice and has drawn up a comprehensive oil spill contingency plan. SVEAG originally envisaged the whole of Sullom Voe, Yell Sound and associated waters as forming a natural geographical area on which to base a contingency plan, and this view was followed by SVOSAC. An ecological survey of the area was carried out to identify:

1. Areas of water with biological interests, including fisheries, bird life, marine mammals, areas of potentially anoxic waters, shallow lagoons, etc.
2. Coastal types and habitats, including amenity beaches and harbours, salt marshes, soft shores, sandy shores, rocky shores and shingle and sand ayres, spits, tombolos and bars.

The whole area divides naturally into four zones (Fig. 43). The first, Yell Sound North, is an area of relatively open water, flushed by a major tidal current and frequently experiencing heavy seas. Fisheries interests here are generally in deep water and the use of dispersants for oil on water is considered the most practical clean-up method, though it is recognized that there may be periods when containment and recovery could be carried out. Zone 2, Yell Sound South, contains many small islands and experiences one of the strongest tidal races in Shetland, reaching as much as 7–8 knots. Speed of reaction is essential in this zone, and because of the very strong currents and numerous navigational hazards, dispersant spraying is the only practical technique for this zone. Zone 3 (Sullom Voe) and Zone 4 (Dales Voe complex) are more enclosed bodies of water, rarely receiving heavy seas. Both have a restricted water exchange and the extreme heads of the voes have deep, still areas, often with a salt marsh complex. The head waters of Sullom Voe are 140 feet deep and input of peat from run-off water is such that the sea bed and bottom layers of water undergo intermittent anoxic periods. Within these zones containment and recovery is recommended. In certain areas including the heads of the voes, houbs and other shallow areas, it is recommended that dispersants must never be used. Around the jetties, however, small handling spills will be treated with dispersant whilst on open water.

There is very little coastline in the oil spill control area that is classified for public amenity use and, therefore, very little that requires intensive clean-up techniques or the use of beach-sprayed dispersants. About 50% of the coastline is rocky and inaccessible from land, and in such situations oil will be left to degrade naturally. There are a number of salt marshes and species-rich soft shores associated with the houbs where the use of dispersants or heavy mechanical clean-up must be avoided, and a number of shingle and sand spits, ayres, tombolos and bars, so characteristic of Shetland's drowning landscape, where the use of heavy clean-up equipment would be similarly damaging.

INOSAC has drawn up contingency plans for the land lines, which total some eight miles. These follow standard clean up practices. There are no areas of biological interest on or adjacent to the wayleaves, nor are there any major courses or standing bodies of water.

THE MONITORING PROGRAMME

A considerable amount of biological and chemical monitoring has taken place within and around Sullom Voe. These studies have been directed towards the establishment of a baseline against which any future changes which may be caused by the terminal operations, and action which may be required, can be judged.

It was SVEAG through its monitoring sub-groups that first identified the need for a biological monitoring programme with adequate control sites and baseline studies were commenced in 1975. SOTEAG, through its monitoring group, has now taken over this programme and enlarged it to include chemical studies. SOTEAG will, of course, ultimately be responsible for the interpretation of the data.

The studies undertaken to date have not only provided the baseline information; because they have been undertaken by experts in their own field, the studies have also provided a considerable amount of scientific data for the Sullom Voe area, and contributed to greater knowledge of the natural environment of Shetland. Indeed some of the information included in other chapters of this book was obtained during this monitoring programme.

The design of the monitoring programme has tried to take into account those areas where monitoring was already taking place and would be likely to continue, for example the Sea Mammals Research Unit of the Natural Environment Research Council have been monitoring seals around Shetland for some years (p. 112f) and the Department of Agriculture and Fisheries for Scotland have been looking at, amongst other things, the hydrocarbon content of the waters in and around Sullom Voe. Nevertheless, there remained many areas where little or no information for Sullom Voe existed. Seabirds and seaduck were identified as being at particular risk. These birds are very mobile and could suffer not only from an oil spill within Yell Sound or Sullom Voe, but from possible oil spills as a result of tanker accidents on the approaches to Shetland. With this in mind, the large breeding colonies of Guillemots and Gannets at Hermaness have been monitored by an oil industry ornithologist annually since 1975. Hermaness, a National Nature Reserve, is particularly significant. Not only is it one of the most important cliff breeding sites in North Europe, it is also one of the closest of several important seabird breeding sites in Shetland to the new oil terminal. More recently other breeding sites have been included in the seabird monitoring programme.

The sea area around Sullom Voe is an important overwintering area for seaduck. About 60% of Shetland's Eider population overwinter in Yell Sound, Sullom Voe and the sea area immediately east of Yell. In the winter of 1975/76 the Nature Conservancy Council started counts of the duck population of these areas and they have been carried out each year since that time (p. 170).

The waters and bottom living animals of Sullom Voe have been investigated by two groups independently, since 1976. The Scottish Marine Biological Association has been particularly concerned with the water chemistry throughout Sullom Voe, and certain species within the animal communities, whereas the Oil Pollution Research Unit of the Field Studies Council, has concentrated on the animal communities in the jetty and diffuser areas around Calback Ness. More recently SOTEAG has integrated these programmes so as to ensure that both the chemical and biological aspects of a number of selected sites within Sullom Voe are studied simultaneously.

Habitats which are at greatest risk from floating oil are the coastal areas, and these have been monitored since 1976. The coastline of Sullom Voe has a variety of habitats. Much is rocky in nature, varying from small shingle to solid rock. The larger boulder and rock shores have been monitored by the Oil Pollution Research Unit along the same lines as those developed at Britain's other great oil port, Milford Haven. The soft shores, and under this heading the sediments of the shallow tidal ponds (houbs) are extremely important species-rich areas, are monitored annually by the Orkney Marine Biological Unit of Dundee University. The houbs are potential oil traps as are the small salt marshes which are dotted around Sullom Voe. The initial survey of the salt marshes showed them to be similar to the species-poor marshes found in Norway, and not at all like the larger estuarine marshes of mainland Britain. The salt marshes were found to form a series within which three types could be recognized:

1. Marshes which are completely open to the influence of waves (one extreme).
2. Marshes which are totally protected behind a shingle spit (the other extreme).

3. Marshes which are behind a protective spit in such a position that at high tide there is a body of open water between the spit and marsh front. Such marshes are probably very dynamic even though the new sediment input to them is very small.

To round off the SVEAG/SOTEAG monitoring programme, the general air quality of the Sullom Voe region is being monitored using colour photographs of lichen quadrats. The lichens growing on rock outcrops, standing stones, walls and gravestones around Sullom Voe are being used for this exercise instead of the more usual corticolous species (there are no suitable trees in Shetland). This is being carried out jointly by the oil industry and the British Museum, Natural History.

Various planning conditions and statutory requirements for monitoring have been imposed upon industry which will be met independently by the industry. They include a comprehensive monitoring programme for the diffuser area, and the monitoring of gaseous hydrocarbon and sulphur dioxide from the terminal. Wherever possible these studies will be carried out in a manner complementary to the SVEAG/SOTEAG programme.

CONCLUSIONS

Although no-one can guarantee that there will not be effects on the environment of Sullom Voe through the day-to-day operation of the terminal, or the infrastructure around Sullom Voe built to support the terminal, or the operation of shipping in and out of the terminal, all identifiable aspects have been considered and solutions sought which should reduce the impact. Great attention has been paid to detail in the design, building and operation of the terminal so that the risk of pollution is diminished and in some cases, eliminated. That there will be oil spills is a fact of human life, but the provision of an ecologically based oil spill clean-up contingency plan at least means that the clean-up itself will be undertaken in a sensible manner, taking various biological factors into account. The monitoring programme will point towards possible troubles at an early stage, even though the actual cause of the trouble may not be identified by changes detected. The causes of any changes which SOTEAG consider unacceptable will be sought and remedial action taken. All decisions on the design and building of the terminal have taken account of the advice on environmental effects or precautions proffered by SVEAG and SOTEAG.

References for Chapter 13
(full citations are given in the Bibliography, p. 353)

Button, 1976; Johnston, 1977; Livesey & Henderson, 1973; Nicolson, 1975; Shetland Islands Council, 1977; Sullom Voe Environmental Advisory Group, 1976; Zetland County Council, 1974.

CHAPTER 14

CONSERVATION

EARLIER chapters have described the multiplicity of outstanding and often unique features of the Shetland archipelago, placing many of them high in both national and international contexts. These features range from the immense and striking seabird colonies to apparently abstruse examples of adaptability and evolution in endemic sub-species. In the same way, the reasons for and techniques of conservation range from the obvious to the subtle. Nevertheless, if the archipelago is viewed as a single living system, the results of destroying any part of it becomes a possible threat to the total system rather than a mere isolated wound. To achieve and maintain a harmonious, attractive, diverse and stable environment for whatever purpose – admiration, investigation or harvest – caution, planning and control are required.

A surprisingly fragile ecosystem

Shetland is an isolated group of islands where many species have very small populations and no adjacent reservoir for replacement; furthermore, some species, both terrestrial and marine, are close to either the northern or southern limits of their distribution, and this means they are in a delicate position within the ecosystem and may easily be displaced. Two further points have a bearing on how carefully we must treat the local environment:

1. There are only 681 vascular plant species in the islands compared with some 2241 for the whole of Britain. A similar species poverty occurs in virtually every other group from phytoplankton to terrestrial mammals. Such a species-poor ecosystem is inherently vulnerable, as a lack of diversity normally means a lack of stability.

2. Compared with the rest of Britain, the climate and especially factors associated with wind, is severe; while the growing season, as a result of the islands' northerly latitude, is extremely short. Disturbance to plant cover can rapidly lead to erosion which may take many years to heal.

The history of Shetland's conservation can be said to have begun with the efforts of Dr L. Edmonston and John Scott in the 19th century to protect the almost extinct Great Skua (p. 200). Much more recently, following the passing of the National Parks and Access to the Countryside Act of 1949, National Nature Reserves (N.N.R.) were declared for Noss, Hermaness and Haaf Gruney in 1955. In the 1960s the Royal Society for the Protection of Birds (R.S.P.B.) appointed their first part-time Warden and the (then) Nature Conservancy their first full-time resident Officer. Since then the R.S.P.B. Officer has become full-time and an R.S.P.B. Reserve has been established at

Fetlar, while the Nature Conservancy Council (N.C.C.) has declared another N.N.R. at the Keen of Hamar and designated 28 Sites of Special Scientific Interest (S.S.S.I.), representative of a wide cross-section of Shetland habitats (see p. 253). With the advent of North Sea oil the N.C.C. launched an ambitious survey of all the environmental interests, through their research colleagues of the Institute of Terrestrial Ecology (I.T.E.), and a continuing programme of monitoring is being carried out in and around sites liable to be affected by oil and oil developments (Chapter 13). The computer-based results of the I.T.E. survey is intended to be accessible in a readily understood form for the use of local planning authorities.

Bitter experience has shown that the statutory designation of a site as an S.S.S.I. is no protection in Shetland and may indeed give a false impression that the remainder of the environment is without value. Examples of mistreatment of S.S.S.I.'s are sand extraction at St Ninian's and Quendale; sewage outfall into the tiny machair Loch of Hillwell; and incredibly, planning permission granted (although never exploited) to construct a road over Ronas Hill with the intention of removing shingle from the beaches on the remote western edge. Agricultural developments fall outwith the Acts, and nothing could be done to prevent the reseeding of half the unique site at the Keen of Hamar. Inappropriate quarry development at Voe and Mavis Grind, and sand-extraction at West Sandwick (none of which are designated sites) show the local preference for pragmatic rather than long-term solutions.

Important as the designation of sites should be, the very nature of the islands and their biological interests, demands a more liberal approach. Many habitats and species are widely and thinly spread, particularly the limited populations of some endemic species where each unit in itself may appear unimportant and yet helps to maintain the viability of the others by its very existence. Every time a habitat is destroyed in Shetland an option closes for a number of species. If a particular habitat is restricted, as with the dwindling natural shrub sites, there may be no further option for a species except extinction. This loss is not just an injury to the Shetland environment or to our aesthetic appreciation of it, but in the long term may be an economic loss. For example the future of shelter-belts for crops and animals in Shetland may be extremely important and the native shrubs could provide an immediate supply of genotypes that have been adapting to the local climate for thousands of years.

Shetland's approach to conservation cannot therefore be the simple designation of sites and an acceptance of free development elsewhere; it must involve the assessment of each case against the total situation. Local Plans and the Conservation Plan in the overall County Structure Plan are steps in the right direction. If these are used in conjunction with a well-organized Management Information System, the right answers should emerge. This approach will not work however, unless the Shetland Islands Council, private developers and the general public all give the natural environment the respect

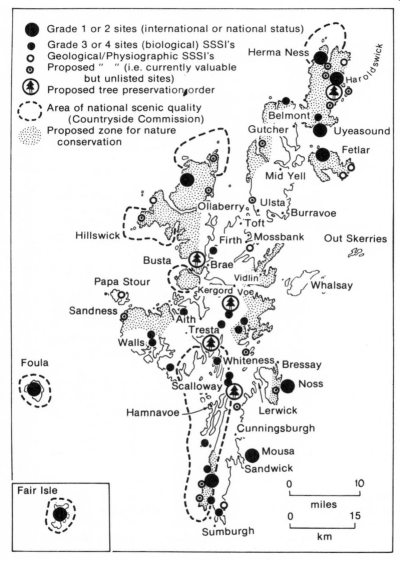

Grade 1 or 2 sites (international or national status)
Grade 3 or 4 sites (biological) SSSI's
Geological/Physiographic SSSI's
Proposed "   " (i.e. currently valuable
    but unlisted sites)
Proposed tree preservation order

Area of national scenic quality
    (Countryside Commission)
Proposed zone for nature
    conservation

Herma Ness
Haroldswick
Har
Belmont
Gutcher
Uyeasound
Fetlar
Mid Yell
Ulsta
Ollaberry
Burravoe
Toft
Hillswick
Firth
Mossbank
Out Skerries
Busta
Brae
Papa Stour
Vidlin
Whalsay
Kergord
Voe
Sandness
Aith
Walls
Tresta
Whiteness
Bressay
Foula
Noss
Scalloway
Hamnavoe
Lerwick
Cunningsburgh
Mousa
Sandwick
Fair Isle
0   10
miles
0   15
km
Sumburgh

FIG 44. Declared and proposed nature conservation areas. (Modified from the *Shetland Structure Plan*, 1979).

it is due. With proper conservation the myriad features which give the unique character to Shetland can be protected and the heritage passed on to future generations. And this is perhaps where conservation should start today, with the younger generation. The islands are ideally suited for the setting up of Local Nature Reserves and outdoor centres where the natural environment may become an integral part of education.

PRACTICAL PROBLEMS

But quite apart from these principles, there are a number of practical problems that deserve attention in addition to the direct impact of the Sullom Voe Oil Terminal and other oil-related developments.

1. The greater part of the Shetland topography consists of moorland varying in character from wet blanket peat, through areas of only partial plant cover such as on the mettagabbros in Unst, to tracts of serpentine and the North Roe plateau which support fellfield. Scattered over these moorlands are numerous water-bodies ranging from lochans to quite large lochs which support numerous breeding birds, particularly waders. Traditionally these areas have received little human disturbance but they have changed greatly in character through human activity (Chapter 4). To some extent the waders may have exploited the low density and cover of vegetation created by man, but other species have gone. Sheep grazing is heavy in the islands and some investigation is required to find an optimal grazing level. Such a study will have to be combined with the exclusion of animals and the managed redevelopment of shrubs in some sites. These might eventually show how to provide stock-shelter, improve the soil, and ultimately the grazing and carrying levels of stock.

2. There are a growing number of visitors and residents who appreciate wilderness areas like these moorlands. Some come just to walk, some to climb or fish the many lochs, but many bring camera and binoculars to study the bird life. Disturbance of breeding birds is becoming alarmingly common and we must all become better disciplined in our approach to wildlife. But inadvertent damage to the environment is a greater danger: more sophisticated pleasures are on the increase in Shetland, as with an improvement in his standard of living the part-time crofter is beginning to spend his money on leisure pursuits. There are large areas of the country which can absorb climbing and wildfowl shooting, skin-diving, water-skiing and speed-boating, but there are many places, such as the preferred roosting areas for wintering wildfowl, Whimbrel, Snowy Owl, Phalarope and Peregrine breeding sites, from which these pursuits must be excluded if they are to retain their wilderness character.

3. The collection of pebbles, minerals and crystals of an attractive or semi-precious nature, is becoming a limited but increasing pastime for a band of enthusiasts, as they are already a business for the stone-polisher. Shetland is rich in such stones as scapolite, garnet, jasper, malachite, serpentine, agate

and amethyst. The best sites must be identified and collectors directed to those less vulnerable or valuable. Sites of geological and fossil interest have been identified by the N.C.C. and Geological Survey, and they too must be protected from amateur and professional alike.

4. On fellfield areas winter weather causes active 'frost-heave' and disturbance by wheeled vehicles or even by foot can cause erosion and destruction of plant life. Particular care should be taken that no developments occur in these areas and that easy access, especially by road, is not encouraged. Ecosystems of this type are very unusual in Britain (particularly on serpentine). In Shetland they occur at unusually low altitudes and deserve special conservation measures.

5. Although the largest shelter-belt in Shetland (at Kergord) was planted early this century, its value is only now becoming fully appreciated. The establishment of shelter-belts requires great care and patience since the majority of tree species do not grow well in Shetland, and it takes several years for them to provide anything like shelter. Whatever the reason or place of their planting – by the croft or on the hill, to protect crops, hill stock or newly planted grasslands – broad-leaved trees and particularly native shrubs ought to be included among the well-tried Sitka Spruce and Lodgepole. This would diversify the wildlife of the islands and encourage the re-colonization of species which probably lived here in the past but became extinct when their habitat disappeared. This would be particularly obvious with birds and one might expect to see Goldcrest, Tree Sparrow, Thrush and Jackdaw as well as the more northern Fieldfare and Redwing becoming established.

6. Because most Shetland soil is acid, areas of natural grassland or even herb-rich heath are restricted to the better sandstones, limestones, serpentine and gneiss. These contain distinctive floras and faunas, much more diverse than the surrounding acidic moorlands. The most important and attractive must be identified and active encouragement given to owners to prevent their reseeding or slagging and being turned into fields of commercial grasses. Similarly hayfields, meadows and marshes in low-lying crofting areas which support an even more diverse flora and fauna and which give the croft land their character, must be overseen to prevent unnecessary ditching and fencing. The loss of 'natural' pastures is a conservation problem throughout the British Isles, but it is particularly acute in Shetland because of the paucity of good land.

7. Freshwater bodies are not under any great threat at present apart from the occasional water scheme. They are peaceful areas and none so large that fishermen need motor boats. Care must be taken with restocking with 'sporting fish' such as the Rainbow Trout, that not too many natural populations are interfered with. Particular restraint must be exercised at Girlsta Loch, the only site in Shetland for Char.

8. The most dramatic attack in recent years on the Shetland environment has been on coastal sand and shingle deposits. In the past only the smallest

sites were damaged, since most exploitation was merely for individual houses. During and since the 1939–45 war, and particularly with the large requirements for building materials associated with oil developments, demand has vastly outstripped the natural reserves and serious damage has been done to a number of sites (Chapter 2). The Islands Council foresaw that the Sullom requirements could not be met from local resources and insisted on the importing of sand for that development. Notwithstanding the planning guidelines have been insufficient adequately to protect sites in general. Even small sites, such as that at West Sandwick, have received permission for extraction which can only lead to their destruction. At Quendale, which is the only complete sand-blow system in Shetland with characteristic physiography and plant communities, and which supports the only native butterfly population, removals are eating away the foredunes and disrupting the natural drainage. More controlled extraction could, with a little more difficulty, have exploited the more inland deposits there without interfering with the system to such an extent.

Tourism and local use is also bringing more pressure to such sites and among the more popular are the few shell sand beaches (such as the one at Meill on Burra). This requires some control of public use before erosion causes excessive damage. No one likes restrictions on their freedom, but the beaches will fast lose their interest and attractiveness unless something is done to control their use. Other coastal systems which require special assessment and protection are the vulnerable and valuable salt-marshes, houbs, bars, spits and tombolos so typical of Shetland.

9. Particular species which may require care are those unique to Shetland, such as Edmonston's Chickweed, and sub-species such as those of moths, domestic animals and mice. Since they all have relatively small populations in the national context, it may be necessary to restrict influences which might adversely affect them. Perhaps the most important action that could be taken is to discourage introductions from the mainland. The seal populations also require careful monitoring. The Common Seal has now largely recovered from its persecution of the 1960s, but if hunting is re-introduced it must be at a level which will not harm the stability of the population. At present the Grey Seal population appears to be stable and not to be increasing as in many places outwith Shetland. The Otter population also appears to be healthy, with little trapping taking place today, but the destruction of ten by an oil spill (see p. 258) is worrying, even though the spill in question was fuel oil and more dangerous than the more usual (and likely) crude oil. The large and growing population of Greater Black-backed Gulls ought to be monitored, in particular the effect on its winter feeding habits and expansion of refuse at rubbish dumps and fish factories.

There are other species which are only rare in terms of their population within Shetland (for example the beautiful Oyster plant or the Purple Saxifrage) but the destruction of a single site could see their extinction; while of the rarer birds, the Peregrine is in desperate need of investigation to find out why its population has collapsed so dramatically in the last ten or twenty years.

In discussing conservation in Shetland one must consider in detail the effect of North Sea oil on Shetland, and of the oil port at Sullom Voe, the largest civil engineering project in Britain. The steps that have been taken to minimize these effects are described in Chapter 13, but we must put them in the context of the whole Shetland environment, because the development with its requirements of people, housing, improved roads and airstrips and demand for building materials has increased the overall pressure on the environment, never mind the particular problems of pollution. The site for the oil port virtually chose itself as the only sheltered deep water site with adequate shore space for the vast complex, and it is to the Council's credit that they endorsed this site and restricted subsidiary developments, such as the service bases, to Lerwick and Sandwick. Providentially the biological interests of the site itself are virtually nonexistent. The marine interests however, both within Sullom and in Yell Sound are quite important, although not exceptional. Within Sullom is the Houb of Scatsta, a significant wader feeding area, while in the winter the voe itself supports up to 500 Eider, 150 Long-tailed Duck and 50 Slavonian Grebes as well as the few Velvet Scoters that occur in Shetland.

Outside the voe Yell Sound in winter harbours 1500 Eider, several hundred Black Guillemot, up to 1000 Shag, plus Great Northern, White and Black-billed Divers; while in late winter and early spring large numbers of Common Guillemots and rather fewer Razorbills pass to and from Ramna Stacks at the northern entrance to the sound. In the summer months the breeding bird populations of Yell Sound include Fulmars, Puffins, Black Guillemots, Shags and Cormorants, and these are joined by feeding Red-throated Divers from the surrounding landward areas. Breeding on islands in the sound are *circa* 250 Common Seals. The monitoring programme of the Shetland Oil Terminal Environmental Advisory Group (SOTEAG) has been designed to detect both the scale of any damage caused and the rate of recovery. Should any adverse changes take place it may be possible to alter the contingency plans and techniques of clear-up. These contingency plans have been discussed in Chapter 13, while the Shetland Islands Council has its own plans for the area within its jurisdiction, up to one mile offshore. Outwith this area the responsibility for oil spill clearance lies with the Department of Trade and Industry. Stocks of dispersants and equipment within Shetland are capable of dealing with 4000 tons of oil.

There have been several predictions concerning the amount of oil which may be accidentally spilled within the port area. The Department of the Environment's Central Unit on Environmental Pollution (CUEP) has estimated that the Scottish east coast oil ports (which includes Sullom and Flotta in Orkney), can expect by 1981 one spill per week between them. However, the first Oil Pollution Officer for Sullom predicted that there would be one spillage per week at Sullom itself, with one of 100 tons annually and one of a minimum of 2000 tons every ten years. These figures have been disputed by SOTEAG, but there is no doubt that there are going to be regular small spillages and occasional large ones. The much acclaimed oil port of Milford Haven has an apparently irreducible minimum of 2–3 spillages per 100 tankers and since there will be an average of 2–3 tankers per day at Sullom, this would give the minimum number of spillages annually at 14–30. However more spillages occur when loading than unloading and since Milford Haven is mainly a port of the latter and Sullom the former, the spillage rate may well reach one per week at Sullom. Action to contain oil spills at Sullom is the responsibility of the Oil Pollution Officer who is employed by the Shetland Islands Council and stationed at Sullom. A watch for incidents is carried out from the pilot launch and tugs. If an incident occurs, immediate action is taken using a converted landing craft equipped for the purpose. Small spills at the jetties are initially handled by the operators using equipment held in the area. 'Apportionment of blame and retrieval of the clean-up operation are gone into after the pollution has been dealt with'.

The situation at Sullom is also potentially more serious than that of Milford Haven as far as damage to the marine environment is concerned. Milford Haven has large tidal and freshwater flows which regularly flush the port, whereas at Sullom there is little tide and a negligible flow of freshwater. Obviously there is a danger of an accumulation of hydrocarbons and also of dispersants if these are used regularly. Either or both of these will affect the local marine environment, but no one can yet hazard a real estimate as to what extent.

Unfortunately within one month of the port being opened there were two oil spills. One was of crude oil which was contained within the holding basin and caused no harm, while the second was of 1200 tons of fuel oil which escaped from a damaged tanker (the *Esso Bernicia*) at the loading jetty. This oil eventually escaped from Sullom into Yell Sound, polluting sections of the coast and killing nearly 4000 seabirds and seaduck, particularly Eiders, Shags, Black Guillemots and Divers (including 155 Great Northern Divers), and claiming the lives of ten Otters and around 50 sheep (with another 2000 contaminated). Ninety-five per cent of all diving seabirds were estimated to have been killed within Sullom Voe and 75% in southern Yell Sound. Following the accident enquiries were set up, but it was obvious that contingency plans and equipment were inadequate. This led to the original plans being revised. In future, efforts will be made to prevent any further spills within the Port from escaping into Yell Sound by placing spur-booms at the mouth of Sullom Voe. Unknown sources of oil pollution since the *Esso Bernicia* incident accounted for a further 2300 seabird deaths up to May 1979.

This incident at the most up-to-date oil port in the world raises the whole question of the type of equipment and the amount of material required to be available for oil spills in Britain as a whole. In 1976 the CUEP recommended that Britain should have the capacity to deal with 16,000 tonnes of oil per day. They also predicted that by 1980 there was a 50% probability of a well blow-out releasing 15,000 tonnes daily before being brought under control. This prediction has already been fulfilled with the Ekofisk blow-out in April 1977. However there has not been the capacity to react adequately if there is a major disaster in the Shetland area. Neither the equipment nor the people have been available; they were intended to be brought in from England, weather permitting! Hopefully a salvage vessel will now remain permanently stationed in the Northern Isles, with pumping equipment, floating oil storage tanks and adequate dispersant locally available.

Other dangers are of oil spills from sources other than wells or accidents within Sullom, for example from the pipelines, from tanker accidents offshore or from discharge of oily ballast water before entering the port. In an effort to make oil available as soon as possible, the Port opened without its Ballast Treatment Plant in operation and at least one tanker was suspected of dumping its oily ballast before arriving. Public outcry led to the oil companies making the carrying of 35% ballast a condition of charter for tankers visiting Sullom so removing any temptation of ballast dumping. Since then there have been no further incidents of this sort. More immediate risks to the Shetland environment however, have come from several incidents of tankers approaching dangerously close to the coast on their approach to Sullom. It is obviously necessary for the Shetland Island Council and the oil companies to agree on sea routes before an oil tanker goes aground while taking an unnecessary short-cut.

Incredibly there is no requirement for Masters or owners of a vessel responsible for releasing oil outwith port authority areas to report such incidents. As far as tanker accidents are concerned there was heavy criticism from a Commons Committee of Enquiry into the handling of the *Eleni V* which grounded off the south English coast. Lack of co-ordination and lack of leadership let the situation deteriorate when prompt action was required. A number of improvements have been suggested to help prevent such tanker accidents off Shetland. For example compulsory pilotage and 'traffic lanes' from at least twelve miles out could regulate the movement of tankers. Secondly since most 'problem' tankers sail under flags of convenience and are often not up to the high standards of construction and command of the fleets of the major maritime nations, it has been suggested that they should all be subject to government inspection when they enter the port and refused further entry if they are considered a hazard. In the event of an accident it is essential that the head of the Marine Pollution Control Unit establishes himself immediately in Shetland and deals with the incident with the help of experienced local advice; and that he has the equipment available to do the job.

When one realizes that the cost of the anti-pollution measures recommended by the CUEP amounts to less than 0.001 % of the value of North Sea oil, one can appreciate why the first oil spills at Sullom were such a disaster. This level of investment in anti-pollution measures makes a mockery of the statement in the fourth report of the Royal Commission on Environmental Pollution, which stated – 'The risk of serious pollution is likely to be concentrated in the area of the Shetlands where there is a hazard to wildlife, particularly to the very large numbers of seabirds, and there the difficulties of applying clean-up measures will be the greatest. There is a need for great care and vigilance in landing operations and the need for exceptional precautions against accidents should be considered. Because of the great increase in the cost of oil, such precautions are likely to be justified on economic as well as environmental grounds'.

There is no indication that any of the precautions taken so far are any more than 'adequate' and certainly not 'exceptional'. This is also reflected in the attitude to chronic pollution, which the majority of biologists agree is more insidious than the occasional accident. The CUEP paper estimated that 1250 tonnes of oil suspended in water will be discharged annually from ballast treatment plants at the four new terminals in this country. This is assuming that the concentration will be at 25 parts per million, as there is no statutory limit on discharge from terminals. The discharge from Sullom will normally be between 10–15 ppm and 'not normally' exceed 25 ppm, which means a daily output of between half and one ton of oil through a diffusor into Yell Sound. The technology exists, by way of bacterial action, to reduce this figure to nearer 5 ppm, but there is no pressure from government to achieve this. The arguments for reducing the concentration arise from the fact that the little that is known of the effects of oil in the natural environment indicate that many marine biological processes rely on extremely low concentrations of chemical messengers, at the parts per billion level, and concentrations of oil in the ppm range might easily interfere in these processes. At a greater density level it is known that lobsters can be tainted by oil and made inedible by concentrations of oil in their fats at 0.01 ppm. It is an unfortunate fact that hydrocarbons are remarkably stable in the marine environment.

The most obvious danger from oil spills and the one that catches the public's imagination however, is to birds which are fouled by an oil slick, lose buoyancy or insulation, or ingest oil in preening and die. The threats in Shetland are in particular seasons and in particular areas where there are large concentrations of birds. The areas most at risk include those adjacent to the seabird colonies on the coasts from Fair Isle to Muckle Flugga, and the sheltered voes and sounds where the Eiders congregate in the autumn during their moult and where in the winter they are joined by Black Guillemots, wintering Long-tailed Duck, Divers and Grebes. However it is impossible to exclude the remaining waters around the Shetland coast. For example an oil slick in May 1971 which moved up the east coast from Sumburgh to Whalsay accounted for 1200 seabirds found dead on the shore and probably killed nearer five times that number.

The diving birds (Auks, Ducks, Divers and Shags) are most vulnerable to oil since their reaction to a slick is to dive, very often resurfacing still within the slick. In both the 1971 and 1979 incidents at least 70% of the oiled birds were diving species. Without doubt the Common Guillemot is the species most at risk, partly because of the immense population in Shetland, but also because after breeding they swim offshore in large concentrations from the colonies in a flightless condition. Similarly Eiders go through a moult in late summer and also congregate in flightless flocks. If either were threatened by an oil slick in this condition they would have difficulty in escaping.

In order to gauge the effects of any oil spills in Shetland on the seabirds and seaduck, work by the N.C.C. began in 1973 to establish the size and distribution of the Eider population, and this was followed by attempts to design a monitoring system for seabirds which would detect changes in these populations. In 1974 the Sullom Voe Environmental Advisory Group (later to become SOTEAG) was founded – see Chapter 13 – and forces and money were joined to expand and intensify these researches. As far as the seaduck are concerned the numbers and yearly pattern of movement have been reasonbly well established (Chapter 9), while the critical sites and techniques for monitoring breeding seabirds have been recognized. Other work has been carried out by oil industry ornithologists and by University groups.

There are however a number of problems concerning the monitoring of seabirds which have yet to be solved before the results are in any way meaningful or relevant to detecting changes in populations caused by pollution. For example – when does one count? – where? – how many? – how often? – and what is one counting? With Common Guillemots for example there are seasonal and diurnal patterns of attendance on the cliffs and these must be established before a particular colony can be sensibly counted. At the same time an estimate of the proportion of non-breeders has to be made. Repeated counts are therefore made over an extended period in order to achieve acceptable accuracy. A relationship must be established between the number counted and the number actually breeding. Then it is necessary to be able to calculate breeding success, since the effects of pollution may very well be sub-lethal, affecting fertility either directly or through behaviour.

Different methods and times of counting have been worked out for the common species at several sites. This took two years work and a lot of man hours. However after all this, no one yet knows the natural variation in breeding numbers or success in different years; or if this varies between colonies, and by how much; or if it varies more at the edge of a colony than in the heart of it. These variables will only be established over a number of years of work.

Unfortunately also there are other unknown variables which might dramatically affect seabird numbers and obscure a chronic effect of pollution.

It may be that the huge increase in industrial fishing for sand-eels, which are the principal food of Guillemots, will remove a substantial part of their food supply. This would lead to an almost inevitable decrease in numbers. Moreover a bird in poor condition from food lack is likely to be particularly susceptible to even small amounts of pollution. There is growing competition between natural predators of commercial fish and our fishermen; it has been estimated that the seabirds of Foula require 29% of the total fish within a 25-mile radius of the island, so this competition could soon come to a head. Undoubtedly numerous birds will be found dead from oiling if there is a large oil spill and counts will show these birds to be absent from the cliffs, but a great deal of work is required before any of the more subtle effects of pollution will be detected.

CONSERVATION AND THE FUTURE OF THE SHETLAND ENVIRONMENT

From the viewpoint of the present, the future of the large Shetland seabird and seaduck populations must be recorded as uncertain. Numbers in Sullom Voe will almost definitely decrease and probably also those in Yell Sound. Small accidents may only affect populations locally in other places, although they could seriously damage smaller seabird populations, such as Cormorants at Muckle Roe or Shearwaters at Fetlar, if they occurred offshore of one of them. On the other hand a large oil slick anywhere around Shetland will inevitably harm a large number of birds. If it is offshore from one of the large seabird colonies of Foula, Unst, Noss, Sumburgh or Fair Isle the effect could be catastrophic with little that could be done in the way of clean-up to prevent it. One can only press for the highest care and standards at all stages in the operation of North Sea oil, and trust that mistakes are not made in these vulnerable areas.

Onshore, strict adherence to a conservation plan, some controls of the impacts of tourism, perhaps an environmental code, and particularly education both at school and later could protect these fascinating islands from the worst excesses of development. In future years we will know how Shetland has been affected by new and continuing pressures on its environment; let us hope that we will be able to report on success – which will only come from conscious and positive co-operation between central and local government, industry, conservation bodies both amateur and professional, and the public at large. Shetlanders profess a pride and jealousy for their islands: it is important for them and for the natural environment of which they are trustees that these emotions are translated into sensible conservation management.

During the Second World War, Robert Rendall wrote a sonnet describing the contentment and adjustment of an island crofter. The crofter of the poem was an Orcadian, but his philosophy could equally well be that of a Shetlander or any from that multitude of naturalists who have found peace in the northern isles and who would bitterly resent the despoliation of *ultima thule*:

Scant are the few green acres I till,
But arched above them spreads the boundless sky,
Ripening their crops, and round them lie
Long miles of moorland hill.

Beyond the cliff-top glimmers in the sun
The far horizon's bright infinity;
And I can gaze across the sea
When my day's work is done.

The solitudes of land and sea assuage
My quenchless thirst for freedom unconfined;
With independent heart and mind
Hold I my heritage.

References for Chapter 14
(full citations are given in the Bibliography on p. 353)

Baker, 1971; Berry, 1972*b*, 1974; Bourne & Johnston, 1971; Button, 1976; Central Unit on Environmental Pollution, 1976; Davis & Anderson, 1976; Dunnet, 1974; Eggeling, 1964; Furness, 1978; Goodier, 1974; Huxley, 1974; Johnston, 1974, 1976; Kinnear, 1976; Lloyd, 1975; Rendall, 1946; Royal Commission on Environmental Pollution, 1974; Shetland Islands Council, 1977; Swan & Senior, 1972; Warren & Harrison, 1974.

APPENDICES

LISTS OF SPECIES

The following pages list all the known species (and in some cases, infra-specific categories) recorded in Shetland from a number of groups. The plant tables are almost comprehensive, but the Shetland invertebrates are poorly known and only four tables are included (Siphonaptera, Lepidoptera, Arachnida, freshwater and terrestrial Mollusca). It has not seemed worthwhile listing the terrestrial' vertebrates because there are so few species represented (Chapter 8). On the other hand, birds are the best known Shetland animals, and details of population sizes, changes and vagrant records are included. The use of vernacular names and taxonomic authorities follow the conventions usual for the groups concerned.

Most of the tables have been compiled by specialists in the different groups. These are acknowledged in the heads of each table.

FUNGI (based on Dennis, 1972)

Mycologists have neglected the largely treeless Northern and Western Isles in favour of woodlands. This may be short-sighted on their part; Møller (1945, 1958) has listed 547 species from Faroe. The following list represents collections almost entirely made by Dennis (1972; Dennis & Gray, 1954), together with records by Traill (1889–90) and some unpublished collections in the Kew herbarium.

TABLE 18. Fungi.

PERONOSPORALES

Albugo tragopogonis S. F. Gray (*Cytopus cubicus* Lev.), on *Cirsium palustre*.
Peronospora alsinearum Casp. (*P. media* Gaum.), on *Stellaria media*.
Peronospora honckenyae Syd., on *Minuartia peploides*.
Peronospora minor (Casp.) Gaum., on *Atriplex* seedlings.
Peronospora radii de By., on flowers of *Tripleurospermum maritimum* var. *inodorum*.
Peronospora ranunculi Gaum., on *Ranunculus flammula*.
Peronospora rumicis Cda., on *Rumex acetosa*.
Plasmopara densa (Rab.) Schroet., on *Rhinanthus minor* and *Euphrasia sp.*

MUCORALES
Pilobolus crystallinus Tode, on sheep and rabbit droppings.
Pilobolus kleinii van Tiegh., on horse dung.

AGARICALES
Coprinus hephthemerus Lange & Smith, on sheep dung.
Coprinus miser (Karst.) Karst., on rabbit droppings.
Coprinus plicatilis (Curt. ex Fr.) Fr.
Coprinus stercorarius Fr. sensu Kuhner & Romagnesi, sheep and rabbit dung.
Stropharia coprophila (Bull. ex Fr.) Lange sensu Møller.

USTILAGINALES
Cintractia caricis (Pers.) Magn., on *Carex* sp.
Ustilago violacea (Pers.) Roussel, on *Lychnis flos-cuculi* and *Silene maritima*.

UREDINALES
Melampsorella caryophyllacearum Schroet., on *Cerastrium holosteoides*.
Puccinia acetosae Kornicke, II on *Rumex acetosa*.
Puccinia calthae Link, II and III on *Caltha palustris*.
Puccinia calthicola Schroet., II and III on *Caltha palustris*.
Puccinia caricina DC., I on *Urtica dioica* and *Carex binervis*.
Puccinia cnici Mart., on *Cirsium vulgare*.
Puccinia galii-verni Ces., on *Galium saxatile*.
Puccinia obscura Schroet., I on *Luzula compestris*.
Puccinia poae-nemoralis on *Anthoxanthum odoratum*.
Puccinia punctiformis (Str.) Rohl., on *Cirsium arvense*.
Puccinia recondita Rob. & Desm., II on *Holcus* sp.
Puccinia virgae-aureae (DC.) Lib., on *Solidago virgaurea*.
Uredo festucae DC., on *Festuca ovina*.
Uromyces nerviphilus (Grogn.) Hots., III on *Trifolium repens*.
Uromyces poae Rabh., II & III on *Poa trivialis*.

PROTOMYCETALES
Taphridium umbelliferarum (Rostr.) Lag. & Juel, on *Heracleum sphondylium*.

PEZIZALES
Ascobolus albidus Crouan, on rabbit droppings.
Ascobolus furfuraceus Pers. ex Hooker, on sheep dung.
Ascophanus aurora (Crouan) Boudier, on rabbit droppings.
Cheilymenia raripila (Phill.) Dennis, on rabbit droppings.
Iodophanus carneus (Pers.) Korf, on rabbit droppings.
Lasiobolus ciliatus (Schmidt ex Fr.) Boudier, on horse dung.
Rhyparobius sexdecimsporus (Crouan) Sacc., on sheep dung.
Saccobolus obscurus (Cke.) Phill., on sheep dung.
Saccobolus versicolor (Karst.) Karst., on rabbit droppings.

HELOTIALES
Dasyscyphus controversus (Cke.) Rehm, on *Phalaris arundinacea*.
Hysteropezizella prahliana (Jaap) Nannf., on *Ammophila arenaria*.
Phaeangellina empetri (Phill.) Dennis, on *Empetrum* sp.
Phialea cyathoidea (Bull. ex Merat) Gillet, on ?*Heracleum*.
Pseudopeziza cerastiorum (Wallr.) Fuckel, on *Cerastium holosteoides*.

PHACIDIALES
Lophodermium arundinaceum (Schrad. ex Fr.) Chev., on *Ammophila arenaria*.
Lophodermium juniperinum (Fr.) de Not., on *Juniperus communis*.

SPHAERIALES
Endodothella junci (Fr.) Theiss. & Syd. on *Juncus* sp.
Physalospora empetri Rostr. on *Empetrum* sp.
Podospora curvula (de By.) Niessl, on sheep dung.
Podospora minuta (Fuckel) Niessl, on sheep dung.
Sordaria fimicola (Rob.) Ces. & de Not., on horse dung.
Sordaria minima Sacc. & Sped., on rabbit droppings.

PLECTASCALES
Erysiphe graminis DC. ex Merat, on *Agropyron repens*.

PLEOSPORALES
Keissleriella culmifida (Karst.) Bose, on *Phalaris arundinacea*.
Sporormia intermedia Auersw., on rabbit droppings.
Trichodelitschia bisporula (Crouan) Munk, on rabbit droppings.

SPHAEROPSIDALES
Dilophospora alopecuri (Fr.) Fr. on *Holcus lanatus*.
Myxosporina subtecta (Rob.) von Hohnel (Rhodesia subtecta (Rob.) Grove), on
    Ammophila arenaria.
Septoria acetosae Oud., on *Rumex acetosa*.
Septoria cerastii Rob. & Desm., on *Cerastium holosteoides*.
Septoria oxyspora Penz. & Sacc., on *Phalaris arundinacea*.
Stagonospora compta (Sacc.) Died., on *Trifolium repens*.

MONILIALES
Cercospora radiata Fuckel, on *Anthyllis vulneraria*.
Endoconospora cerastii Gjaerum on *Cerastium holosteoides*.
Fusarium avenaceum (Fr.) Sacc. on *Holcus* sp.
Geotrichum candidum Link, on horse dung.
Ovularia obliqua (Cke.) Oud., on *Rumex* sp.
Ramularia pratensis Sacc., on *Rumex acetosa*.

MARINE ALGAE (David E. G. Irvine)

The winding voes and innumerable rocks and skerries of Shetland carry a
rich vegetation of seaweeds, with over 300 different species (Burrows, 1963;
Dixon, 1963; Irvine, 1962, 1974). On rocky shores there are forests of great
Oarweeds extending to 100ft or more below low water level, while sheltered
voes may carry great stands of the treacherous Sea Laces (*Chorda filum*), the
long slimy 30ft fronds of which may all too easily entrap the unwary swimmer.
Between the tides a dense covering of Wracks occupies the more sheltered
shores, and the houbs are often partly filled with the bright green fronds of
Codium fragile var. *atlanticum*, which in spite of its name is an immigrant from
Pacific waters. As might be expected, the flora includes characteristically

northern species such as *Callophyllis cristatus* and *Fucus distichus*. Of the latter, subspecies *distichus* is not known elsewhere in the British Isles (Powell, 1957, 1963); neither is *Sphacelaria arctica* nor the curious hollow-stemmed form of *Laminaria saccharina* which Børgesen (1903) named *L. faeroensis*. On the other hand, several southern species appear to come no further north than the Orkneys, for instance *Bostrychia scorpioides* and *Nemalion helminthoides*.

The appended list is compiled from the work of many botanists, from the list of 90 species produced by Thomas Edmonston in 1845 up to the present day. Species here are named in accordance with the *Check-list of British Marine Algae*.

TABLE 19. Marine algae

CYANOPHYTA: CYANOPHYCEAE
Anabaena variabilis Kütz. ex Born. et Flah.
Anacystis dimidiata (Kütz.) Dr. et D.
A. marina (Hansg.) Dr. et D.
Calothrix crustacea Thur. ex Born. et Flah.
Coccochloris stagnina Spreng.
Entophysalis conferta (Kütz.) Dr. et D.
E. deusta (Menegh.) Dr. et D.
Microcoleus lyngbyaceus (Kütz.) Crouan frat. ex Gom.
O. submembranacea Ardiss. et Straff. ex Gom.
Porphyrosiphon notarisii (Menegh.) Kütz. ex Gom.
Schizothrix arenaria (Berk.) Gom.
S. calcicola (C. Ag.) Gom. ex Gom.
S. rubella Gom.
Spirulina subsalsa Oerst. ex Gom.

RHODOPHYTA: FLORIDEOPHYCEAE
Acrosorium reptans (Crouan frat.) Kylin
Ahnfeltia plicata (Huds.) Fries
Antithamnion floccosum (O. F. Müll.) Kleen
A. plumula (Ellis) Thur. in Le Jol. var. *plumula*
Apoglossum ruscifolium (Turn.) J. Ag.
Audouinella alariae (Jónss.) Woelkerling
A. daviesii (Dillw.) Woelkerling
A. floridula (Dillw.) Woelkerling
A. parvula (Kylin) Dixon
A. purpurea (Lightf.) Woelkerling

A. secundata (Lyngb.) Dixon
A. sparsa (Harv.) Dixon
A. spetsbergensis (Kjellm.) Woelkerling
A. virgatula (Harv.) Dixon
Brongniartella byssoides (Good. et Woodw.) Schmitz
Callithamnion arbuscula (Dillw.) Lyngb.
C. corymbosum (Sm.) Lyngb.
C. decompositum J. Ag.
C. granulatum (Ducluz.) C. Ag.
C. hookeri (Dillw.) S. F. Gray
C. roseum (Roth) Lyngb.
C. tetragonum (With.) S. F. Gray var. *tetragonum*
var. *brachiatum* (Bonnem.) Rosenv.
[*C. tetricum* (Dillw.) S. F. Gray – probably in error for *C. tetragonum*]
Callocolax neglectus Schmitz ex Batt.
Callophyllis cristata (C. Ag.) Kütz.
C. laciniata (Huds.) Kütz.
Catenella caespitosa (With.) L. Irvine in Parke et Dixon
[*Ceramium ciliatum* (Ellis) Ducluz. – probably in error for *C. shuttleworthianum*]
C. circinatum (Kütz.) J. Ag.
C. deslongchampsii Chauv. in Duby
C. diaphanum (Lightf.) Roth
C. fastigiatum Harv.
C. pedicellatum DC
C. rubrum (Huds.) C. Ag.
C. shuttleworthianum (Kütz.) Rabenh.
C. strictum Harv.

Ceratocolax hartzii Rosenv.
Chondrus crispus Stackh.
Choreocolax polysiphoniae Reinsch
Chylocladia verticillata (Lightf.) Bliding
Corallina officinalis L.
Cruoria pellita (Lyngb.) Fries
Cryptopleura ramosa (Huds.) Kylin ex
    Newton
Cystoclonium purpureum (Huds.) Batt.
Delesseria sanguinea (Huds.) Lamour.
Dermatolithon corallinae (Crouan frat.)
    Fosl.
D. pustulatum (Lamour.) Fosl.
Dilsea carnosa (Schmidel) O. Kuntze
Dumontia incrassata (O. F. Müll.)
    Lamour.
Falkenbergia rufolanosa – tetrasporangial
    phase of *Asparagopsis armata* Harv.
Fosliella minutula (Fosl.) Ganesan
F. tenuis Adey et Adey
F. valida Adey et Adey
Furcellaria lumbricalis (Huds.) Lamour.
Gelidium pusillum (Stackh.) Le Jol.
[*G. versicolor* (*G. cartilagineum*) –an
    exotic species found only in drift.]
Gigartina stellata (Stackh. in With.)
    Batt.
Gloiosiphonia capillaris (Huds.) Carm.
    ex Berk.
Gracilaria verrucosa (Huds.) Papenf.
Griffithsia corallinoides (L.) Batt.
G. flosculosa (Ellis) Batt.
Haematocelis rubens J. Ag.
Halarachnion ligulatum (Woodw.) Kütz.
Halosacciocolax lundii Edelstein
Helminthora divaricata (C. Ag.) J. Ag.
Heterosiphonia plumosa (Ellis) Batt.
Hildenbrandia crouanii J. Ag.
H. rubra (Sommerf.) Menegh.
Hypoglossum woodwardii Kütz.
Kallymenia reniformis (Turn.) J. Ag.
Laurencia hybrida (DC) Lenorm. ex
    Duby
L. pinnatifida (Huds.) Lamour.
Leptophytum laeve (Strömf.) Adey
Lithophyllum incrustans Phil.
L. orbiculatum (Fosl.) Fosl.
Lithothamnion glaciale Kjellm.
Lomentaria articulata (Huds.) Lyngb.

L. clavellosa (Turn.) Gaill.
L. orcadensis (Harv.) Coll. ex Taylor
Membranoptera alata (Huds.) Stackh.
Myriogramme bonnemaisonii (C. Ag.)
    Kylin
Nitophyllum punctatum (Stackh.) Grev.
Odonthalia dentata (L.) Lyngb.
Palmaria palmata (L.) O. Kuntze
Petrocelis cruenta J. Ag.
Peyssonelia dubyi Crouan frat.
Phycodrys rubens (L.) Batt.
Phyllophora crispa (Huds.) Dixon
P. pseudoceranoides (S. G. Gmel.) Newr.et
    A. R. A. Taylor
P. truncata (Pall.) Zinova
Phymatolithon calcareum (Pall.) Adey et
    McKibbin
P. laevigatum (Fosl.) Fosl.
P. lenormandii (Aresch. in J. Ag.) Adey
P. polymorphum (L.) Fosl.
P. rugulosum Adey
Plocamium cartilagineum (L.) Dixon
Plumaria elegans (Bonnem.) Schmitz
Polyides rotundus (Huds.) Grev.
Polyneura gmelinii (Lamour.) Kylin
P. hilliae (Grev.) Kylin
Polysiphonia brodiaei (Dillw.) Spreng.
P. elongata (Huds.) Spreng.
P. elongella Harv. in Hook.
P. fibrata (Dillw.) Harv. in Hook.
P. fibrillosa (Dillw.) Spreng.
P. fruticulosa (Wulf.) Spreng.
P. lanosa (L.) Tandy
P. macrocarpa Harv. in Mackay
P. nigra (Huds.) Batt.
P. nigrescens (Huds.) Grev.
P. urceolata (Lightf. ex Dillw.) Grev.
P. violacea (Roth) Spreng.
Pterosiphonia parasitica (Huds.) Falkenb.
Ptilota plumosa (Huds.) C. Ag.
Ptilothamnion pluma (Dillw.) Thur. in
    Le Jol.
Rhodomela confervoides (Huds.) Silva
R. lycopodioides (L.) C. Ag.
Rhodophyllis divaricata (Stackh.)
    Papenf.
[*Schmitziella endophloea* – probably
    recorded in error]
Scinaia forcellata Biv.

Seirospora seirosperma (Harv.) Dixon
Spermothamnion repens (Dillw.) Rosenv.
Trailliella intricata – tetrasporangial
phase of *Bonnemaisonia hamifera* Hariot

RHODOPHYTA: BANGIOPHYCEAE
Bangia atropurpurea (Roth) C. Ag.
Colacodictyon reticulatum (Batt.) J. Feldm.
Conchocelis rosea – alternate phase of
Porphyra and *Bangia* spp.
Erythrocladia subintegra Rosenv.
Erythrotrichia carnea (Dillw.) J. Ag.
E. ciliaris (Carm. ex Harv. in Hook.)
Thur. in Le Jol.
Porphyra leucosticta Thur. in Le Jol.
P. linearis Grev.
P. miniata (C. Ag.) C. Ag.
P. purpurea (Roth) C. Ag.
P. umbilicalis (L.) J. Ag.
Porphyropsis coccinea (J. Ag. ex Aresch.)
Rosenv.

CHRYSOPHYTA: XANTHOPHYCEAE
Vaucheria subsimplex Crouan frat.
V. velutina C. Ag.

PHAEOPHYTA: PHAEOPHYCEAE
Acinetospora crinita (Carm. ex Harv.
in Hook.) Kornm.
Acrothrix gracilis Kylin
Aglaozonia parvula – diploid phase of
Cutleria multifida
Alaria esculenta (L.) Grev.
Ascophyllum nodosum (L.) Le Jol.
Asperococcus compressus Griff. ex Hook.
A. fistulosus (Huds.) Hook. f. *fistulosus*
f. *vermicularis* (Griff.) Harv.
A. turneri (Sm.) Hook.
Battersia mirabilis Reinke
Chilonema ocellatum (Kütz.) Sauv.
Chorda filum (L.) Stackh.
Chordaria flagelliformis (O. F. Müll.)
C. Ag.
Cladostephus spongiosus (Huds.) C. Ag.
f. *spongiosus*
f. *verticillatus* (Lightf.) P.v.R.
Colpomenia peregrina Sauv.
Cutleria multifida (Sm.) Grev.
Desmarestia aculeata (L.) Lamour.
D. ligulata (Lightf.) Lamour.

D. viridis (O. F. Müll.) Lamour.
Desmotrichum undulatum (J. Ag.) Reinke
Dictyosiphon chordaria Aresch.
D. foeniculaceus (Huds.) Grev.
Dictyota dichotoma (Huds.) Lamour.
Ectocarpus fasciculatus Harv.
E. siliculosus (Dillw.) Lyngb. var.
siliculosus
var. *confervoides* Cardinal
Elachista flaccida (Dillw.) Aresch.
E. fucicola (Vell.) Aresch.
E. scutulata (Sm.) Aresch.
Endodictyon infestans Gran.
Eudesme virescens (Carm. ex Harv. in
Hook.) J. Ag.
Fucus ceranoides L.
F. distichus L. subsp. *distichus*
subsp. *anceps* (Harv. et Ward ex
Carr.) Powell
subsp. *edentatus* (Pyl.) Powell
F. serratus L.
F. spiralis L. f. *spiralis*
f. *nanus* (Stackh.) Børg.
F. vesiculosus L. f. *vesiculosus*
f. *linearis* (Huds.) Powell
Giffordia granulosa (Sm.) Hamel
G. hincksiae (Harv.) Hamel
G. ovata (Kjellm.) Kylin
G. sandriana (Zanard.) Hamel
G. secunda (Kütz.) Batt.
Halidrys siliquosa (L.) Lyngb.
Hecatonema maculans (Coll.) Sauv.
Herponema velutinum (Grev.) J. Ag.
Himanthalia elongata (L.) S. F. Gray
Isthmoplea sphaerophora (Carm. ex
Harv. in Hook.) Kjellm.
Laminaria digitata (Huds.) Lamour.
[*L. faeroensis* Børg. – probably a
growth form of *L. saccharina*]
L. hyperborea (Gunn.) Fosl.
L. saccharina (L.) Lamour.
Laminariocolax tomentosoides (Farl.)
Kylin
Leathesia difformis (L.) Aresch.
Leptonematella fasciculata (Reinke) Silva
Litosiphon filiformis (Reinke) Batt.
L. laminariae (Lyngb.) Harv.
L. pusillus (Carm. ex Hook.) Harv.
Mesogloia lanosa Crouan frat.

M. vermiculata (Sm.) S. F. Gray
Mikrosyphar polysiphoniae Kuck.
M. porphyrae Kuck.
Myriactula areschougii (Crouan frat.)
Hamel.
M. clandestina (Crouan frat.) J. Feldm.
Myrionema aecidioides (Rosenv.) Sauv.
M. papillosum Sauv.
M. strangulans Grev.
Myriotrichia clavaeformis Harv.
M. filiformis Harv.
M. repens Hauck
Pelvetia canaliculata (L.) Decne et Thur.
  – including ecad *muscoides* of
  saltmarshes.
Petalonia fascia (O. F. Müll.) O. Kuntze
Petroderma maculiforme (Wollny) Kuck.
Phaeostroma pustulosum Kuck.
Pilayella littoralis (L.) Kjellm.
Protectocarpus speciosus (Børg.) Kuck.
Pseudolithoderma extensum (Crouan
  frat.) S. Lund
Punctaria plantaginea (Roth) Grev.
P. tenuissima (C. Ag.) Grev.
Ralfsia clavata (Harv. in Hook.)
  Crouan frat.
R. verrucosa (Aresch.) J. Ag.
Saccorhiza polyschides (Lightf.) Batt.
Sauvageaugloia griffithsiana (Grev. ex
  Harv. in Hook.) Hamel ex Kylin
Scytosiphon lomentaria (Lyngb.) Link
Spermatochnus paradoxus (Roth) Kütz.
Sphacelaria arctica Harv.
S. bipinnata (Kütz.) Sauv.
S. britannica Sauv.
S. cirrosa (Roth) C. Ag.
S. furcigera Kütz.
S. plumigera Holm.
S. plumosa Lyngb.
S. radicans (Dillw.) C. Ag.
Sphaerotrichia divaricata (C. Ag.) Kylin
Spongonema tomentosum (Huds.) Kütz.
Stictyosiphon griffithsianus (Le Jol.)
  Holm. et Batt.
S. soriferus (Reinke) Rosenv.
S. tortilis (Rupr.) Reinke
Streblonema breve (Sauv.) De Toni
S. fasciculatum Thur. in Le Jol.
S. parasiticum (Sauv.) Levr.

S. sphaericum (Derb. et Sol. in
  Castagne) Thur. in Le Jol.
Ulonema rhizophorum Fosl.

CHLOROPHYTA: CHLOROPHYCEAE
Prasinocladus marinus (Cienk.) Waern

CHLOROPHYTA: CHLOROPHYCEAE
Blastophysa rhizopus Reinke
Blidingia minima (Näg. ex Kütz.) Kylin
Bolbocoleon piliferum N. Pringsh.
Bryopsis hypnoides Lamour.
B. plumosa (Huds.) C. Ag.
Capsosiphon fulvescens (C. Ag.) Setch.
  et Gardn.
Chaetomorpha capillaris (Kütz.) Børg.
C. linum (O. F. Müll.) Kütz.
C. melagonium (Web. et Mohr) Kütz.
Chlorochytrium cohnii Wright
C. inclusum Kjellm. – non-specific
  phase in life-history of *Spongomorpha*
  spp.
C. willei Printz
Cladophora albida (Huds.) Kütz.
C. fracta (O. F. Müll. ex Vahl) Kütz.
C. hutchinsiae (Dillw.) Kütz.
C. pygmaea Reinke
C. rupestris (L.) Kütz.
C. sericea (Huds.) Kütz.
Codiolum petrocelidis – non-specific phase
  in life-history of *Spongomorpha* spp.
Codium fragile (Sur.) Hariot subsp.
  atlanticum (Cotton) Silva
Derbesia marina (Lyngb.) Solier
Endoderma perforans Huber
Enteromorpha clathrata (Roth) Grev.
E. compressa (L.) Grev.
E. intestinalis (L.) Link
E. linza (L.) J. Ag.
E. prolifera (O. F. Müll.) J. Ag.
E. ralfsii Harv.
E. ramulosa (Sm.) Hook.
E. torta (Mert. in Jürg.) Reinb.
Epicladia flustrae Reinke var. *flustrae*
  var. *phillipsii* Batt.
Eugomontia sacculata Kornm.
Halicystis ovalis – haploid phase of
  Derbesia marina
Monostroma fuscum (Post. et Rupr.)
  Wittr.

M. grevillei (Thur.) Wittr.
Ochlochaete ferox Huber
Ostreobium quekettii Born. et Flah.
Percursaria percursa (C. Ag.) Rosenv.
Phaeophila dendroides (Crouan frat.) Batt.
P. leptochaete (Huber) Nielsen
P. viridis (Reinke) Burrows
P. wittrockii (Wille) Nielsen
Prasiola crispa (Lightf.) Kütz. subsp.
   marina Børg.
P. stipitata Suhr in Jessen
Pringsheimiella scutata (Reinke)
   Marchew
Pseudopringsheimia fucicola (Rosenv.)
   Wille

Rhizoclonium riparium (Roth) Harv.
Spongomorpha aeruginosa (L.) Hoek
S. arcta (Dillw.) Kütz.
S. bombycina (Kjellm.) Wille
S. sonderi Kütz.
Ulothrix flacca (Dillw.) Thur. in Le Jol.
U. pseudoflacca Wille
U. speciosa (Carm. ex Harv. in Hook.)
   Kütz.
Ulva lactuca L.
U. rigida (C. Ag.) Thur.
Uvella lens Crouan frat.
Urospora pencilliformis (Roth) Aresch.

BRYOPHYTA (work of M. O. Hill and Jean A. Paton, cited by permission of the Nature Conservancy Council) (see also Paton, 1965, 1973).

As a general rule, bryophytes have larger geographical ranges than higher plants. The majority of Shetland bryophytes have circumpolar distributions and many are found also in the southern hemisphere. Wind-borne tree pollen arriving in Shetland is about 20% of that within a forest in a continental area, and there are 15 days in April to July when measurable amounts of tree pollen occur in Lerwick (Tyldesley, 1973). It is therefore not surprising that the sea is only a slight barrier to wind-distributing plants. For example the southern hemisphere moss *Campylopus introflexus* was first recorded in Britain in 1941, in Surrey; the first record for Shetland was in 1971 at a time when it was still being found frequently in new localities in the rest of Britain. It has been claimed that relict bryophyte species persist in Shetland, but there is no firm evidence for this. For example, *Dicranum montanum* has been found on peat in Foula despite the fact that it is a moss of rotting wood (Hawksworth, 1969b). It is more likely that this is a sporadic occurrence rather than a survival from a wooded Shetland.

A detailed analysis of the species and habitats of bryophytes in Shetland lead to the conclusion that the bryophyte flora differs only marginally from what would be present if Shetland was connected to mainland Britain (Ratcliffe, 1968). Habitats which are well represented in Shetland (such as peat moorland and loch banks) have an effectively complete bryophyte flora; absent bryophytes are those of steep rocky slopes, ravines, and epiphytic habitats.

TABLE 20. Liverworts

Conocephalum conicum	C. arguta	C. starkei
Lunularia cruciata	Lophozia ventricosa	C. bicuspidata
Preissia quadrata	L. alpestris	C. pleniceps
Marchantia polymorpha	L. incisa	C. loitlesbergeri
Riccardia incurvata	Leiocolea muelleri	C. connivens
R. multifida	L. gillmanii	C. media
R. sinuata	Barbilophozia floerkii	C. catenulata
R. latifrons	Tritomaria quinqudentata	C. leucantha
R. palmata	T. exsectiformis	Cladopodiella fluitans
R. pinguis	Sphenolobus minutus	Nowellia curvifolia
Pellia epiphylla	Anastrepta orcadensis	Odontoschisma sphagni
P. neesiana	Gymnocolea inflata	O. denudatum
P. endiviifolia	Solenostoma triste	O. elongatum
Metzgeria furcata	S. pumilum	Douinia ovata
Moerckia flotoviana	S. cordifolium	Diplophyllum albicans
Blasia pusilla	Solenostoma sphaerocarpum	D. obtusifolium
Fossombronia foveolata	S. crenulatum	Scapania scandica
F. incurva	Plectocolea obovata	S. irrigua
F. wondraczekii	P. subelliptica	S. umbrosa
Haplomitrium hookeri	P. paroica	S. gracilis
Anthelia julacea	Nardia compressa	S. nemorea
A. juratzkana	N. scalaris	S. degenii
Herberta straminea	N. geoscyphus	S. undulata
Hygrobiella laxifolia	Marsupella emarginata	S. uliginosa
Mastigophora woodsii	M. aquatica var. pearsonii	S. subalpina
Ptilidium ciliare	Gymnomitrion crenulatum	S. compacta
Blepharostoma trichophyllum	Mylia taylori	S. ornithopodioides
Bazzania trilobata	M. anomala	Radula complanata
B. tricrenata	Plagiochila carringtonii	R. aquilegia
Lepidozia pinnata	P. asplenioides	Pleurozia purpurea
L. reptans	P. spinulosa	Porella laevigata
L. pearsonii	Lophocolea bidentata	P. thuja
L. setacea	L. cuspidata	P. platyphylla
L. trichoclados	Chiloscyphus polyanthos	P. cordaeana
L. sylvatica	C. pallescens	Lejeunea cavifolia
Calypogeia neesiana	Harpanthus flotovianus	L. patens
C. muellerana	H. scutatus	Frullania tamarisci
C. trichomanis	Saccogyna viticulosa	F. germana
C. fissa	Cephaloziella subdentata	F. fragilifolia
C. sphagnicola	C. hampeana	F. dilatata

TABLE 21. Mosses

Sphagnum palustre
S. magellanicum
S. papillosum
S. imbricatum
S. compactum
S. teres
S. squarrosum
S. lindbergii
S. riparium
S. recurvum
S. tenellum
S. cuspidatum
S. contortum
S. subsecundum var.
   inundatum
S. subsecundum var.
   auriculatum
S. fimbriatum
S. girgensohnii
S. robustum
S. nemoreum
S. plumulosum
Andreaea alpina
A. rupestris
A. rothii
Atrichum undulatum
Oligotrichum hercynicum
Polytrichum nanum
P. aloides
P. urnigerum
P. alpinum
P. piliferum
P. juniperinum
P. alpestre
P. formosum
P. commune
Diphyscium foliosum
Fissidens viridulus
F. bryoides
F. curnowii
F. osmundoides
F. taxifolius
F. cristatus
F. adianthoides
Archidium alternifolium
Pleuridium acuminatum

Ditrichum cylindricum
Ditrichum cylindricum
D. heteromallum
D. flexicaule
Distichium capillaceum
D. inclinatum
Ceratodon purpureus
Blindia acuta
Pseudephemerum nitidum
Dicranella palustris
D. schreberana
D. varia
D. staphylina
D. rufescens
D. subulata
D. cerviculata
D. heteromalla
Rhabdoweisia fugax
R. denticulata
Dichodontium pellucidum
Dicranoweisia cirrata
Dicranum montanum
D. elongatum
D. fuscescens
D. majus
D. bonjeanii
D. scoparium
Dicranodontium denudatum
Campylopus schimperi
C. fragilis
C. pyriformis
C. flexuosus
C. atrovirens
C. introflexus
C. brevipilus
Leucobryum glaucum
Encalypta rhabdocarpa
Tortula ruraliformis
T. intermedia
T. subulata
T. muralis
Pottia heimii
P. truncata
P. crinita
Cinclidotus fontinaloides
Barbula convoluta

B. unguiculata
B. hornschuchiana
B. fallax
B. spadicea
B. rigidula
B. tophacea
B. cylindrica
B. recurvirostra
Gymnostomum aeruginosum
G. recurvirostrum
G. calcareum
Eucladium verticillatum
Tortella tortuosa
T. flavovirens
Trichostomum sinuosum
T. crispulum
T. brachydontium
Weissia controversa
W. perssonii
W. microstoma
Grimmia maritima
G. apocarpa
G. alpicola
G. doniana
G. pulvinata
G. trichophylla
G. patens
Rhacomitrium ellipticum
R. aciculare
R. aquaticum
R. fasciculare
R. heterostichum
R. canescens
R. lanuginosum
Funaria hygrometrica
F. attenuata
F. obtusa
Physcomitrium pyriforme
Ephemerum serratum var.
   serratum
E. serratum var.
   minutissimum
Splachnum sphaericum
Pohlia cruda
P. nutans
P. gracilis

P. rothii
P. annotina
P. wahlenbergii
P. delicatula
Anomobryum filiforme
Bryum pendulum
B. inclinatum
B. pallens
B. pseudotriquetrum
B. argenteum
B. bicolor
B. micro-erythro-
carpum
B. rubens
B. bornholmense
B. ruderale
B. klinggraeffii
B. sauteri
B. alpinum
B. capillare
Mnium hornum
M. stellare
M. cuspidatum
M. longirostrum
M. rugicum
M. seligeri
M. undulatum
M. punctatum
M. pseudopunctatum
M. cinclidioides
Aulacomnium palustre
Amblyodon dealbatus
Catoscopium nigritum
Bartramia ithyphylla
Conostomum tetragonum
Philonotis fontana
P. tomentella
P. calcarea
Breutelia chrysocoma
Ptychomitrium polyphyllum
Amphidium mougeotii
Zygodon viridissimus

Orthotrichum rupestre
O. anomalum
O. cupulatum
O. pulchellum
O diaphanum
Ulota phyllantha
U. vittata
U. crispa
U. hutchinsiae
Fontinalis antipyretica
Climacium dendroides
Hedwigia ciliata
Antitrichia curtipendula
Neckera companata
Omalia trichomanoides
Thamnium alopecurum
Hookeria lucens
Heterocladium heteropterum
Thuidium tamariscinum
T. delicatulum
Cratoneuron filicinum
C. commutatum var.
commutatum
C. commutatum var.
falcatum
Campylium stellatum
C. chrysophyllum
C. polygamum
C. elodes
Leptodictyum riparium
Amblystegium serpens
Drepanocladus aduncus
D. fluitans
D. exannulatus
D. revolvens
D. uncinatus
Hygrophypnum ochraceum
H. luridum
H. eugyrium
H. dilatatum
Scorpidium scorpioides
Acrocladium stramineum

A. cordifolium
A. giganteum
A. sarmentosum
A. cuspidatum
Isothecium myurum
I. myosuroides
Camptothecium sericeum
C. lutescens
Brachythecium albicans
B. rutabulum
B. rivulare
B. velutinum
B. populeum
B. plumosum
Cirriphyllum crassinervium
Eurhynchium striatum
E. praelongum
E. swartzii
E. riparioides
E. murale
E. confertum
Pterigynandrum filiforme
Orthothecium intricatum
Pseudoscleropodium purum
Pleurozium schreberi
Isopterygium elegans
Plagiothecium
denticulatum
P. succulentum
P. sylvaticum
P. undulatum
Hypnum cupressiforme
var. cupressiforme
H. cupressiforme var.
resupinatum
H. ericetorum
Ctenidium molluscum
Hyocomium flagellare
Rhytidiadelphus triquetrus
R. squarrosus
R. loreus
Hylocomium splendens

LICHENS (D. L. Hawksworth)

Lichens (intimate associations between a fungus and an alga which act as a single reproducible organism: Hale, 1974) are a conspicuous feature of the Shetland landscape. Several species were formerly collected for dyeing in Shetland (*e.g. Ochrolechia* species, *Parmelia omphalodes, P. saxatilis, Ramalina siliquosa*) and received common names but today they are largely passed over by the islands' inhabitants – with the exception of sheep which find several species to their taste (*e.g. Cladonia uncialis, Ramalina siliquosa*). Lichens are particularly sensitive monitors of environmental conditions and for this reason have been used extensively in surveys designed to ascertain the effects or estimate the levels of particular pollutants (Hawksworth & Rose, 1976). In Shetland species on coastal rocks can, with other organisms, be used as monitors of damage arising from any possible oil spillages, while those on inland rocks and fence-posts may serve as monitors of pollutants in the air. Active monitoring of the environmental impact of the development of Sullom Voe using permanent lichen quadrats is now in progress.

Of the habitats colonized by lichens in Shetland the coastal rocks and cliffs comprise the largest single unit. These are usually completely covered by lichens from the intertidal zone (dominated by the black tar-like *Verrucaria maura* and *V. mucosa* with black coralloid tufts of *Lichina confinis* often also present), through a zone in which orange lichens predominate (particularly *Caloplaca marina, C. thallincola* and *Xanthoria parietina*), and grading into the upper parts of the shore where greyish lichens intermixed with greenish-grey scrawny tufts of *Ramalina cuspidata* and *R. siliquosa* are seen. As the whole of the islands are under the influence of salt-laden winds and sea spray, the maritime greyish lichen assemblage is to be found everywhere in Shetland, commonly on the walls of crofts and planticribs. Amongst the commonest crustose lichens on sandstones and other non-basic rocks in Shetland are *Caloplaca ferruginea, Candelariella vitellina, Fuscidea cyathoides, F. tenebrica, Huilia albocaerulescens, Lecanora atra, L. gangaleoides, L. polytropa, Lecidea sulphurea, Lecidella subincongrua, Ochrolechia parella, O. tartarea* and *Pertusaria pseudocorallina*. The normally rather local northern species *Lecidea diducens* is especially widespread in Shetland on quartzites and other non-calcareous rocks. Bright emerald green patches of *Rhizocarpon geographicum* are a conspicuous feature of smoother-textured hard siliceous rocks, and several leafy (foliose) lichens are also widespread on non-basic rocks not too close to the sea (*e.g. Hypogymnia physodes, Parmelia glabratula* subsp. *fuliginosa, P. omphalodes, P. saxatilis* and *P. sulcata*).

Limestone is rather scarce in Shetland but when it does occur (see Fig. 5) it supports a distinctive assemblage of lichens many of which are restricted to it, including *Agonimia tristicula, Aspicilia calcarea, A. contorta, Bacidia sabuletorum, Dermatocarpon miniatum, Lecidella stigmatea, Protoblastenia rupestris, Thelidium decipiens* and *Verrucaria sphinctrina*. Mortar, concrete and asbestos-cement also provide habitats for lichens requiring base-rich rocks; *Caloplaca citrina, Candelariella aurella, Lecanora dispersa, Lecidella stigmatea, Verrucaria hochstetteri* and *V. muralis* are especially common in these situations. The serpentine rocks on Unst are rather disappointing lichenologically and lack several species known only from this rock type elsewhere in Europe; *Polyblastia cupularis* is, however, abundant on the southern serpentine outcrops associated with soapstones. Wall tops, boulders and cliffs used as bird-perches are rich in nutrients and also have particular lichen communities which include, for example, *Aspicilia leproscescens, Caloplaca verruculifera, Lecanora muralis, Physcia adscendens, P. dubia, Phaeophyscia orbicularis, Xanthoria candelaria* and *X. parietina.*

The massive granite boulders on the lower slopes of Collafirth and Ronas Hills support a lichen community including several conspicuous species unknown elsewhere in Shetland: *Cornicularia normoerica, Pseudephebe pubescens, Umbilicaria cylindrica, U. polyphylla* and *U. torrefacta.* The summit *Rhacomitrium*-heath is an important site for montane lichens in Shetland amongst which *Alectoria nigricans, Pertusaria xanthostoma* and *Thamnolia vermicularis* merit particular mention; these three species are absent from the second highest hill in Shetland, The Sneug (Foula), which does, however, have the montanesuboceanic *Bryoria bicolor.*

Cetraria islandica, Cornicularia aculeata, Cladonia and *Peltigera* species are widespread in heathlands and grasslands throughout the islands but *Cladonia* species become exceptionally well-developed on areas scalped of peat fifty or more years ago; it is in such a scalped area that *C. rangiferina* occurs on Foula. The lips of old peat hags and cuttings are also usually rich in *Cladonia*s together with *Baeomyces rufus* and *Pycnothelia papillaria.*

The few trees to be encountered in Shetland are generally very poor in lichens, most of the species recorded being ubiquitous in the rest of Britain, perhaps partly due to the effects of salt spray and the isolation of clumps of trees from one another. Weathered wooden window frames and particularly fence-posts do, however, provide a habitat on which a luxuriant lichen vegetation develops. Fence posts are often crowned by soft yellowish-green tufts of *Usnea fragilescens* s.l., *U. hirta* and *U. subfloridana* intermixed with *Bryoria fuscescens, Cetraria chlorophylla, Hypogymnia physodes, H. tubulosa, Parmelia saxatilis, P. sulcata* and *Platismatia glauca. Evernia prunastri, Pseudevernia furfuracea* and *Ramalina farinacea* are amongst other macrolichens which can be found on this substrate. Of the crustose species to be found on wooden window frames and fence-posts on the islands the commonest are *Caloplaca holocarpa, Lecanora chlarona, L. expallens* and *Lecidella elaeochroma. Lecanora conizaeoides*, an extremely pollution tolerant species, is quite widespread on conifer fence-posts in Shetland showing that it can thrive in areas which are also virtually pollution free.

Although a considerable amount of lichenological survey work has been carried out in Shetland during the last 20 years (Duncan, 1961, 1963; Hawksworth, 1966; Hawksworth & Seaward, 1977), the lichen flora of the islands must still be regarded as inadequately known. No comprehensive survey of the lichens of Shetland has been published and the following check-list includes only those species which have been reliably recorded from Shetland since 1960; earlier reports and doubtful records in need of confirmation have been omitted, while numerous species not previously published as occurring in Shetland are included.

TABLE 22. Lichens

Acarospora fuscata (Nyl.) Arnold
A. sinopica (Wahlenb.) Körb.
A. smaragdula (Wahlenb. ex Ach.) Massal.
Acrocordia alba (Schrad.) B. de Lesd.
A. macrospora Massal.
A. salweyi (Leight. ex Nyl.) A.L.Sm.
Agonimia tristicula (Nyl.) Zahlbr.
Alectoria nigricans (Ach.) Nyl.
Anaptychia fusca (Huds.) Vain.
Arthonia phaeobaea (Norm.) Norm.
A. punctiformis Ach.
A. radiata (Pers.) Ach.
Arthopyrenia biformis (Borr.) Massal.
A. halodytes (Nyl.) Arnold
A. punctiformis (Pers.) Massal.
Aspicilia caesiocinerea (Nyl. ex Malbr.) Arnold
A. calcarea (L.) Sommerf.
A. contorta (Hoffm.) Kremp.
A. lacustris (With.) Th. Fr.
A. leproscescens (Sandst.) Hav.

Bacidia arceutina (Ach.) Arnold
B. egenula (Nyl.) Arnold
B. inundata (Fr.) Körb.
B. naegelii Hepp ex Müll. Arg.
B. sabuletorum (Schreb.) Lett.
B. umbrina (Ach.) Bausch.
Baeomyces roseus Pers.
B. rufus (Huds.) Rebent.'
Botrydina vulgaris Bréb.
Bryophagus gloeocapsa Nitschke ex Arnold
Bryoria bicolor (Ehrh.) Brodo & D. Hawksw.
B. chalybeiformis (L.) Brodo & D. Hawksw.
B. fuscescens (Gyeln.) Brodo & D. Hawksw.

B. subcana (Nyl. ex Stiz.) Brodo & D. Hawksw.
Buellia aethalea (Ach.) Th. Fr.
B. alboatra (Hoffm.) Deichm. Br. & Rostr.
B. disciformis (Fr.) Mudd
B. punctata (Hoffm.) Massal.
B. stellulata (Tayl.) Mudd
B. verruculosa (Sm.) Mudd

Caloplaca arnoldii (Wedd.) Zahlbr. ex Ginzb.
C. cerina (Ehrh. ex Hedw.) Th. Fr.
C. citrina (Hoffm.) Th. Fr.
C. ferruginea (Huds.) Th. Fr.
C. flavovirescens (Wulf.) Dalla Torre & Sarnth.
C. heppiana (Mül. Arg.) Zahlbr.
C. holocarpa (Hoffm.) Wade
C. marina (Wedd.) Zahlbr.
C. microthallina (Wedd.) Zahlbr.
C. saxicola (Hoffm.) Nordin
C. thallincola (Wedd.) DR.
C. verruculifera (Nyl.) Zahlbr.
Candelariella aurella (Hoffm.) Zahlbr.
C. vitellina (Hoffm.) Müll. Arg.
Catillaria biformigera (Leight.) P. James.
C. chalybeia (Borr.) Massal.
C. griffithii (Sm.) Malme
C. lenticularis (Ach.) Th. Fr.
Cetraria chlorophylla (Willd.) Vain.
C. islandica (L.) Ach.
Cladonia arbuscula (Wallr.) Rabenh.
C. bellidiflora (Ach.) Schaer.
C. cervicornis (Ach.) Flot.
C. chlorophaea (Flörke ex Sommerf.) Spreng.
C. ciliata Stirt.
C. coccifera (L.) Willd.

C. coniocraea (Flörke) Spreng.
C. cornuta (L.) Hoffm.
C. crispata var. *cetrariiformis* (Del.
   ex Duby) Vain.
C. fimbriata (L.) Fr.
C. floerkeana (Fr.) Sommerf.
C. foliacea (Huds.) Willd.
C. furcata (Huds.) Schrad.
C. gracilis (L.) Willd.
C. luteoalba Wheld. & Wils.
C. macilenta Hoffm.
C. ochrochlora Flörke
C. pityrea (Flörke) Fr.
C. pocillum (Ach.) O. J. Rich.
C. polydactyla (Flörke) Spreng.
C. portentosa (Duf.) Zahlbr.
C. pyxidata (L.) Hoffm.
C. rangiferina (L.) Web.
C. rangiformis Hoffm.
C. squamosa (Scop.) Hoffm.
C. strepsilis (Ach.) Vain.
C. subcervicornis (Vain.) Kernst.
C. subulata (L.) Web.
C. uncialis subsp. *biuncialis* (Hoffm.)
   Choisy
C. verticillata (Hoffm.) Schaer.
Clathroporina calcarea W. Wats.
Collema auriculatum Hoffm.
C. crispum (Huds.) Web.
C. cristatum (L.) Web.
C. flaccidum (Ach.) Ach.
C. multipartitum Sm.
C. polycarpon Hoffm.
C. tenax (Sw.) Ach.
   var. *ceranoides* (Borr.) Degel.
   (var. *tenax* also occurs)
C. tuniforme (Ach.) Ach.
Coriscium viride (Ach.) Vain.
Cornicularia aculeata (Schreb.) Ach.
C. muricata (Ach.) Ach.
C. normoerica (Gunn.) DR.
Cystocoleus niger (Huds.) Hariot

Dermatocarpon cinereum (Pers.) Th. Fr.
D. fluviatile (Web.) Th. Fr.
D. hepaticum (Ach.) Th. Fr.
D. cf. *meiophyllum* Vain.
D. miniatum (L.) Mann
Dimerella diluta (Pers.) Trevis.

Diploschistes scruposus (Schreb.) Norm.
   var. *bryophilus* (Ach.) Müll. Arg.
   var. *scruposus* also occurs
Ephebe lanata (L.) Vain.
Evernia prunastri (L.) Ach.
Fuscidea cyathoides (Ach.) V. Wirth &
   Vězda
F. lightfootii (Sm.) Coppins & P. James
F. tenebrica (Nyl.) V. Wirth & Vězda
Gyalecta jenensis (Batsch) Zahlbr.
Haematomma ochroleucum (Neck.) Laund.
H. ventosum (L.) Massal.
Huilia albocaerulescens (Wulf.) Hertel
H. crustulata (Ach.) Hertel
H. macrocarpa (DC.) Hertel
H. percontigua (Nyl.) Hertel
Hypogymnia physodes (L.) Nyl.
H. tubulosa (Schaer.) Hav.
Icmadophila ericetorum (L.) Zahlbr.
Lecania aipospila (Wahlenb. ex Ach.) Th.
   Fr.
L. cyrtella (Ach.) Th. Fr.
L. erysibe (Ach.) Mudd
L. rupicola (Nyl.) P. James
Lecanora actophila Wedd.
L. atra (Huds.) Ach.
L. badia (Hoffm.) Ach.
L. carpinea (L.) Vain.
L. campestris (Schaer.) Hue
L. chlarona (Ach.) Nyl.
L. chlarotera Nyl.
L. confusa Almb.
L. conizaeoides Nyl. ex Cromb.
L. crenulata (Dicks.) Hook.
L. dispersa (Pers.) Sommerf.
L. expallens Ach.
L. gangaleoides Nyl.
L. helicopis (Wahlenb. ex Ach.) Ach.
L. intricata (Ach.) Ach.
L. muralis (Schreb.) Rabenh.
L. poliophaea (Wahlenb. ex Ach.) Ach.
L. polytropa (Hoffm.) Rabenh.
L. rupicola (Hoffm.) Zahlbr.
L. straminea (Wahlenb. ex Ach.) Ach.
L. tenera (Nyl.) Cromb.
L. varia (Hoffm.) Ach.

Lecidea atrata (Ach.) Wahlenb.
L. diducens Nyl.
L. fuscoatra (L.) Ach.
L. goniophila Flörke
L. granulosa (Hoffm.) Ach.
L. grumosa Leight.
L. lapicida (Ach.) Ach.
L. leucophaea (Flörke ex Rabenh.) Nyl.
L. lactea Flörke ex Schaer.
L. lithophila (Ach.) Ach.
L. pantherina (Hoffm.) Th. Fr.
L. pelobotryon (Wahlenb. ex Ach.) Th. Fr.
L. phaeops Nyl.
L. plana (Lahin) Nyl.
L. speirea (Ach.) Ach.
L. sulphurea (Hoffm.) Wahlenb.
L. symmicta (Ach.) Ach.
L. tenebrosa Flot.
L. turgidula Fr.
L. uliginosa (Schrad.) Ach.
Lepraria incana (L.) Ach.
L. membranacea (Dicks.) Vain.
L. neglecta auct.
Lecidella elaeochroma (Ach.) Haszl.
    f. soralifera (Erichs.) D. Hawksw.
L. scabra (Tayl.) Hertel & Leuckert
L. stigmatea (Ach.) Hertel & Leuckert
L. subincongrua (Nyl.) Hertel & Leuckert.
Leptogium lichenoides (L.) Zahlbr.
L. plicatile (Ach.) Leight.
L. teretiusculum (Wallr.) Arnold
L. sinuatum (Huds.) Massal.
Lichina confinis (O. F. Müll.) C. Ag.
L. pygmaea (Lightf.) C. Ag.
Lithographa tesserata (DC.) Nyl.
Lobaria laetevirens (Lightf.) Zahlbr.

Micarea leprosula (Th. Fr.) Coppins & Fletcher
M. lignaria (Ach.) Hedl.
M. sylvicola (Flot.) V. Wirth & Vězda s.l.
M. violacea (Crouan ex Nyl.) Hedl.
Microglaena muscorum (Fr.) Th. Fr.

Nephroma laevigatum Ach.
Normandina pulchella (Borr.) Nyl.

Ochrolechia androgyna (Hoffm.) Arnold
O. frigida (Sw.) Lynge
O. parella (L.) Massal.
O. tartarea (L.) Massal.
Opegrapha atra Pers.
O. chevallieri Leight.
O. confluens (Ach.) Stiz.
O. gyrocarpa Flot.
O. herbarum Mont.
O. saxatilis DC.
O. saxicola Ach.
O. varia Pers.
O. vulgata (Ach.) Ach.
O. zonata Körb.

Pannaria pezizoides (Web.) Trevis.
Parmelia conspersa (Ach.) Ach.
P. crinita Ach.
P. glabratula (Lamy) Nyl.
    subsp. fuliginosa (Fr. ex Duby) Laund.
P. omphalodes (L.) Ach.
P. perlata (Huds.) Ach.
P. pulla Ach.
P. saxatilis (L.) Ach.
P. subaurifera Nyl.
P. sulcata Tayl.
Peltigera canina (L.) Willd.
P. polydactyla (Neck.) Hoffm.
P. praetextata (Flörke ex Sommerf.) Zopf
P. rufescens (Weiss) Humb.
Pertusaria amara (Ach.) Nyl.
P. corallina (L.) Arnold
P. dealbata (Ach.) Cromb.
P. flavicans Lamy
P. lactea (L.) Arnold
P. pseudocorallina (Liljebl.) Arnold
P. xanthostoma (Sommerf.) Fr.
Phaeophyscia orbicularis (Neck.) Moberg
Phlyctis argena (Spreng.) Flot.
Physcia adscendens (Th. Fr.) Oliv.
P. aipolia (Ehrh. ex Humb.) Hampe
P. caesia (Hoffm.) Hampe
P. dubia (Hoffm.) Lett.
P. tenella (Scop.) DC. subsp. marina (E. Nyl.) D. Hawskw.
Placidiopsis custanii (Massal.) Körb.
Placynthium nigrum (Huds.) Gray
Platismatia glauca (L.) Culb. & C. Culb.

Polyblastia cupularis Massal.
P. cruenta (Körb.) P. James & Swinsc.
P. dermatodes Arnold
P. inumbrata (Nyl.) Arnold
P. succedens Rehm
P. theleodes (Sommerf.) Th. Fr.
Porina carpinea (Pers.) Zahlbr.
P. chlorotica (Ach.) Müll. Arg.
P. lectissima (Fr.) Zahlbr.
P. persicina (Körb.) Zahlbr.
Protoblastenia calva (Dicks.) Zahlbr.
P. immersa (Hoffm.) Steiner
P. monticola (Ach.) Steiner
P. rupestris (Scop.) Steiner
Pseudephebe pubescens (L.) Choisy
Pseudevernia furfuracea (L.) Zopf
var. *ceratea* (Ach.) D. Hawksw.
var. *furfuracea* also present
Psoroma hypnorum (Vahl) Gray
Pycnothelia papillaria (Ehrh.) Duf.

Ramalina cuspidata (Ach.) Nyl.
R. farinacea (L.) Ach.
R. fastigiata (Pers.) Ach.
R. fraxinea (L.) Ach.
R. siliquosa (Huds.) A. L. Sm.
R. subfarinacea (Nyl. ex Cromb.) Nyl.
Rhizocarpon constrictum Malme
R. geographicum (L.) DC.
R. hochstetteri (Körb.) Vain.
R. obscuratum (Ach.) Massal.
R. oederi (Web.) Körb.
R. petraeum (Wulf.) Massal.
R. polycarpon (Grogn.) Th. Fr.
R. umbilicatum (Ram.) Flag.
Rinodina atrocinerea (Dicks.) Körb.
R. exigua (Ach.) Gray
R. sophodes (Ach.) Massal.
R. subexigua (Nyl.) Oliv.

Sarcogyne privigena (Ach.) Anzi
S. regularis Körb.
S. simplex (Dav.) Nyl.
Schaereria lugubris Körb.
Sphaerophorus fragilis (L.) Pers.

S. globosus (Huds.) Vain.
Staurothele catalepta (Ach.) Blomb. & Forss.
S. fissa (Tayl.) Zwackh
Stereocaulon evolutum Graewe
S. vesuvianum Pers.

Thamnolia vermicularis (Sw.) Ach. ex Schaer.
Thelidium decipiens (Nyl.) Kremp.
T. incavatum Mudd
T. pyrenophorum (Ach.) Mudd
Toninia aromatica (Sm.) Massal.
T. coeruleonigricans (Lightf.) Th. Fr.
Trapelia coarctata (Sm.) Choisy s.l.

Umbilicaria cylindrica (L.) Del. ex Duby
U. polyphylla (L.) Baumg.
U. torrefacta (Lightf.) Schrad.
Usnea flammea Stirt.
U. fragilescens Hav. ex Lynge s.l.
U. hirta (L.) Web.
U. inflata Del.
U. subfloridana Stirt.

Verrucaria aethiobola Wahlenb. ex Ach.
V. aquatilis Mudd
V. coerulea DC.
V. degelii R. Sant.
V. fusconigrescens Nyl.
V. glaucina Ach.
V. hochstetteri Fr.
V. margacea Wahlenb.
V. maura Wahlenb. ex Ach.
V. microspora Nyl.
V. mucosa Wahlenb. ex Ach.
V. muralis Ach.
V. nigrescens Pers.
V. sphinctrina Ach.
V. striatula Wahlenb. ex Ach.
V. viridula (Schrad.) Ach.

Xanthoria candelaria (L.) Th. Fr.
X. parietina (L.) Beltm.
X. polycarpa (Hoffm.) Oliv.

FLOWERING PLANTS AND FERNS (W. Scott and R. C. Palmer)

This list is a revised version of the *Check-list of Flowering Plants and Ferns of the Shetland Islands* produced by the authors in 1969. It replaces the last full inventory of Shetland plants, which was in G. C. Druce's *Flora Zetlandica* (1922). This was a great advance on its predecessors, Thomas Edmonston's *A Flora of Shetland* (1845) and C. F. A. Saxby's so-called revision of it (1903), but suffered in that it was a derivative work, being largely a digest of the researches of these and other workers, notably the Surrey botanist W. H. Beeby whose fine Shetland herbarium, now at the South London Botanical Institute, is the largest outside Shetland. Moreover Druce, at the time of his visits, was too elderly for the arduous field-work (sometimes entailing swimming or rock-climbing) demanded by such an enterprise. None of the earlier floras showed much knowledge of Yell and Fetlar, the second and fourth largest islands respectively; these, and many smaller islands, have now been intensively searched, sometimes with surprising results.

It may seem that there can have been few changes in the Shetland flora comparable with those seen in some southern countries. This is true, but changes there have been: Juniper (*Juniperus communis*), once apparently a feature of the landscape, is now, it seems, a steadily diminishing species, while some plants rare or unknown in Druce's day, such as Earthnut (*Conopodium majus*) and Cat's Ear (*Hypochoeris radicata*), are now common in inhabited areas. Further, some interesting escapes from cultivation have established themselves recently, such as the spectacular Magellan Ragwort (*Senecio smithii*) and that feature of the sub-antarctic landscape, the tussock-forming Tussi-girse (*Poa flabellata*).

A dagger is placed against each species not considered to be a native or established colonist. Species believed endemic to Shetland are designated by an asterisk.

The sequence of families and genera normally follows A. R. Clapham, T. G. Tutin, and E. F. Warburg, *Flora of the British Isles*, 2nd ed. (1962). The Latin names used are normally taken from this work.

TABLE 23.　Flowering plants and ferns

Huperzia selago (L.) Bernh. ex Schrank & Mart. (*Lycopodium selago* L.) subsp. *selago*
　Fir Clubmoss. Frequent.
Lycopodium clavatum L. Stag's-horn Moss. Rare.
Diphasium alpinum (L.) Rothm. (*Lycopodium alpinum* L.). Alpine Clubmoss. Very
　local.
Selaginella selaginoides (L.) Link Lesser Clubmoss. Common.
Isoetes lacustris L. Quill-wort. Widely distributed.
I. echinospora Durieu. Quill-wort. Probably widespread, especially in west
　Mainland.

Equisetum fluviatile L. Water Horsetail. Common.

E. palustre L. Marsh Horsetail. Very common.

E. sylvaticum L. Wood Horsetail. Occasional.

E. arvense L. Common Horsetail. Common.

E. arvense × *fluviatile* = *E.* × *litorale* Kühlew. ex Rupr. Probably widespread.

Osmunda regalis L. Royal Fern. Now confined to holms in a few lochs in west Mainland.

Hymenophyllum wilsonii Hook. Wilson's Filmy Fern. Widespread and sometimes locally abundant.

Pteridium aquilinum (L.) Kuhn Bracken. Locally common, especially so in west Mainland.

Blechnum spicant (L.) Roth Hard-fern. Common.

Phyllitis scolopendrium (L.) Newm. Hart's-tongue Fern. Presumed lost.

Asplenium adiantum-nigrum L. Black Spleenwort. Occasional.

Asplenium cuneifolum Viv. Serpentine rocks only.

A. marinum L. Sea Spleenwort. Local.

A. trichomanes L. Maidenhair Spleenwort. Rare, chiefly on limestone.

A. viride Huds. Green Spleenwort. Very rare on serpentine rocks in Unst.

A. ruta-muraria L. Wall-rue. Very rare.

Athyrium filix-femina (L.) Roth Lady-fern. Common.

Cystopteris fragilis (L.) Bernh. Brittle Bladder-fern. Very local and found chiefly on limestone.

Dryopteris filix-mas (L.) Schott Male Fern. Local.

D. pseudomas (Woll.) Holub & Pouzar. Very rare.

D. dilatata (Hoffm.) A. Gray Broad Buckler-fern. Very common and very variable.

†*D. assimilis* S. Walker Kergord plantations

Thelypteris limbosperma (All.) H. P. Fuchs Mountain Fern. Uncommon and mainly in north Mainland.

T. phegopteris (L.) Slosson Beech Fern. Rare, almost confined to Northmavine.

Carpogymnia dryopteris (L.) Löve & Löve (*Thelypteris dryopteris* (L.) Slosson). Oak Fern. Rare, most frequently seen in Northmavine.

Polypodium vulgare L. subsp. *vulgare* Polypody. Common. The only subspecies so far known from Shetland.

Botrychium lunaria (L.) Sw. Moonwort. Occasional.

Ophioglossum azoricum C. Presl (*O. vulgatum* L. subsp. *ambiguum* (Coss. & Germ.) E. F. Warb.). Adder's Tongue. Local and almost confined to coastal turf especially on small islands.

†*Picea sitchensis* (Bong.) Carr. Sitka Spruce. Rarely seen outside enclosures.

Juniperus communis L. subsp. *nana* Syme Juniper. Frequent in Fair Isle, local in Northmavine and Muckle Roe, and very rare in Yell and Dunrossness. Possibly decreasing and certainly extinct at some stations.

Caltha palustris L. Marsh Marigold. Common.

†*Trollius europaeus* L. subsp. *europaeus* Globe Flower. Garden outcast or planted.

†*Anemone nemorosa* L. Wood Anemone. Kergord plantations.

†*Aconitum napellus* L., *sensu lato*. Monkshood. Lerwick garden outcast or relic, 1967.

Ranunculus acris L. Meadow Buttercup. Very common and variable.

R. repens L. Creeping Buttercup. Common weed.

R. bulbosus L. subsp. *bulbosus* Bulbous Buttercup. Known at present only from coastal pasture, St. Ninian's Isle.

R. flammula L. subsp. *flammula* Lesser Spearwort. Very common and variable; the doubtfully distinct subsp. *minimus* (A. Benn.) Padmore was recorded by its describer from Dunrossness.

R. hederaceus L. Ivy-leaved Water Crowfoot. Occasional in Fair Isle and Dunrossness, and northwards to Lerwick.

R. trichophyllus Chaix subsp. *trichophyllus* Thread-leaved Water Crowfoot. Very rare.

R. baudotii Godr. Southern Dunrossness.

R. baudotii × *trichophyllus* subsp. *trichophyllus* Common in Maa Loch, Vementry, 1960 (W. Scott); neither parent seems now to grow in the loch.

R. ficaria L. subsp. *ficaria* Lesser Celandine. Fairly frequent.

†*R. aconitifolius* L. (double-flowered form). Fair Maids of France. Outside a yard at Easter Quarff, planted, 1967.

†*Aquilegia vulgaris* L. Columbine. Garden escape or outcast.

Thalictrum alpinum L. Alpine Meadow Rue. Frequent at all levels.

Nymphaea alba L. White Water-lily. In a few lochs and pools in west Mainland; also planted.

Papaver rhoeas L. Field Poppy. Appears to have been a rare colonist in the last century.

P. dubium L. Long-headed Poppy. Local on sandy soils, mainly in southern Dunrossness and in Unst and north Yell.

†*P. somniferum* L. subsp. *somniferum* Opium Poppy. Usually a garden outcast, perhaps sometimes a casual.

†*P. orientale* L. Oriental Poppy. Rarely seen outside gardens.

†*Meconopsis cambrica* (L.) Vig. Welsh Poppy. Garden outcast or escape, rare.

Glaucium flavum Crantz Yellow Horned-poppy. Anciently recorded from Sullom Voe.

†*Fumaria muralis* Sond. ex Koch subsp. *boraei* (Jord.) Pugsl. Weed in vegetable patch, Cutts, Trondra, 1968.

F. officinalis L. subsp. *officinalis* Common Fumitory. Frequent on sandy soils.

†*Brassica oleracea* L., cult. Cabbage. Outcast or relic of cultivation.

†*B. napus* L. var. *napobrassica* (L.) Rchb. Swedish Turnip. Outcast or relic of cultivation.

†*B. rapa* L. subsp. *rapa* Turnip. Outcast or relic of cultivation.

†*Brassica nigra*. (L.) Koch Black Mustard. Once seen in Lerwick.

Sinapis arvensis L. Charlock. Locally common, especially on sand or limestone, but rare or absent on peatier soils.

†*S. alba* L. subsp. *alba* White Mustard. Rare casual.

†*Diplotaxis tenuifolia* (L.) DC. Perennial Wall Rocket. Very rare in gardens where it is perhaps an intentional introduction in origin though now regarded as a weed.

Raphanus raphanistrum L. subsp. *raphanistrum* Wild Radish. Very common, particularly in cornfields.

†*Rapistrum rugosum*. (L.) All. Bastard Cabbage. Two plants on waste ground, Scalloway, 1977 (R. C. Palmer).

Cakile maritima Scop. subsp. *maritima* Sea Rocket. Widespread but often only fugitive, permanent perhaps on large sandy beaches as in southernmost Mainland.

†*Lepidium sativum* L. Garden Cress. Rare casual.

†*Iberis umbellata* L. Candytuft. Scalloway Rubbish Dump, garden outcast, 1960.

†*Thlaspi arvense* L. Field Penny-cress. Rare casual.

Capsella bursa-pastoris (L.) Medic. Shepherd's Purse. A common weed of the populated and arable areas.

Cochlearia officinalis L. (incl. the apparently very similar *C. scotica* Druce). Scurvy-grass. Common around the coast, very rarely inland.

C. pyrenaica DC. On the Unst and Fetlar serpentine.

C. danica L. Danish Scurvy-grass. Local, typically in old stonework (brochs, etc) by the sea.

Subularia aquatica L. Awlwort. Lochs in west Mainland.

†*Lunaria annua* L. subsp. *annua* Honesty. Scalloway Rubbish Dump, garden outcast, 1961.

†*Lobularia maritima* (L.) Desv. Sweet Alison. Rare outcast, as on Scalloway Rubbish Dump, 1961.

Draba incana L. Hoary Whitlow Grass. Occasional, found mainly on limestone in Mainland and on serpentine in Unst and Fetlar.

†*Armoracia rusticana* Gaertn., Mey. & Scherb. Horse-radish. Waste ground on edge of playing-field, Lerwick, 1959.

Cardamine pratensis L. Lady's Smock. Very common.

†*C. flexuosa* With. Wood Bitter-cress. Weed in flower garden, Brough Lodge, Fetlar, 1928 (Col. H. H. Johnston), and more recently in similar situations elsewhere.

C. hirsuta L. Hairy Bitter-cress. Local.

†*Barbarea vulgaris* R. Br. Yellow Rocket. Rare casual.

†*B. verna* (Mill.) Aschers. Early-flowering Yellow Rocket. In a garden at Sandwick, Dunrossness, regarded as a weed.

Cardaminopsis petraea (L.) Hiit. Northern Rock-cress. Known only on serpentine in Unst and (very rarely) Fetlar.

†*Arabis hirsuta* (L.) Scop. Hairy Rock-cress. Recorded as a garden weed on Fetlar.

Nasturtium officinale R.Br. (*Rorippa nasturtium-aquaticum* (L.) Hayek). Watercress. Dunrossness, probably introduced long ago but now looking native.

†*N. microphyllum* × *officinale* = *N.* × *sterile* (Airy Shaw) Oefelein Hybrid Watercress. Cloka Burn, near Walls, very scarce, 1968.

†*Rorippa palustris* (L.) Besser subsp. *palustris* (*R. islandica* auct. eur. occident., non (Oeder ex Murray) Borbás). Marsh Yellow-cress. Once found near Voe, casual.

†*Malcolmia maritima* (L.) R.Br. Virginia Stock. Garden outcast.

†*Matthiola longipetala* (Vent.) DC. subsp. *bicornis* (Sibth. & Sm.) P. W. Ball. Night-scented Stock. Lerwick, casual, 1976 (R. C. Palmer).

†*Hesperis matronalis* L. subsp. *matronalis* Dame's Violet. Garden outcast.

†*Alliaria petiolata* (Bieb.) Cavara & Grande. Garlic Mustard. Garden weed, Lerwick, one plant, 1971 (Mrs W. Hutchison).

†*Sisymbrium officinale* (L.) Scop. Hedge Mustard. Lerwick only.

†*S. orientale* L. Eastern Rocket. Casual at Lerwick.

†*Arabidopsis thaliana* (L.) Heynh. Thale Cress. Rare casual.

†*Camelina sativa* (L.) Crantz. Gold of Pleasure. Lerwick Rubbish Dump, casual, 1967.

Viola riviniana Rchb. Common Violet. Widespread.

V. canina L. subsp. *canina* Heath Violet. At present known certainly only from the Unst serpentine.

V. palustris L. subsp. *palustris* Marsh Violet. Common.

†*V. cornuta* L. Garden Viola. Rare garden escape or outcast.

V. tricolor L. subsp. *tricolor* Wild Pansy. Occasional colonist (often perennating in coastal pasture).

V. arvensis Murr. Field Pansy. Rare colonist of sandy soils.

V. arvensis × *tricolor*. Rare or overlooked.

Polygala vulgaris L. Common Milkwort. Occasional, frequent on limestone and serpentine.

P. serpyllifolia Hose Heath Milkwort. Common, especially on acid soils.

Hypericum pulchrum L. Slender St John's Wort. Frequent, sometimes as a procumbent form (f. *procumbens* Rostrup).

Elatine hexandra (Lapierre) DC. Waterwort. Rare.

Silene dioica (L.) Clairv. Red Campion. Widespread by the coast, less so inland. Mostly represented by the dense-flowered, heavy-seeded race known as subsp. *zetlandica* (Compton) Clapham.

†*S. alba* (Mill.) E. H. L. Krause subsp. *alba* White Campion. Rare casual as in sandy fields in Dunrossness.

S. alba subsp. *alba* × *dioica* With the parents.

S. vulgaris (Moench) Garcke subsp. *maritima* (With.) Á. & D. Löve (*S. maritima* With.). Sea Campion. Frequent, occasionally inland.

S. acaulis (L.) Jacq. Moss Campion. Frequent, especially near the sea and on limestone and serpentine.

Lychnis flos-cuculi L. subsp. *flos-cuculi* Ragged Robin. Common.

Agrostemma githago L. Corn Cockle. Colonist, now presumed extinct.

†*Cerastium tomentosum* L., *sensu lato* Snow-in-Summer. Occasional outside gardens and usually persisting.

* *C. arcticum* Lange subsp. *edmondstonii* (H. C. Wats.) A. & D. Löve (*C. nigrescens* Edmondst. ex H. C. Wats.). Shetland Mouse-ear Chickweed. Only on a limited stretch of serpentine in Unst, and unfortunately in some danger of extinction.

C. fontanum Baumg. subsp. *triviale* (Link) Jalas (*C. holosteoides* Fr.). Common Mouse-ear Chickweed. Very common and variable.

C. glomeratum Thuill. Sticky Mouse-ear Chickweed. Common.

C. diffusum Pers. subsp. *diffusum* (*C. atrovirens* Bab.). Dark-green Mouse-ear Chickweed. Common.

Stellaria media (L.) Vill. subsp. *media* Chickweed. Common.

†*S. holostea* L. Greater Stitchwort. Kergord plantations, *c.* 1955 (W. Scott).

†*S. graminea* L. Lesser Stitchwort. Very scarce casual.

S. alsine Grimm Bog Stitchwort. Common.

Sagina maritima Don Sea Pearlwort. Common.

S. procumbens L. subsp. *procumbens* Procumbent Pearlwort. Very common.

S. subulata (Sw.) C. Presl Awl-leaved Pearlwort. Frequent, especially in north and west Mainland.

S. nodosa (L.) Fenzl Knotted Pearlwort. Local, often on serpentine and limestone.

Minuartia rubella (Wahlenb.) Hiern Alpine Sandwort. Unst serpentine, but not seen since 1901.

Honkenya peploides (L.) Ehrh. Sea Sandwort. Common.

Arenaria serpyllifolia L. Thyme-leaved Sandwort. Rare in sandy dune-pasture, on rocks (chiefly limestone), etc.

A. norvegica Gunn. subsp. *norvegica* Norwegian Sandwort. Scattered over the Unst serpentine.

Spergula arvensis L. Corn Spurrey. Ubiquitous in cornfields.

Spergularia media (L.) C. Presl Greater Sea Spurrey. Frequent in saltmarsh vegetation.

S. marina (L.) Griseb. Sea Spurrey. Frequent in the stonework of wharves, among coastal rocks, etc.

Montia fontana L. subsp. *fontana* Blinks. Very common; subsp. *variabilis* S. M. Walters known only from Fair Isle.

†*M. sibirica* (L.) Howell Pink Purslane. Occasional garden outcast or escape.

Chenopodium album L. subsp. *album* Fat Hen. Rare, perhaps preferring sand.

Atriplex prostrata group *Orache*. Common on seashores. Many populations appear to be of complex hybrid origin, involving the next three species and *A. longipes* Drej., but analysis is difficult.

A. prostrata Boucher ex DC. subsp. *prostrata*. Certain only in Fair Isle, 1977 (R. C. Palmer).

A. praecox Hülphers. Frequent on damp shingle of relatively sheltered voes.

A. glabriuscula Edmondst. Babington's Orache. Apparently much over-recorded; perhaps most frequent on the more exposed beaches.

A. patula L. Common Orache. Frequent.

A. laciniata L. Frosted Orache. Once seen in Dunrossness, now apparently lost.

Suaeda maritima (L.) Dum. subsp. *maritima* Herbaceous Seablite. Baltasound, very rare elsewhere.

Salicornia europaea L. Glasswort. Recently only at Baltasound.

†*Sidalcea* sp. Greek Mallow. Rarely outside gardens.

†*Linum usitatissimum* L. Cultivated Flax. Very rare casual, not seen recently.

L. catharticum L. Purging Flax. Common.

Radiola linoides Roth All-seed. Very locally abundant.

†*Geranium pratense* L. Meadow Cranesbill. Frequent garden escape, often long-persisting.

†*G. endressii* Gay French Cranesbill. Grassy waste ground among rubble, site of demolished house, Fox Lane, Lerwick, 1967.

†*G. phaeum* L. Dusky Cranesbill. Appears to have occurred as an escape or outcast in the last century.

†*G. dissectum* L. Cut-leaved Cranesbill. Casual, temporarily established on rocks at Scalloway.

G. molle L. Dove's-foot Cranesbill. Scarce, mainly in sandy cornfields, on rocky outcrops, etc.

G. robertianum L. Herb Robert. Confined to shingle at Boddam, perhaps not native.

†*G. ibericum* Cav. This or its hybrid *G.* × *magnificum* Hyl. sometimes persists as an outcast.

†*Erodium cicutarium* (L.) L'Hérit. subsp. *cicutarium* Common Storksbill. Sandy fields in Dunrossness, apparently established 200 years ago, now only a very rare casual.

Oxalis acetosella L. Wood-sorrel. North half of Mainland, very scarce.

†*O. incarnata* Pale Oxalis. Among rubble by steps, Scalloway, 1978 (W. Scott).

†*Tropaeolum speciosum* Poepp. & Endl. Flame Nasturtium. Among planted honeysuckle near Vementry, Mainland, planted (A. Tait); rare elsewhere.

†*Limnanthes douglasii* R.Br. Poached Egg Flower. One in old quarry between Southpunds and Gord, Levenwick, 1978 (W. Scott).

†*Impatiens glandulifera* Royle Policeman's Helmet. Rare, mainly in Scalloway.

†*Acer pseudoplatanus* L. Sycamore. Occasionally seen outside enclosures.

†*Aesculus hippocastanum* L. Horse-chestnut. Leagarth, Fetlar, garden relic, 1967.

†*Lupinus nootkatensis* Donn ex Sims Lupin. Garden outcast or planted.

†*Laburnum anagyroides* Medic. Laburnum. Self-sown at Scalloway, also as a relic.

†*Ulex europaeus* L. subsp. *europaeus* Gorse. Planted, especially in the Tingwall valley.

†*U. gallii* Planchon. Western Gorse. Fair Isle, planted.

†*Cytisus scoparius* (L.) Link (*Sarothamnus scoparius* (L.) Wimmer ex Koch) subsp. *scoparius* Broom. Baltasound, planted.

†*Medicago sativa* L. subsp. *sativa* Lucerne. Very rare in sandy fields in Dunrossness.

†*Melilotus indica* (L.) All. Small Melilot. One plant on waste ground by Loch of Clickimin, 1971 (W. Scott).

Trifolium dubium Sibth. Lesser Yellow Trefoil. Rare (except in southern Dunrossness), and often introduced.

†*T. hybridum* L. subsp. *hybridum* Alsike Clover. Occasional escape or relic of cultivation.

T. repens L. subsp. *repens* White Clover. Very common.

(*T. medium* L. subsp. *medium* Zigzag Clover. Recorded in the past but perhaps only a casual, if authentic.)

T. pratense L. Red Clover. Very common.

Anthyllis vulneraria L. Kidney-vetch. Common, and mainly, if not all subsp. *lapponica* (Hyl.) Jalas.

Lotus corniculatus L. Birdsfoot-trefoil. Very common and beautiful.

†*L. uliginosus* Schkuhr. Greater Birdsfoot-trefoil. Lerwick in two places.

†*Vicia hirsuta* (L.) S. F. Gray Hairy Tare. Very rare casual.

V. cracca L. Tufted Vetch. Common.

V. sepium L. Bush Vetch. Common.

†*V. sativa* L., *sensu lato*. Common Vetch. Very rare casual.

Lathyrus pratensis L. Meadow Vetchling. Frequent.

L. japonicus Willd subsp. *maritimus* (L.) Bigel. Sea Pea. Burrafirth, Unst (as var. *acutifolius* Bab.), but not seen since about 1900; the type recently at Easter Quarff (since lost), and Norwick, Unst.

(*L. montanus* Bernh. Bitter Vetch. Recorded by Edmonston but never confirmed.)

†*Pisum sativum* L. subsp. *sativum* Garden Pea. Rare casual.

†*Spiraea salicifolia* L. Willow Spiraea. Rarely planted or escaped.

Filipendula ulmaria (L.) Maxim. subsp. *ulmaria* Meadowsweet. Frequent, especially on limestone.

Rubus saxatilis L. Stone Bramble. Local, mainly on limestone and serpentine.

†*R. idaeus* L. Raspberry. Occasional escape or outcast.

†*R. spectabilis* Pursh Salmonberry. Planted locally and thriving remarkably well.

†*R. fruticosus* L., *sensu lato*. Bramble. Rarely planted or escaped.

Potentilla palustris (L.) Scop. Marsh Cinquefoil. Common.

P. anserina L. Silverweed. Very common.

P. erecta (L.) Räusch. Common Tormentil. Everywhere.

(*Sibbaldia procumbens* L. Least Cinquefoil. Recorded from Ronas Hill but never confirmed.)

(*Fragaria vesca* L. Wild Strawberry. Recorded by several botanists but unconfirmed.)

†*F.* × *ananassa* Duchesne Garden Strawberry. Lerwick, 1973 (R. C. Palmer).

Geum rivale L. Water Avens. Local and chiefly on limestone.

(*Dryas octopetala* L. Mountain Avens. Apparently seen on Weisdale Hill by Druce but sought in vain since.)

Alchemilla alpina L. Alpine Lady's Mantle. Only on Ronas Hill.

†*A. conjuncta* Bab. Greater Alpine Lady's Mantle. Very rare escape from gardens where it is liable to become a weed.

A. filicaulis Buser subsp. *filicaulis* Lady's Mantle. Frequent along the limestone belts of Mainland, occasional elsewhere.

†*A. glabra* Neygenfind. Naturalized in a number of places, particularly in Unst and Yell.

Aphanes microcarpa (Boiss. & Reut.) Rothm. Parsley Piert. Rare and perhaps impermanent.

†*Acaena anserinifolia* (J. R. & G. Forst.) Druce Pirripirri Bur. Formerly by a roadside near Scalloway.

†*Rosa rugosa* Thunb. Japanese Rose. Planted or garden straggler. A very popular garden rose.

R. canina L. *R sensu lato*. Dog Rose. Ocasional and mainly in the north and west.

R. tomentosa Sm. Downy Rose. This or some other member of the *Villosae* seems to have been known in the last century.

†*R. sherardii* Davies. Vassa, South Nesting, 1976 (W. Scott).

†*R. rubiginosa* L. Sweet Briar. Ham Burn, Foula, 1965 (W. Scott).

†*Crataegus monogyna* Jacq. subsp. *nordica* Franco Hawthorn. Rarely planted, as in the Tingwall valley.

Sorbus aucuparia L. Rowan. Local in the north and west and often very dwarfed.

†*S. intermedia* (Ehrh.) Pers. Swedish Whitebeam. Walls of ruined houses in the old lanes area, Lerwick, only twice recorded.

†*Malus domestica* Borkh. (*M. sylvestris* Mill. subsp. *mitis* (Wallr.) Mansf.). Apple. Rare casual, rarely persisting.

Rhodiola rosea L. (*Sedum rosea* (L.) Scop.). Rose-root. Frequent.

†*Sedum telephium* L. Orpine. Garden outcast or straggler.

†*S. spurium* M. Bieb. Caucasian Stonecrop. Planted at Scalloway.

S. anglicum Huds. English Stonecrop. Frequent in Out Skerries, rare in South Nesting.

S. acre L. Wall-pepper. Occasionally planted.

†*Saxifraga spathularis* × *umbrosa* = *S.* × *urbium* D. A. Webb London Pride. Garden outcast or planted.

S. oppositifolia L. Purple Saxifrage. Northernmost Mainland (at low levels), very rare elsewhere. Shetland's only native saxifrage.

Parnassia palustris L. subsp. *palustris* Grass of Parnassus. Occasional to frequent; very abundant and beautiful on the Spiggie links.

†*Ribes rubrum* L. Red Currant. Very rarely planted in non-enclosed areas.

†*R. nigrum* L. Black Currant. Occasionally planted by streams, etc.

†*R. sanguineum* Pursh Flowering Currant. Rarely planted outside gardens.

†*R. uva-crispa* L. Gooseberry. Rarely planted outside gardens.

Drosera rotundifolia L. Sundew. Common on the moors.

D. anglica Huds. Great Sundew. Very scarce, recently only in Northmavine.

†*Epilobium hirsutum* L. Great Hairy Willow-herb. Planted by a stream, Wester Quarff, 1965.

E. montanum L. Broad-leaved Willow-herb. Occasional, usually as a garden weed.

E. montanum × *obscurum* Rocks below Fort Charlotte, Lerwick, with both parents, 1966.

†*E. montanum* × *roseum* Lerwick, 1973 (R. C. Palmer).

E. roseum Schreb. subsp. *roseum* Small-flowered Willow-herb. Lerwick only, as a weed of gardens and waste places, etc.

E. obscurum Schreb. Short-fruited Willow-herb. Uncommon or overlooked.

E. obscurum × *palustre* Roadside ditch, Omunsgarth, near Sandsound, with both parents, 1966.

E. palustre L. Marsh Willow-herb. Very common and variable.

(*E. alsinifolium* Vill. Chickweed Willow-herb. Recorded from Ronas Hill, a likely station, but not confirmed.)

E. angustifolium L. (*Chamaenerion angustifolium* (L.) Scop.). Rosebay Willow-herb. Now very rare in a native state, but an occasional escape.

†*Fuchsia magellanica* Lam. Fuchsia. Planted or outcast, rarely bird- or self-sown.

Myriophyllum spicatum L. Spiked Water-milfoil. So far known only in Loch of Hillwell, Dunrossness.

M. alterniflorum DC. Alternate-flowered Water-milfoil. Very common.

Hippuris vulgaris L. Mare's-tail. Occasional in Unst, very local in Yell and Fetlar, and very rare in Mainland.

Callitriche stagnalis Scop. Water Starwort. Very common.

C. platycarpa Kütz. Water Starwort. Local or under-recorded, often in running water.

C. intermedia Hoffm. Water Starwort. Very common.

C. hermaphroditica L. Autumnal Starwort. Occasional.

Cornus suecica L. (*Chamaepericlymenum suecicum* (L.) Aschers. & Graebn.). Dwarf Cornel. High moorland in Foula, and at low levels at two places in Yell.

†*Hedera helix* L. Ivy. Planted, sometimes in wild-looking places.

Hydrocotyle vulgaris L. Pennywort. Common.

Eryngium maritimum L. Sea Holly. Not seen this century, probably extinct.

Anthriscus sylvestris (L.) Hoffm. Cow Parsley. Very common.

†*Scandix pecten-veneris* L. subsp. *pecten-veneris* Shepherd's Needle. Once recorded, probably only casual.

†*Myrrhis odorata*(L.) Scop. Sweet Cicely. Garden escape or outcast.

†*Conium maculatum* L. Hemlock. Lerwick, now nearly if not quite extinct.

†*Bupleurum rotundifolium* group. Very rare.

Apium inundatum (L.) Rchb. f. Marshwort. Fair Isle, Papa Stour, and recently near Uyea, Unst (R. C. Palmer) and at Esha Ness (A. Fitter).

†*Carum carvi* L. Caraway. Well naturalised in a number of places, especially in Dunrossness.

Conopodium majus (Gouan) Loret Earthnut. Frequent in hayfields, etc.

†*Aegopodium podagraria* L. Goutweed. Occasional weed of gardens and waste places, etc.

Berula erecta (Huds.) Coville Narrow-leaved Water-parsnip. Tingwall valley, rare.

Ligusticum scoticum L. Lovage. Frequent on precipitous cliffs, rarely on sand or shingle.

Angelica sylvestris L. Wild Angelica. Common.

†*A. archangelica* L. subsp. *archangelica* Angelica. Relic of cultivation in Dunrossness.

†*Levisticum officinale* Koch Garden Lovage. Garden straggler at Brough Lodge, Fetlar, 1958.

†*Peucedanum ostruthium* (L.) Koch Master-wort. Occasional garden escape or relic.

Heracleum sphondylium L. subsp. *sphondylium* Cow Parsnip. Common.

†*H. mantegazzianum* Somm. & Lev., *sensu lato*. Giant Hogweed. Roadside, Leagarth House, Fetlar.

†*Daucus carota* subsp. *sativus* (Hoffm.) Arcangeli Carrot. Occasional outcast.

Euphorbia helioscopia L. Sun Spurge. Occasional, though rather frequent in Dunrossness.

†*E. peplus* L. Petty Spurge. Rare garden weed.

Polygonum aviculare L., *sensu stricto*. Knotgrass. Known certainly only from Fair Isle.

P. boreale (Lange) Small. The common Shetland knotgrass

P. arenastrum Bor. Small-leaved Knotgrass. Probably frequent about farmyards, etc.

P. oxyspermum Meyer & Bunge ex Ledeb. subsp. *raii* (Bab.) D. A. Webb & Chater (*P. raii* Bab.). Ray's Knotgrass. Burrafirth, Unst, but not seen for a century.

P. viviparum L. Alpine Bistort. Occasional in coastal turf, and on high ground on Ronas Hill and Foula.

†*P. bistorta* L. Bistort. Very rarely as an escape, or planted.

P. amphibium L. Amphibious Bistort. Locally common, both land and water states occurring.

P. persicaria L. Persicaria. Frequent but seldom in quantity.

†*Bilderdykia convolvulus* (L.) Dumort. (*Polygonum convolvulus* L.). Black Bindweed. Rare and usually casual.

†*B. aubertii* (Louis Henry) Moldenke (*Polygonum baldschuanicum* auct., non Regel). Lace Vine. Remains of garden, Leagarth, Fetlar, 1967.

†*Reynoutria japonica* Houtt. (*Polygonum cuspidatum* Sieb. & Zucc.). Japanese Knotweed. Occasional escape or straggler, often established. The related, distinct-looking taxon originally called *Polygonum compactum* Hook. f. was found running wild near houses, Reafirth, Mid Yell, 1967.

†*R. sachalinensis* (Friedrich Schmidt Petrop.) Nakai (*Polygonum sachalinense* Friedrich Schmidt Petrop.). Giant Knotweed. Established by a house, Houbie, Fetlar.

Oxyria digyna (L.) Hill Mountain Sorrel. Ronas Hill area, rare.

†*Rheum* × *cultorum* Thorsrud & Reisaeter. Rhubarb. Outcast or relic of cultivation, often long-persisting.

Rumex acetosella L., *sensu stricto*. Sheep's Sorrel. Very common.

R. acetosa L. Sorrel. Very common.

R. longifolius DC. Butter Dock. The commonest Shetland dock and often found in more or less natural habitats.

R. longifolius × *obtusifolius* subsp. *obtusifolius* Probably a frequent hybrid.

R. crispus L. Curled Dock. Common and often by the shore.

R. crispus × *longifolius* Probably rare.

R. obtusifolius L. subsp. *obtusifolius* Broad-leaved Dock. Frequent in the more inhabited parts.

†*Helxine soleirolii* Req. Mind-your-own-business. Leagarth, Fetlar, 1967 (R. C. Palmer).

Urtica urens L. Small Nettle. Occasional, frequent on sand.

U. dioica L. Stinging Nettle. Very common, especially by abandoned crofts.

†*Humulus lupulus* L. Hop. Garden straggler in two places, Baltasound, 1962.

†*Ulmus glabra* Huds. Wych Elm. Once or twice recorded.

Betula pubescens Ehrh. subsp. *carpatica* (Willd.) Aschers. & Graebn. Birch. Now only in two or three places in Northmavine.

Corylus avellana L. Hazel. Known only in one ravine in South Nesting, and one holm in Punds Water, Northmavine, 1967.

Populus tremula L. Aspen. Very local, and only in the north and west.

†*Salix pentandra* L. Bay Willow. Very rare.

†*S. alba* L. subsp. *vitellina* (L.) Arcangeli Golden Willow. Planted in the ravine at Effirth, Bixter, 1959.

†*S. fragilis* L. Crack Willow. Rarely planted.

†*S. purpurea* L. Purple Willow. Streamside, Gardin, Vidlin, 1973 (W. Scott).

†*S. daphnoides* Vill. Rarely planted.

†*S. viminalis* L. Common Osier. Rarely planted.

†*S.* × *calodendron* Wimmer. Several bushes by burn above Northdale, Fetlar, planted, 1967.

†*S. caprea* L. Goat Willow. Hardly, if ever, seen outside enclosures.

†*S. nigricans* × *phylicifolia* Widely planted, especially in West Mainland.

S. atrocinerea Brot. Common Sallow. Rare, chiefly on holms in lochs in Northmavine, but also in small quantity in Yell and Fair Isle. Sometimes planted.

S. atrocinerea × *aurita* Rare, in some places persisting in the apparent absence of both parents.

†*S. atrocinerea* × *viminalis* = *S.* × *smithiana* Willd. Often planted near crofts and by streams.

S. aurita L. Eared Sallow. Occasional.

S. aurita × *repens* = *S.* × *ambigua* Ehrh. Widespread, often persisting in the absence of one or both parents.

S. repens L., *sensu lato*. Creeping Willow. Frequent; galled forms often occur.

S. lapponum L. Downy Willow. Known from one holm in a loch, North Roe.

S. herbacea L. Least Willow. On many of the higher summits but descending to low levels, especially in Northmavine.

Loiseleuria procumbens (L.) Desv. Wild Azalea; Loiseleuria. Ronas Hill.

†*Pernettya mucronata* (L. fil.) Gaud. ex Spreng. Prickly Heath. Planted in one or two places.

Arctostaphylos uva-ursi (L.) Spreng. Bearberry. Muckle Roe, and parts of Northmavine, locally common.

Arctous alpinus (L.) Niedenzu Black Bearberry. Very local, Ronas Hill and northwards, sometimes with the preceding.

Calluna vulgaris (L.) Hull Heather. Ubiquitous.

Erica tetralix L. Cross-leaved Heath. Very common.

E. cinerea L. Bell-heather. Very common.

Vaccinium vitis-idaea L. Cowberry. Local on the higher hills of Mainland. Not seen in flower.

V. myrtillus L. Blaeberry. Common, but fruiting only in sheltered sites.

V. uliginosum L. Bog Whortleberry. Local, and very rarely flowering.

(*Pyrola media* Sw. Intermediate Wintergreen. Recorded near Walls, but unconfirmed. *P. rotundifolia* L. is known from Orkney.)

Empetrum nigrum L. Crowberry. Very common. (Including *E. hermaphroditum* Hagerup which, if it really occurs, is rare or overlooked.)

Armeria maritima (Mill.) Willd. Thrift. Ubiquitous on the coast, very rarely seen some way inland.

Primula vulgaris Huds. Primrose. Common in some areas, absent in others.

†*Primula* sp. Primrose. Garden forms are sometimes seen, usually near houses.

†*Lysimachia punctata* L. Dotted Loosestrife. Outcast or planted in a few places.

Trientalis europaea L. Chickweed Wintergreen. Very local and mainly in Dunrossness, but also in Fair Isle, Foula, Bressay, the Isle of Noss and Unst.

Anagallis tenella (L.) Bog Pimpernel. Local.

†*A. arvensis* L. subsp. *arvensis* Scarlet Pimpernel. Rare garden weed.

Glaux maritima L. Sea Milkwort. Common, particularly by the muddier shores.

†*Fraxinus excelsior* L. Ash. Rarely seen outside gardens.

Centaurium littorale (D. Turner) Gilmour Seaside Centaury. (Recorded by Edmonston but not confirmed.)

Gentianella campestris (L.) Börner Field Gentian. Widespread.

G. amarella (L.) Börner subsp. *septentrionalis* (Druce) Pritchard Felwort. Local in dune pasture, extremely rare on limestone outcrops.

Menyanthes trifoliata L. Buckbean. Widespread.

†*Phacelia tanacetifolia* Benth. Fiddle-neck. Once as a garden weed, Scalloway.

†*Polemonium caeruleum* L. Jacob's Ladder. Very rare outcast.

†*Symphytum officinale* L. Comfrey. Rare garden escape or relic of cultivation.

†*S. asperum* × *officinale* = *S.* × *uplandicum* Nyman Russian Comfrey. Occasional, mainly on waste ground or near gardens.

†*S. tuberosum* L. Tuberous Comfrey. Rare garden escape or outcast.

Anchusa arvensis (L.) Bieb. Bugloss. Frequent, especially on sand.

†*Pulmonaria officinalis* L. Lung-wort. Planted or outcast in one or two spots.

Myosotis scorpioides (*M. palustris* (L.) Hill) Water Forget-me-not. Perhaps native in southern Dunrossness, elsewhere established locally near houses, always as a form with appressed hairs.

M. repens G. Don (*M. secunda* A. Murr.). Creeping Water Forget-me-not. Very common.

M. caespitosa C. V. Schultz Tufted Forget-me-not. Common.

M. arvensis (L.) Hill Common Forget-me-not. Common.

M. discolor Pers. Yellow and blue Forget-me-not. Common.

†*Lithospermum arvense* L. Corn Gromwell. Sparingly in new garden, Scalloway, 1963.

Mertensia maritima (L.) S. F. Gray Oyster Plant; Northern Shore-wort. Now fast approaching extinction.

†*Convolvulus arvensis* L. Bindweed. Once seen as a garden weed, Bressay.

†*Calystegia sepium* (L.) R. Br. subsp. *sepium* Larger Bindweed. Uncommon garden escape or outcast.

†*Solanum nigrum* L. Black Nightshade. Once seen near Scalloway.

†*S. tuberosum* L. Potato. Outcast or relic of cultivation.

†*Lycopersicum esculentum* Mill. Tomato. A casual of rubbish tips.

†*Linaria vulgaris* Mill. Toadflax. Rare garden straggler or planted.

†*L. maroccana* Hook f. Annual Toadflax. Scalloway Rubbish Dump, garden outcast, 1961.

†*Kickxia spuria* (L.) Dum. Fluellen. Garden weed, Scalloway, very rare, 1959.

†*Cymbalaria muralis* Gaertn., Mey. & Scherb. Ivy-leaved Toadflax. Planted near Lerwick, and as a rare casual.

†*Mimulus guttatus* DC. Monkey-flower. Naturalised in many places.

†*M. guttatus* × *luteus* Mimulus. Naturalised locally, usually as a form with one large reddish spot on the central lobe of the lower lip.

†*M. luteus* L. Blood-drop-emlets. Nounsbrough, in ditch, 1976 (R. C. Palmer).

†*M. cupreus* × *guttatus* Mimulus. Naturalised locally, nearly always as a form with a petaloid calyx.

†*Digitalis purpurea* L. Foxglove. Rare garden escape or outcast, also planted.

Veronica beccabunga L. Brooklime. Rare, mostly in Tingwall valley.

V. anagallis-aquatica L. Water Speedwell. Tingwall valley and southern Dunrossness.

V. scutellata L. Marsh Speedwell. Widespread but rather uncommon, most frequent in west Mainland.

V. officinalis L. Common Speedwell. Common.

†*V. chamaedrys* L. Germander Speedwell. Doubtfully native, but well established in Tingwall valley; rare elsewhere.

V. serpyllifolia L. subsp. *serpyllifolia* Thyme-leaved Speedwell. Common.

V. arvensis L. Wall Speedwell. Not uncommon.

V. hederifolia L., *sensu lato*. Ivy Speedwell. Local.

†*V. persica* Poir. Buxbaum's Speedwell. Occasional, usually as a garden weed.

V. polita Fr. Grey Speedwell. Rare.

V. agrestis L. Field Speedwell. Occasional, mainly on sand.

†*V. filiformis* Sm. Slender Speedwell. Occasional outcast or planted; well established at Tingwall Churchyard.

Pedicularis palustris L. Red-rattle. Common.

P. sylvatica L. Lousewort. Very common.

Rhinanthus serotinus (Schönh.) Oborny subsp. *apterus* (Fr.) Hyl. Greater Yellow-rattle. Very rare colonist with no recent records.

R. minor L. Yellow-rattle. Common and mainly as subsp. *stenophyllus* (Schur) O. Schwarz; subsp. *monticola* (Sterneck) O. Schwarz is local or under-recorded, while subsp. *borealis* (Sterneck) Sell appears to be rare.

Melampyrum pratense L. Common Cow-wheat. Extremely rare.

Euphrasia Eyebright. This genus presents great problems in Shetland on account of the extreme variability of many species and conflicting interpretations of some of them. In addition, hybrids appear frequently, at least eight of the possible combinations being recorded with a fair degree of certainty; others are likely to occur.

E. micrantha Rchb. Very common in moorland, etc.

E. scottica Wettst. Frequent in marshes.

E. frigida Pugsl. Upland grassland, Foula.

E. foulaensis Towns. ex Wettst. Common in coastal turf, more sparingly inland.

E. rotundifolia Pugsl. Recognized only from Ronas Voe.

E. marshallii Pugsl. Coastal turf, apparently rare and untypical.

E. ostenfeldii (Pugsl.) Yeo. Apparently the most frequent of the hairy coastal eyebrights; found also on the serpentine of Unst.

E. nemorosa (Pers.) Wallr. Short grassland, locally common often in dune pasture as a large-flowered form simulating *E. arctica*.

**E. heslop-harrisonii* Rich grassland. At present known only from Foula and the holms of Uyea-sound, near Vementry.

E. confusa Pugsl. Common in closely grazed turf.

E. arctica Lange ex Rostrup (*E. borealis* auct. mult). Widespread and often a large showy plant. Its hybrid with *E. confusa* is frequent.

Odontites verna (Bell.) Dum. subsp. *verna* Red Bartsia. Rare, mainly in the south.

Pinguicula vulgaris L. Common Butterwort. Common.

Utricularia vulgaris L., *sensu lato*. Greater Bladderwort. Occasional, only once reported in flower.

U. intermedia Hayne. Intermediate Bladderwort. Rare. Flowering not reported.

U. minor L. Lesser Bladderwort. Local, very rarely flowering.

†*Mentha arvensis* × *spicata* = *M.* × *gentilis* L. Bushy Mint. Escape in Foula.

M. aquatica L. Water Mint. Somewhat local, mainly in the south but extending to Unst.

†*M. aquatica* × *spicata* = *M.* × *piperita* L. Peppermint. Naturalised locally by streams, etc.

†*M. spicata* L. Spearmint. The glabrous form (Spearmint) is established locally as an escape.

M. longifolia (L.) Huds. × *M. suaveolens* Ehrh. = *M.* × *rotundifolia* (L.) Huds. nm. *webberi* (Fraser) R. M. Harley. A distinctive mint sometimes escaping, especially in Dunrossness where it is established locally.

†*M. spicata* L. × *M. suaveolens* Ehrh. = *M.* × *villosa* Huds. nm.

M. alopecuroides (Hull) Stream between Cott and Sound, Weisdale, but not seen recently.

Thymus drucei Ronn. Thyme. Very common.

Prunella vulgaris L. Self-heal. Very common.

Stachys palustris L. Marsh Woundwort. Occasional.

†*S. palustris* × *sylvatica* = *S.* × *ambigua* Sm. A frequent garden escape or outcast well established in many places.

Lamium amplexicaule L. Henbit. Sandy fields, etc., mainly in Dunrossness, rare and usually cleistogamous.

L. moluccellifolium Fr. Intermediate Dead-nettle. Frequent.

L. hybridum Vill. Cut-leaved Dead-nettle. Apparently entirely confined to gardens and waste ground about Lerwick.

L. purpureum L. Red Dead-nettle. Common.

†*L. maculatum* L. Spotted Dead-nettle. Garden outcast, Kergord, 1967.

Galeopsis tetrahit L., *sensu lato*. Common Hemp-nettle. Common.

†*G. speciosa* Mill. Large-flowered Hemp-nettle. A few plants among cabbages, Burravoe, Yell, 1973 (R. Tulloch).

†*Glechoma hederacea* L. Ground Ivy. Grown in gardens and a rare escape or outcast.

(*Ajuga reptans* L. Bugle. Recorded by Edmonston but unconfirmed.)

Plantago major L. Great Plantain. Common.

P. lanceolata L. Ribwort. Very common and variable.

P. maritima L. Sea Plantain. Ubiquitous and varying greatly.

P. coronopus L. Buck's-horn Plantain. Very common.

Littorella uniflora (L.) Aschers. Shore-weed. Very common.

Campanula rotundifolia L. Harebell. Extremely rare, perhaps more so now than formerly.

Jasione montana L. Sheep's-bit. Abundant, varying greatly in stature and flower colour.

Lobelia dortmanna L. Water Lobelia. Common but not always flowering.

†*Sherardia arvensis* L. Field Madder. Rare colonist or casual.

†*Galium odoratum* (L.) Scop. Sweet Woodruff. Formerly recorded as an escape.

(*G. boreale* L. Northern Bedstraw. Recorded, but perhaps of garden origin, if genuine.)

G. mollugo L. *sensu lato* Great Hedge Bedstraw. Rare casual.

G. verum L. Lady's Bedstraw. Common.

G. saxatile L. Heath Bedstraw. Very common.

G. palustre L. subsp. *palustre* Marsh Bedstraw. Common.

G. aparine L. Goosegrass. Almost confined to shingle beaches.

†*Sambucus nigra* L. Elder. Often planted about crofts.

†*Symphoricarpos rivularis* Suksdorf Snowberry. Planted in a number of stations.

Lonicera periclymenum L. Honeysuckle. Local, mainly in the north and west.

Valerianella locusta (L.) Betcke Lamb's Lettuce. Sandy arable ground, very rare.

†*Dipsacus fullonum* L. Teasel. Lerwick Rubbish Dump, 1967.

Succisa pratensis Moench Devil's-bit Scabious. Very common.

†*Galinsoga parviflora* Cav. Gallant Soldier. Garden weed, Eastshore, 1971 (Mrs. R. A. Garriock).

Senecio jacobaea L. Ragwort. Rare colonist, long established at Scalloway.

S. aquaticus Hill Marsh Ragwort. Very common, in dry as well as wet habitats; occurs in a form differing markedly from the southern plant.

Senecio aquaticus × *jacobaea* = *S.* × *ostenfeldii* Druce. Formerly found at Scalloway.

†*S. squalidus* L. Oxford Ragwort. Lerwick and Scalloway.

S. vulgaris L. Groundsel. Common.

†*S. fluviatilis* Wallr. Broad-leaved Ragwort. Brettabister, North Nesting, 1971 (J. Blance).

†*S. smithii* DC. Magellan Ragwort. Frequent by streams, etc., either escaped or planted.

†*Tussilago farfara* L. Coltsfoot. Occasional, often by roadsides or on waste ground.

†*P. albus* (L.) Gaertn. White Butterbur. Rare garden outcast.

†*P. fragrans* (Vill.) C. Presl Winter Heliotrope. An even rarer outcast.

†*Calendula officinalis* L. Pot Marigold. Rarely seen outside gardens.

†*Inula helenium* L. Elecampane. Rare garden escape or outcast.

Gnaphalium sylvaticum L. Wood Cudweed. Occasional.

(*G. supinum* L. Dwarf Cudweed. Recorded from Ronas Hill but requires confirmation.)

G. uliginosum L. Marsh Cudweed. Rather local.

†*Anaphalis margaritacea* (L.) Benth. Pearly Everlasting. Rare garden straggler.

Antennaria dioica (L.) Gaertn. Cat's-foot. Frequent.

Helichrysum bellidioides (Forst. f.) Willd. Planted at Tagon, Voe.

Solidago virgaurea L. Golden-rod. Widespread.

Aster tripolium L. Sea Aster. Known only from Isbister Holm, off Whalsay, and on the east side of Whalsay.

Aster novi-belgii L. Michaelmas Daisy. Often well-established outside gardens.

†*A. lanceolatus* Willd. Old wall by Burns Lane, Lerwick, 1967 (W. Scott).

†*Oleariax haastii* Hook. f. Daisy Bush. Roadside, Freefield, Lerwick, 1976 (W. Scott).

Bellis perennis L. Daisy. Abundant.

†*Anthemis arvensis* L. Corn Chamomile. Once as a casual near Scalloway.

(*A. cotula* L. Stinking Mayweed. Recorded by Edmonston from 'near Tingwall' but unconfirmed.)

Achillea ptarmica L. Sneezewort. Common.

A. millefolium L. Yarrow. More common than the preceding.

Tripleurospermum maritimum (L.) Koch subsp. *maritimum* Scentless Mayweed. Very common.

Matricaria matricarioides (Less.) Porter Rayless Mayweed. Now very common.

†*M. recuitita* L. Wild Chamomile. Weedy roadside, Cunningsburgh, 1978 (R. C. Palmer).

Chrysanthemum segetum L. Corn Marigold. Rare.

C. leucanthemum L. Ox-eye Daisy. Local colonist.

†*C. maximum* Ramond Shasta Daisy. Rare outcast.

†*C. parthenium* (L.) Bernh. Feverfew. Rare garden escape or outcast.

†*C. vulgare* (L.) Bernh. Tansy. Occasional escape, often well established.

†*Cotula squalida* Hook. f. Leptinella. Established at Voe and formerly Graven.

Artemisia vulgaris L. Mugwort. Occasional, commonest on sand.

†*A. abrotanum* L. Southernwood. Waste ground by Loch of Clickimin, garden outcast, 1955.

Arctium minus Bernh. subsp. *nemorosum* (Lej.) Syme. Lesser Burdock. Very rare and confined to the vicinity of Sumburgh Airport.

Cirsium vulgare (Savi) Ten. Spear Thistle. Very common, often on beaches.

C. palustre (L.) Scop. Marsh Thistle. Very common.

C. arvense (L.) Scop. Creeping Thistle. Very common; the var. *setosum* C. A. Mey. occurs very locally on sandy soils.

†*C. heterophyllum* (L.) Hill Melancholy Thistle. Rare garden escape or outcast.

Saussurea alpina (L.) DC. Alpine Saussurea. Very rare, known only from the Ronas Hill summit and at a much lower level on dry stony ground in Unst. Flowers seldom produced.

†*Centaurea cyanus* L. Cornflower. Colonist, now extremely rare.

†*C. nigra* L. subsp. *nigra* Lesser Knapweed. Rare.

†*C. melitensis* L. Maltese Star Thistle. Once seen on waste ground by Loch of Clickimin, casual, 1956.

†*C. diluta* Aiton Lesser Star Thistle. One plant on Lerwick Rubbish Dump, casual, 1961.

†*C. montana* L. Mountain Bluet. Established locally as an escape.

†*Lapsana communis* L. Nipplewort. Rare colonist or casual.

Hypochoeris radicata L. Cat's Ear. Rare in Druce's day, now common in the inhabited areas.

Leontodon autumnalis L. Autumnal Hawkbit. Very common.

†*Lactuca sativa* L. Garden Lettuce. Lerwick Rubbish Dump, 1967.

Sonchus arvensis L. Field Milk-thistle. Common in crops and on some beaches; the var. *glabrescens* Günth., Grab. & Wimm. is known from Fair Isle.

S. oleraceus L. Milk-thistle. Uncommon and not well established.

S. asper (L.) Hill Spiny Milk-thistle. Frequent.

†*Cicerbita macrophylla* (Willd.) Wallr. Blue Sow-thistle. Rarely established.

Hieracium Hawkweed. Twenty-one microspecies are at present found in the islands mainly in the north and west. Twelve of these are confined to Shetland and come under Section *Alpestria* [Fries] F. N. Williams. Nearly all the hawkweeds are rare or local, some known from only one spot, and only *H. orimeles* is at all frequent.

H. obesifolium Pugsl. Holm in Burga Water, near Sandness, now extinct.

H. gothicoides Pugsl. Very rare, as in the ravine of burn from Mill Loch, near Swining, Lunnasting.

H. sparsifolium Lindeb. Local in north half of Mainland, and in Unst, Yell, and Fetlar.

H. lissolepium (Zahn) Roffey. On rocks in geo on coast east of Stoal, near Aywick, Yell, apparently this, 1961 (R. C. Palmer); now lost.

*H. zetlandicum Beeby. North Roe, very rare elsewhere.

*H. breve Beeby. Ronas Voe, very rare.

*H. gratum P. D. Sell & C. West. Only at Burrafirth and Loch of Cliff, Unst.

*H. difficile P. D. Sell & C. West. Only near Okraquoy, Dunrossness.

*H. australius (Beeby) Pugsl. North end of Unst and the Wick of Tresta cliffs, Fetlar.

*H. praethulense Pugsl. Northmavine, local.

*H. hethlandiae (F. J. Hanb.) Pugsl. Mavis Grind, now extinct.

*H. attenuatifolium P. D. Sell & C. West. Central and west Mainland, local.

*H. pugsleyi P. D. Sell & C. West. Cunningsburgh, central Mainland, and Yell, very local.

*H. dilectum P. D. Sell & C. West. Mainly in central and west Mainland, local.

*H. subtruncatum Beeby. Mainly in north Mainland but extending very locally south to Dunrossness.

*H. northroense Pugsl. One spot in North Roe.

*H. vinicaule P. D. Sell & C. West. Here and there, chiefly in the north and west.

H. caledonicum F. J. Hanb. Very local, as on rocky cliffs by sea, west side of Stead of Aithness.

H. argenteum Fr. Northmavine and central Mainland, very local.

H. scoticum F. J. Hanb. Northmavine and west Mainland, very local.

H. orimeles F. J. Hanb. ex W. R. Linton. The most frequently encountered hawkweed in north, west, and central Mainland.

H. uistense (Pugsl.) P. D. Sell & C. West. About Ronas Voe, very rare.

†*Pilosella aurantiaca* (L.) C. H. & F. W. Schultz, *sensu lato* (*Hieracium aurantiacum* L., *sensu lato*). Fox and Cubs. Escaping locally.

*P. flagellaris (Willd.) P. D. Sell & C. West subsp. *bicapitata* P. D. Sell & C. West Shetland Mouse-ear Hawkweed. Known only from White Ness, West Burrafirth, and Ronas Voe. First discovered in 1962.

†*Crepis capillaris* (L.) Wallr. Smooth Hawk's-beard. Probably little more than an uncommon casual.

Taraxacum Sect. *Erythrosperma* Dandelion. Very rare. Two species are known.

T. sect *Spectabilia* Dandelion. *T. faeroense* (Dahlst). Dahlst. is common in damp places, and about 16 other species are known.

T. sect. *Vulgaria* Dandelion. Largely confined to the more populous areas. About 28 species are known.

Triglochin palustris L. Marsh Arrow-grass. Common.

T. maritima L. Sea Arrow-grass. Common and not exclusively maritime.

Zostera marina L. Grass-wrack. Apparently rare, and at its best in Whiteness Voe.

Potamogeton natans L. Broad-leaved Pondweed. Common in lochs.

P. polygonifolius Pourr. Bog Pondweed. Very common in hill bogs, etc.

P. gramineus L. Various-leaved Pondweed. Common.

P. gramineus × *lucens* = *P.* × *zizii* Koch ex Roth Loch of Hillwell, in the apparent absence of *P. lucens*.

P. gramineus × *perfoliatus* = *P.* × *nitens* Weber. Local, or under-recorded.

P. gramineus × *polygonifolius*? A hybrid pondweed believed to be of this parentage occurs in the Loch of Cliff.

P. alpinus Balb. Reddish Pondweed. Recently found at Loch of Voe, Delting.

P. praelongus Wulf. Long-stalked Pondweed. Very local.

P. perfoliatus L. Perfoliate Pondweed. In every large loch.

P. friesii Rupr. Flat-stalked Pondweed. Loch of Clickimin, 1975 (R. C. L. Howitt), and the Loch of Hillwell, 1977 (R. C. Palmer).

P. rutilus Wolfg. Shetland Pondweed. Lochs of Tingwall and Asta, and near Walls.

P. pusillus L. Lesser Pondweed. Occasional.

P. berchtoldii Fieb. Small Pondweed. Occasional.

P. filiformis Pers. Slender-leaved Pondweed. Frequent, especially near the coast in shallow water on a sandy bottom.

P. pectinatus L. Fennel-leaved Pondweed. Rare, perhaps only in the Tingwall valley and southern Dunrossness.

Ruppia spiralis L. ex Dum. Coiled Pondweed. Rare.

R. maritima L. Tassel Pondweed. Occasional.

Zannichellia palustris L. Horned Pondweed. Very local.

Narthecium ossifragum (L.) Huds. Bog Asphodel. Common.

†*Hosta* sp. Plantain Lily. Very rare garden outcast.

†*Lilium pyrenaicum* Gouan. Pyrenean Lily. An outcast or planted, sometimes persisting. Grows 'like a weed' in Shetland gardens.

Scilla verna Huds. Spring Squill. Common in many places.

†*Endymion hispanicus* × *non-scriptus* Bluebell. Probably the usual garden bluebell, frequently occurring as an outcast.

†*Allium ursinum* L. Ramsons. Sound, Weisdale, 1975 (R. C. Palmer).

Juncus squarrosus L. Heath Rush. Very common.

J. gerardii Lois. Mud Rush. Common by the coast.

J. trifidus L. Three-leaved Rush. Only at high altitudes on Ronas Hill.

J. bufonius L. Toad Rush. Common.

J. effusus L. Soft Rush. Ubiquitous.

J. conglomeratus L. Compact Rush. Frequent.

J. acutiflorus Ehrh. ex Hoffm. Sharp-flowered Rush. Local and behaving like a colonist, being almost confined to roadsides.

J. articulatus L. Jointed Rush. Very common.

J. bulbosus L., *sensu lato*. Bulbous Rush. Very common (often as a submerged aquatic), probably always as *J. kochii* F. W. Schultz.

J. triglumis L. Three-flowered Rush. Damp stony ground in south-east Unst, very rare.

Luzula pilosa (L.) Willd. Hairy Woodrush. Occasional to frequent among heather or on dry heathy pastures.

L. sylvatica (Huds.) Gaud. Greater Woodrush. Common.

L. spicata (L.) DC. Spiked Woodrush. Only on Ronas Hill, very sparingly.

L. campestris (L.) DC. Field Woodrush. Common, at least on the less acid soils.

L. multiflora (Retz.) Lej. Many-headed Woodrush. Very common in hilly places and acid pastures, producing small forms closely simulating the last.

†*Narcissus* spp. or hybrids. Narcissus; Daffodil. Planted or outcast in many places.

†*Alstroemeria aurantiaca* D. Don Peruvian Lily. Rare garden straggler or outcast.
†*Iris spuria* L. Butterfly Iris. Sometimes planted or outcast near houses, rarely established.
I. pseudacorus L. Yellow Flag. Common.
†*Crocosmia* × *crocosmiflora* (Lemoine) N.E.Br. Montbretia. Frequent escape or planted.
Listera cordata (L.) R.Br. Lesser Twayblade. Occasional or frequent among heather.
Hammarbya paludosa (L.) O. Kuntze Bog Orchid. Known only from one station in north Yell.
Coeloglossum viride (L.) Hartm. Frog Orchid. Frequent, especially by the coast and on limestone and serpentine.
Gymnadenia conopsea (L.) R.Br. Fragrant Orchid. Rare, mainly in Unst.
(*Leucorchis albida* (L.) E. Mey. ex Schur Small White Orchid. Recorded from Bressay but unconfirmed.)
Orchis mascula (L.) L. Early Purple Orchid. Frequent on the Unst serpentine, very rare elsewhere.
Dactylorhiza incarnata (L.) Soó subsp. *incarnata* Meadow Orchid. Occasional, mainly in marshes on limestone; subsp. *coccinea* (Pugsl.) Soó in dune pasture in southern Dunrossness.
D. maculata (L.) Soó subsp. *ericetorum* (Linton) P. F. Hunt & Summerh. Moorland Spotted Orchid. Common.
D. maculata subsp. *ericetorum* × *purpurella* A frequent hybrid, often large and showy.
D. fuchsii (Druce) Soó subsp. *hebridensis* (Wilmott) Soó. Common Spotted Orchid. Spiggie, 1952 (H. T. Powell), and elsewhere in Dunrossness, in damp sandy pasture.
D. fuchsii subsp. *hebridensis* × *purpurella* Near Mails, north of Exnaboe, and by the lower end of the Burn of Mail, Cunningsburgh, 1979 (W. Scott).
D. purpurella (T. & T. A. Steph.) Soó. Northern Fen Orchid. Common, though less so than *D. maculata*.
Lemna minor L. Duckweed. Lerwick (not seen recently) and Bressay, very rare.
Sparganium erectum L. Branched Bur-reed. Certain only near Lerwick.
S. angustifolium Michx. Floating Bur-reed. Widespread in lochs and pools.
S. minimum Wallr. Small Bur-reed. Rare, certain only in Unst.
Eriophorum angustifolium Honck. Common Cotton-grass. Very common.
E. vaginatum L. Hare's-tail Cotton-grass. Very common.
Trichophorum cespitosum (L.) Hartman subsp. *germanicum* (Palla) Hegi Deer-grass. Very common.
Eleocharis acicularis (L.) Roem. & Schult. Needle Spike-rush. Lochs of Spiggie and Brow.
E. quinqueflora (F. X. Hatmann) Schwarz. Few-flowered Spike-rush. Common, sometimes in saltmarsh turf.
E. multicaulis (Sm.) Sm. Many-stemmed Spike-rush. Frequent and sometimes plentiful over wide areas, as in parts of west and north Mainland.
E. palustris (L.) Roem. & Schult. subsp. *palustris* Common Spike-rush. Common.
E. uniglumis (Link) Schult. Slender Spike-rush. Uncommon in saltmarshes, other records need confirmation.
Blysmus rufus (Huds.) Link Narrow Blysmus. Occasional in saltmarsh turf.

Schoenoplectus lacustris (L.) Palla Bulrush. Local but possibly increasing; said to be spread by swans.

Isolepis setacea (L.) R.Br. Bristle Scirpus. Rare or overlooked.

Eleogiton fluitans (L.) Link Floating Scirpus. Very local.

Schoenus nigricans L. Bog-rush. Frequent.

Carex hostiana DC. Tawny Sedge. Frequent.

C. binervis Sm. Green-ribbed Sedge. Common on heaths and moors.

C. lepidocarpa Tausch Long-stalked Yellow Sedge. Probably frequent, at least on limestone.

C. demissa Hornem. Common Yellow Sedge. Very common.

C. serotina Mérat Small-fruited Yellow Sedge. Occasional or under-recorded, often in coastal turf. Plants formerly referred to the related taxon *C. scandinavica* E. W. Davies probably belong here.

C. flava (*sensu lato*) × *hostiana* Hybrids of *C. hostiana* with *C. demissa* or *C. lepidocarpa* are locally common, sometimes in the apparent absence of *C. hostiana*.

C. rostrata Stokes Bottle Sedge. Common.

C. rostrata × *vesicaria* = *C.* × *involuta* (Bab.) Syme. Deep drains at west side of Grass Water, Sandsting, where it seems to have ousted the second parent, 1965.

C. vesicaria L. Bladder Sedge. Formerly known in the neighbourhood of Grass Water, Sandsting, but not recorded since 1924.

C. panicea L. Carnation Sedge. Very common.

C. limosa L. Mud Sedge. Rare.

C. flacca Schreb. Glaucous Sedge. Common.

C. pilulifera L. Pill Sedge. Frequent.

C. aquatilis Wahlenb. Northern Sedge. Known only from Papil Water, Fetlar.

C. nigra (L.) Reichard Common Sedge. Very common and variable.

C. bigelowii Torr. ex Schwein. Stiff Sedge. Widespread on the higher summits and sometimes descending to low levels.

C. pulicaris L. Flea Sedge. Common.

C. dioica L. Dioecious Sedge. Frequent.

C. paniculata L. Greater Tussock Sedge. Known only from Fetlar, and Foula.

C. arenaria L. Sand Sedge. Local.

C. maritima Gunn. Curved Sedge. Very local.

C. echinata Murr. Star Sedge. Very common.

C. curta Good. White Sedge. Rare.

C. ovalis Good. Oval Sedge. Common.

Bromus hordeaceus L. subsp. *hordeaceus* (*B. mollis* L.). Soft Brome. Common in the lowlands.

†*B. hordeaceus* subsp. *hordeaceus* × *lepidus* = *B.* × *pseudothominii* Philip Smith (*B. thominii* sensu Tutin). Rare or under-recorded.

†*B. lepidus* Holmb. Slender Brome. Frequent, at least formerly, in hayfields, etc.

†*B. pseudosecalinus* Philip Smith. Very rare weed of hayfields.

Agropyron repens (L.) Beauv. Couch. Common, even found on a few skerries.

A. junceiforme (A. & D. Löve) A. & D. Löve Sand Couch. Rather local.

A. junceiforme × *repens* = *A.* × *laxum* (Fries) Almq. Local but sometimes plentiful where *A. junceiforme* has died out.

Elymus arenarius L. Lyme Grass. Frequent.

†*Hordeum vulgare* L. Barley. Occurring widely as a cornfield casual. Grown as a crop, especially in Dunrossness.

†*H. distichon* L. Barley. Cornfield casual.

† *Triticum aestivum* L. Wheat. Rare casual, mainly on rubbish dumps.

Glyceria declinata Bréb. Glaucous Sweet-grass. Certain only near Kergord, Weisdale.

G. fluitans (L.) R.Br. Floating Sweet-grass. Common.

Festuca vivipara (L.) Sm. Viviparous Fescue. Common.

F. rubra L. Creeping Fescue. Very common. Has recently been divided into numerous subspecies differing in habitat, etc., but the distribution of these in Shetland is not yet fully worked out.

†*F. pratensis* Huds. Meadow Fescue. Frequent hay grass.

†*F. arundinacea* Schreb. Tall Fescue. Very rare.

× *Festulolium loliaceum* (Huds.) P. Fourn. Hybrid Fescue. With the parents (*Festuca pratensis* and *Lolium perenne*), very rare.

Lolium perenne L. Perennial Rye-grass. Common.

†*L. multiflorum* Lam. Italian Rye-grass. Occasional.

†*L. temulentum* L. Darnel. Very rare, now only as a casual of rubbish dumps.

†*Vulpia bromoides* (L.) S. F. Gray Squirrel-tail Fescue. Rare casual of hayfields, etc.

Poa annua L. Annual Meadow-grass. Very common, sometimes a perennial.

P. trivialis L. Rough Meadow-grass. Common.

P. subcaerulea Sm. Spreading Meadow-grass. Very common.

†*P. pratensis* L. *sensu stricto* Meadow-grass. Scalloway, and doubtless elsewhere.

†*P. flabellata* (Lam.) Hook. Tussi-girse. Planted on crofts and established locally in their vicinity, mostly in Dunrossness.

Puccinellia capillaris (Liljebl.) Jansen Northern Salt-marsh-grass. Very frequent by the coast but seldom or never in saltmarshes; the taxon formerly called *P. distans* var. *prostrata* (Beeby) Druce.

P. maritima (Huds.) Parl. Common Salt-marsh-grass. Mainly in saltmarsh turf, rather local.

†*Briza media* L. Common Quaking-grass. Rare and probably not native.

†*Dactylis glomerata* L. Cocksfoot. Common.

†*Cynosurus echinatus* L. Rough Dog's-tail. Once found by Edmonston as a casual on Bressay.

C. cristatus L. Crested Dog's-tail. Common.

Catabrosa aquatica (L.) Beauv. Water Whorl-grass. Wet ground in sandy coastal areas, very local.

Helictotrichon pubescens (Huds.) Pilger Hairy Oat-grass. Frequent.

Arrhenatherum elatius (L.) Beauv. ex J. & C. Presl False Oat-grass. Common.

†*Avena strigosa* Schreb. Bristle Oat. Once the normal Shetland oat, now much less grown but still seen here and there as a casual or relic of cultivation.

†*A. sativa* L. Now the commonly cultivated oat, seen frequently as a casual or relic of cultivation.

†*A. fatua* L. Common Wild Oat. Nowadays at least only a rare casual.

† *Trisetum flavescens* (L.) Beauv. Yellow Oat-Grass. Rare and doubtfully native.

Deschampsia setacea (Huds.) Hack. Bog Hair-grass. Rare and recently only to the north of Ronas Hill.

D. flexuosa (L.) Trin. Wavy Hair-grass. Very common.

D. caespitosa (L.) Beauv. Tufted Hair-grass. Very common.

Aira caryophyllea L. Silvery Hair-grass. Local.
A. praecox L. Early Hair-grass. Very common.
Holcus lanatus L. Yorkshire Fog. Ubiquitous.
H. mollis L. Creeping Soft-grass. Local colonist.
Anthoxanthum odoratum L. Sweet Vernal-grass. Ubiquitous.
†*Phalaris canariensis* L. Canary Grass. Occasional casual.
P. arundinacea L. Reed Canary-grass. Common; the cultivated var. *picta* L. (Ribbon Grass) persisting locally where outcast.
Ammophila arenaria (L.) Link Marram Grass. Locally common.
Agrostis canina L. subsp. *montana* (Hartm.) Hartm. Brown Bent. Common.
A. tenuis Sibth. Common Bent. Common.
A. gigantea Roth Black Bent. At present known only from sandy fields in Dunrossness.
A. stolonifera L. Creeping Bent. Very common.
A. stolonifera × *tenuis* Recorded from Foula and doubtless occurring elsewhere.
†*Phleum pratense* L. Timothy Grass. Occasional relic or escape from cultivation.
†*Alopecurus myosuroides* Huds. Slender Fox-tail. Once as a casual at Lerwick.
A. geniculatus L. Marsh Fox-tail. Common.
†*A. pratensis* L. Meadow Fox-tail. Occasionally naturalised by roadsides, etc., in the lowlands.
Nardus stricta L. Mat-grass. Very common.
Phragmites australis (Cav.) Trin. ex Steudel (*P. communis* Trin.). Common Reed. Very local.
Molinia caerulea (L.) Moench Purple Moor-grass. Very common.
Sieglingia decumbens (L.) Bernh. Heath Grass. Common.

SIPHONAPTERA (R. S. George)

There are only twelve species of fleas recorded from Shetland (and eleven from Orkney). This compares with 43 found in Hertfordshire, 42 in Gloucestershire, and 41 in (old) Yorkshire (Smit, 1955, 1957).

TABLE 24. Fleas

PULICIDAE
Pulex irritans L.
Spilopsyllus cuniculi (Dale)

HYSTRICHOPSYLLIDAE
Typhloceras poppei Wagner
Ctenophthalmus nobilis vulgaris Smit

LEPTOPSYLLIDAE
Leptopsylla segnis (Schonherr)

CERATOPHYLLIDAE
Dasypsyllus gallinulae gallinulae (Dale)
Nosopsyllus fasciatus (Bosc)
Ceratophyllus gallinae (Schrank)
C. fringillae (Walker)
C. vagabundus insularis Rothschild
C. garei Rothschild
C. borealis Rothschild

LEPIDOPTERA (based on Wolff, 1971)

The moths (and few butterflies) of Shetland are described in Chapter 8. The following list is taken from the *Zoology of Iceland*, in which Wolff compares the Lepidopteran faunas of Greenland, Iceland, Faroe, Shetland, Orkney and Scandinavia. A recent summary of the Orkney lepidoptera has been given by Lorimer (1975). The terminology is that of Kloet & Hincks (1972).

TABLE 25. Lepidoptera

HEPIALIDAE
Hepialus lupulinus L.
H. humuli L.
H. fusconebulosus de Geer

OCHSENHEIMERIIDAE
Ochsenheimeria bisontella Zell.

TINEIDAE
Tinea trinotella Thnbg.
Monopis rusticella Hb.

GRACILLARIIDAE
Aspilapteryx tringipennella Zell.
Caloptilia syringella F.

GLYPHIPTERIGIDAE
Aechmia thrasonella Se.
Anthophila fabriciana L.

YPONOMEUTIDAE
Plutella maculipennis Curt.
P. senilella Zett.
P. annulatella Curt.

EPERMENIIDAE
Cataplectica fulviguttella Zell.

ELACHISTIDAE
Elachista albidella Tgstr.

MOMPHIDAE
Mompha locupletella (*schrankella* Hb.) Den & Schiff.

OECOPHORIDAE
Endrosis sarcitrella L.
Hofmannophila pseudospretella Stt.
Agonopterix applana F.
Depressaria badiella Hb.

GELECHIIDAE
Monochroa tenebrella Hb.
Bryotropha terrella Hb.
Scrobipalpa samadensis Pfaff.
Neofaculta betula Haw.

TORTRICIDAE
Dichrorampha plumbagana Tr.
D. consortana Wilk.
D. montana Dup.
Laspeyresia succedana Den. & Schiff.
Epinotia semifuscana Stph.
E. mercuriana Frol.
Ancylis unguicella L.
Bactra lanceolana Hb.
Lobesia littoralis Humphr. & Westw.
Endothemia antiquana Hb.
Argyroploce lacunana Den. & Schiff.
A. schulziana F.
Syndemis musculana Hb.
Clepis helvolana Froel.
Philodone gerningana Den. & Schiff.
Eana penziana Thnbg.
E. osseana Scop.
Acleris aspersana Hb.

COCHYLIDAE
Falseuncaria ciliella Hb.
Aethes cnicana Westw.
Eupoecilia angustana Hb.

PYRALIDAE
Crambus pascuellus L.
C. pratellus L.
C. perlellus Scop.
C. hortuellus Hb.
Agriphila culmella L.
Catoptria furcatella Zett.

Eudoria angustea Curt.
E. borealis Tgstr.
Scoparia ambigualis Tr.
Pyrausta cespitalis Den. & Schiff.
Udea lutealis Hb.
Nomophila noctuella Den. & Schiff.

PTEROPHORIDAE
Stenoptilia bipunctidactyla Sc.

PIERIDAE
Pieris brassicae L.
P. rapae L.

LYCAENIDAE
Polyommatus icarus Rott.

NYMPHALIDAE
Vanessa atalanta L.
V. cardui L.
Aglias urticae L.
Nymphalis antiopa L.

DANAIDAE
Danaus plexippus L.

SATYIDAE
Coenonympha tullia Mull.
Xanthorhoe munitata Hb.
X. montanata Den. & Schiff.
X. fluctuata L.
Camptogramma bilineata L.
Entephria caesiata Den. & Schiff.
Eulithis testata L.
E. populata L.
Chloroclysta miata L.
C. citrata L.
Hydriomena furcata Thnbg.
Rheumaptera hastata L.
Operophtera brumata L.
Perizoma blandiata Den. & Schiff.
P. albulata Stph.
P. didymata L.
Eupithecia venosata F.
E. satyrata Hb.
E. nanata Hb.
Carsia sororiata Hb.

SPHINGIDAE
Acherontia atropos L.
Agrius convolvuli L.
Celerio lineata F.

ARCTIIDAE
Parasemia plantaginis L.

NOCTUIDAE
Euxoa tritici L.
E. nigricans L.
E. cursoria Hufn.
Agroris ipsilon Hufn.
Rhyacia simulans Hufn.
Standfussiana lucernea L.
Noctua pronuba L.
N. comes Hb.
Paradiarsia glareosa Esp.
Lycophotia porphyrea Den. & Schiff.
Peridroma saucia Hb.
Diarsia mendica F.
D. brunnea Den. & Schiff.
D. rubi View.
Amathes c-nigrum L.
A. xanthographa Den. & Schiff.
A. baja Den. & Schiff.
A. alpicola Zettl.
Eurois occulta L.
Anarta melanopa Thnbg.
Hada nana Hufn.
Mamestra brassicae L.
M. oleracea L.
Hadena bicuris Hufn.
H. conspersa Den. & Schiff.
Cerapteryx graminis L.
Orthosia gothica L.
Mythimna impura Hb.
M. pallens L.
Xylena vetusta Hb.
Blepharita adusta Esp.
Dasypolia templi Thnbg.
Agrochola circellaris Hufn.
Apatele euphorbiae Den. & Schiff.
Phlogophora meticulosa L.
Apamea monoglypha Hufn.
A. crenata Hufn.
A. furva Den. & Schiff.
A. maillardi Hb.-G
A. remissa Hb.
A. basilinea Den. & Schiff.
Oligia fasciuncula Haw.
Mesapamea secalis L.
Hydraecia micacea Esp.
Celaena haworthii Curt.

C. *leucostigma* Hb.
Rhizedra lutosa Hb.
Caradrina clavipalpis Sc.
Chloridea armigera Hb.
Catocala fraxini L.

Chrysaspidea festucae L.
Autographa gamma L.
A. pulchrina Haw.
Syngrapha interrogationis L.
Scoliopteryx libatrix L.

BEETLES (M. Bacchus)

The first recorded collection of Coleoptera of any importance from Shetland was made by Thomas Blackburn and C. E. Lilley in 1874. Their five papers and varied publications since then, together with the results of several recent collections, provide a good general picture of the beetle fauna. The 340 species known from the islands represents no more than 9% of the total recorded from the British Isles as a whole, and about 20% of the species to be found in an area of the same size in the south of England.

Perhaps the most notable feature of the fauna is the high proportion of predaceous species (Carabidae, Dytiscidae, Staphylinidae) which form 70% of the total. The limited flora, virtual absence of woodland with its associated fungi, and sparse humus deposits (other than peat) offer a very restricted range of habitats and are the main reason for the paucity of species from other families. The main phytophagous families Curculionidae (26 out of 500 British species) and Chrysomelidae are very poorly represented. Only two wood-feeding species have been found, both living in structural timbers. Species living in humus and fungi are almost absent and the omnivorous Tenebrionidae completely so.

Other notable absentees are the synanthropic species, *i.e.* those almost entirely associated with human habitation or activities. Of the better-known species only *Ptinus tectus* Boieldieu (the Australian Spider beetle) has been found in Shetland. Even then there is no evidence that the two individuals found were from breeding colonies rather than being casual imports.

In 1874 Blackburn described *Apion ryei* as a species new to science from his Shetland collection. Although there is some doubt about its status as a valid species, similar individuals have been found in the Hebrides. Several distinct varieties have also been described from Shetland although only one is now regarded as having any status (*Philonthus varius* (Gyllenhal) var. *shetlandicus* Poppius). One species on the British list is found only on the Shetland Islands, *Athous subfuscus* (Muëller), one of the click beetles. It is quite common in Europe and Scandinavia where it is generally found in woods and copses! It is thought possible that it was introduced in feeding stuff or plants during the long association between Norway and the Shetland Islands.

TABLE 26. Beetles

*Indicates species recorded in the literature which have not been verified by the examination of specimens.

CARABIDAE
Cychrus caraboides (Linnaeus) s.sp.
  rostratus (Linnaeus)
Carabus problematicus Herbst s.sp. gallicus
  Gehin
Leistus ferrugineus (Linnaeus)
Pelophila borealis (Paykull)
Nebria gyllenhali (Schoenherr)
  salina Fairmaire & Laboulbéne
Notiophilus aestuans (Motschulsky)
  aquaticus (Linnaeus)
  biguttatus (Fabricius)
  germinyi Fauvel
  palustris (Duftschmid)*
Elaphrus cupreus Duftschmid
Loricera pilicornis (Fabricius)
Dyschirius globosus (Herbst)
  politus (Dejean)*
Clivinia fossor (Linnaeus)
Broscus cephalotes (Linnaeus)
Patrobus assimilis Chaudoir
  atrorufus (Ström)
  septentrionis (Dejean)
Trechus fulvus Djean
  obtusus Erichson
  quadristriatus (Schrank)
  rubens (Fabricius)
Bembidion atrocoeruleum Stephens
  bruxellense Wesmael
  tetracolum Say
  unicolor Chaudoir
Pterostichus diligens (Sturm)
  minor (Gyllenhal)
  niger (Schaller)
  nigrita (Paykull)
  oblongopunctatus (Fabricius)
  strenuus (Panzer)
Calathus fuscipes (Goeze)
  melanocephalus (Linnaeus)
  mollis (Marsham)
Laemostenus terricola (Herbst)
Olisthopus rotundatus (Paykull)
Agonum albipes (Fabricius)
  ericeti (Panzer)*

  fuliginosum (Panzer)
Amara apricaria (Paykull)
  aulica (Panzer)
  bifrons (Gyllenhal)
  familiaris (Duftschmid)
  lunicollis Schiödte
Harpalus affinis (Schrank)
  latus (Linnaeus)
  quadripunctatus Dejean
Dicheirotrichus gustavi Crotch
Trichocellus cognatus (Gyllenhal)
Bradycellus harpalinus Serville
Cymindis vaporariorum (Linnaeus)

HALIPLIDAE
Haliplus confinis Stephens
  fulvus (Fabricius)
  lineatocollis (Marsham)

DYTISCIDAE
Hydroporus erythrocephalus (Linnaeus)
  gyllenhali Schiödte
  longulus Mulsant
  memnonius Nicolai*
  morio Aubé*
  nigrita (Fabricius)
  obscurus Sturm
  obsoletus Aubé
  palustris (Linnaeus)
  pubescens (Gyllenhal)
  tristis (Paykull)
  umbrosus (Gyllenhal)
Potamonectes assimilis (Paykull)
  griseostriatus (Degeer)
Oreodytes davisi (Curtis)*
Agabus arcticus (Paykull)
  bipustulatus (Linnaeus)
  guttatus (Paykull)
  melanocornis Zimmermann
  nebulosus (Forster)*
Ilybius fuliginosus (Fabricius)
Rhantus bistriatus (Bergstraesser)
  frontalis (Marsham)*
Colymbetes fuscus (Linnaeus)
Acilius sulcatus (Linnaeus)

Dytiscus lapponicus Gyllenhal
   sulcatus (Linnaeus)

GYRINIDAE
Gyrinus opacus Sahlberg
   substriatus Stephens

HYDROPHILIDAE
Helophorus aquaticus (Linnaeus)
   brevipalpis Bedel
   flavipes (Fabricius)
   grandis Illiger*
   granularis (Linnaeus)
Cercyon analis (Paykull)
   depressus Stephens*
   haemorrhoidalis (Fabricius)
   littoralis (Gyllenhall)
   melanocephalus (Linnaeus)
Megasternum obscurum (Marsham)
Anacaena globulus (Paykull)
Laccobius bipunctatus (Fabricius)
Enochrus quadripunctatus (Herbst)
Chaetarthria seminulum (Herbst)

HYDRAENIDAE
Ochthebius dilatatus Stephens*
Hydraena gracilis Germar
Limnebius truncatellus (Thunberg)

PTILIIDAE
Ptenidium laevigatum Erichson
   nitidum (Heer)
   pusillum (Gyllenhal)
Acrotrichis danica Sundt

LEIODIDAE
Hydnobius punctatus (Sturm)
Anisotoma dubia (Kugelann)
   obesa (Schmidt)
Agathidium laevigatum Erichson*
Sciodrepa watsoni (Spence)
Catops fuscus (Panzer)
   morio (Fabricius)

SILPHIDAE
Nicrophorus humator (Gleditsch)
Thanatophilus rugosus (Linnaeus)
Aclypea opaca (Linnaeus)*

SCYDMAENIDAE
Stenichnus collaris (Müller & Kunze)

STAPHYLINIDAE
Megarthrus denticollis (Beck)
   depressus (Paykull)
Olophrum piceum (Gyllenhal)
Arpedium brachypterum (Gravenhorst)
Acidota crenata (Fabricius)*
Lesteva heeri Fauvel
   longoelytrata (Goeze)
   monticola Kiesenwetter
   pubescens Mannerheim
Eusphalerum torquatum (Marsham)
Pyllodrepa floralis (Paykull)
Omalium excavatum Stephens
   laeviusculum Gyllenhal
   riparium Thomson
   rivulare (Paykull)
Xylodromus concinnus (Marsham)
   depressus (Gravenhorst)
Micralymma marinum (Ström)
Bledius subterraneus Erichson*
Carpelimus pusillus (Gravenhorst)
Platystethus arenarius (Fourcroy)*
Anotylus complanatus (Erichson)
   maritimus Thomson
   nitidulus (Gravenhorst)*
   rugosus (Fabricius)
   sculpturatus (Gravenhorst)
Stenus brevipennis Thomson
   brunnipes Stephens
   clavicornis (Scopoli)
   geniculatus Gravenhorst
   impressus Germar
   juno (Paykull)
   nitidiusculus Stephens
   ossium Stephens
   picipes Stephens*
Lathrobium brunnipes (Fabricius)
   fulvipenne (Gravenhorst)
Othius angustus (Stephens)
   myrmecophilus Kiesenwetter
   punctulatus (Goeze)
Gyrophypnus fracticornis (Müller)
   punctulatus (Paykull)
Xantholinus glabratus (Gravenhorst)
   linearis (Olivier)
Philonthus cephalotes (Gravenhorst)
   decorus (Gravenhorst)
   fimetarius (Gravenhorst)
   marginatus (Ström)

politus (Linnaeus)
sordidus (Gravenhorst)
varius (Gyllehhal)
 var. *shetlandicus* Poppius
Gabrius nigritulus (Gravenhorst)*
 trossulus (von Nordmann)
Cafius xantholoma (Gravenhorst)
Staphylinus aeneocephalus Degeer
 ater Gravenhorst
 olens (Müller)
Creophilus maxillosus (Linnaeus)
Quedius aridulus Jansson
 assimilis (von Nordmann)*
 boops (Gravenhorst)
 cinctus (Paykull)
 curtipennis Bernhauer
 fuliginosus (Gravenhorst)*
 fulvicollis (Stephens)*
 mesomelinus (Marsham)
 molochinus (Gravenhorst)
 nitipennis (Stephens)
 scintillans (Gravenhorst)
 semiaeneus (Stephens)
 schatzmayri Gridelli
 tristis (Gravenhorst)
 umbrinus Erichson
Mycetoporus angularis (Mulsant & Rey)*
 splendidus (Gravenhorst)
Tachyporus atriceps Stephens
 chrysomelinus (Linnaeus)
 hypnorum (Fabricius)*
 nitidulus (Fabricius)
 pusillus (Gravenhorst)
Tachinus laticollis Gravenhorst
 signatus Gravenhorst
Cypha laeviusculus (Mannerheim)
Myllaena brevicornis (Matthews)
Autalia puncticollis Sharp
Boreophila islandica (Kraatz)
Aloconota gregaria (Erichson)
Amischa cavifrons Sharp
Lyprocorrhe anceps (Erichson)
Geostiba circellaris (Gravenhorst)
Liogluta longiuscula (Gravenhorst)
Atheta debilis (Erichson)
 elongatula (Gravenhorst)
 fallaciosa (Sharp)
 hygrobia (Thomson)

melanocera (Thomson)
excellens (Kraatz)
harwoodi Williams
amicula (Stephens)
atricolor (Sharp)
cadaverina (Brisout)
tibialis (Heer)
trinotata (Kraatz)
fungi (Gravenhorst)
aterrima (Gravenhorst)
celata (Erichson)
nigra (Kraatz)
zosterae (Thomson)
graminicola (Gravenhorst)
pertyi (Heer)
strandiella Brundin
atramentaria (Gyllenhal)
ischnocera Thomson
nigripes (Thomson)*
longicornis (Gravenhorst)
vestita (Gravenhorst)
Ocalea picata (Stephens)*
Ocyusa hibernica (Rye)
Mniusa incrassata (Mulsant & Rey)*
Oxypoda haemorrhoa (Mannerheim)
 nigricornis Motschulsky
 opaca (Gravenhorst)
 umbrata (Gyllenhal)
Aleochara algarum Fauvel
 grisea Kraatz
 lanuginosa Gravenhorst
 obscurella Gravenhorst
 sparsa Heer

PSELAPHIDAE
 Bryaxis bulbifer (Reichenbach)

GEOTRUPIDAE
Geotrupes stercorarius (Linnaeus)
 stercorosus (Scriba)*

SCARABAEIDAE
Aphodius ater (Degeer)
 borealis Gyllenhal
 contaminatus (Herbst)
 depressus (Kugelann)
 fimetarius (Linnaeus)
 lapponum Gyllenhal
 rufipes (Linnaeus)
 rufus (Moll)

sphacelatus (Panzer)

CLAMBIDAE
Calyptomerus dubius (Marsham)

SCIRTIDAE
Elodes marginata (Fabricius)
    marginata (Linnaeus)

BYRRHIDAE
Simplocaria semistriata (Fabricius)
Cytilus sericeus (Forster)
Byrrhus fasciatus (Forster)
    pilula (Linnaeus)

DRYOPIDAE
Dryops griseus (Erichson)

ELATERIDAE
Hypnoidus riparius (Fabricius)
Athous subfuscus (Müller)
Dalopius marginatus (Linnaeus)
Denticollis linearis (Linnaeus)

CANTHARIDAE
Malthodes pumilis (Brébisson)*

ANOBIIDAE
Anobium punctatum (Degeer)

PTINIDAE
Ptinus tectus Boieldieu

NITIDULIDAE
Brachypterus urticae (Fabricius)
Meligethes aeneus (Fabricius)
Epuraea aestiva (Linnaeus)

CRYPTOPHAGIDAE
Cryptophagus acutangulus (Gyllenhal)
    cellaris (Scopoli)
    dentatus (Herbst)
    pilosus Gyllenhal
    pseudodentatus Bruce
    saginatus Sturm
    scanicus (Linnaeus)
    setulosus Sturm*
Atomaria apicalis Erichson
    atricapilla Stephens
    berolinensis Kraatz
    fuscipes (Gyllenhal)
    lewisi Reitter
    nitidula (Marsham)

ruficornis (Marsham)
Ephistemus globulus (Paykull)

COCCINELLIDAE
Nephus redtenbacheri (Mulsant)
Adonia variegata (Goeze)*

LATHRIDIIDAE
Aridius nodifer (Westwood)
Lathridius pseudominutus (Strand)
Enicmus histrio Joy & Tomlin
Corticaria elongata (Gyllenhal)
Corticarina fuscula (Gyllenhal)
    umbilicata (Beck)
Corticarina fuscula (Gyllenhal)*

CHRYSOMELIDAE
DONACIINAE
Plateumaris discolor (Panzer)

CHRYSOMELINAE
Chrysolina sanguinolenta (Linnaeus)
    staphylaea (Linnaeus)
Hydrothassa marginella (Linnaeus)

HALTICINAE
Longitarsus luridus (Scopoli)*
Psylliodes marcida (Illiger)
    picina (Marsham)

APIONIDAE
Apion violaceum Kirby
    cruentatum Walton
    aethiops Herbst
    loti Kirby
    ryei Blackburn

CURCULIONIDAE
Otiorhynchus arcticus (Fabricius)
    atroapterus (Degeer)
    nodosus (Müller)
    porcatus (Herbst)
    singularis (Linnaeus)
    sulcatus (Fabricius)
Strophosomus melanogrammus (Forster)
Philopedon plagiatus (Schaller)
Barynotus squamosus Germar
Tropiphorus elevatus (Herbst)*
    obtusus (Bonsdorff)
Sitona lepidus Gyllenhal
    lineelus (Bonsdorff)
    puncticollis Stephens*

Hypera plantaginis (Degeer)
Leiosoma deflexum (Panzer)
Euophyrum confine (Broun)
Notaris acridulus (Linnaeus)
Micrelus ericae (Gyllenhal)
Cidnorhinus quadrimaculatus (Linnaeus)

Ceutorhynchus assimilis (Paykull)*
    contractus (Marsham)
    erisymi (Fabricius)*
    pollinarius (Forster)
Rhinoncus pericarpius (Linnaeus)
Phytobius quadrituberculatus (Fabricius)

SPIDERS (N. P. Ashmole)

Shetland has a substantial array of mountain spiders. The principal published information hitherto has been that provided by W. S. Bristowe (1931) after a brief visit in July 1930. He found 30 species and listed two others as having been recorded previously. Of these 32, all but one were found in recent expeditions – an expedition in summer 1974 by staff and students from Edinburgh University Zoology Department led by Drs Philip Ashmole and John Godfrey; by members of the Institute of Terrestrial Ecology Survey Teams, also in 1974; by a party from Leicester Polytechnic to Unst led by Dr J. A. Fowler in 1969; and by Philip Ashmole and George McGavin in April 1975.

Short lists of spiders from Fair Isle have been published by Lindroth (1955), Cloudsley-Thompson (1956) and Carpenter (1962), but these have not been incorporated in the list that follows because of the isolated nature of Fair Isle and the incomplete knowledge of its fauna.

TABLE 27. Spiders.

AMAUROBIIDAE
Amaurobius fenestralis (Stroem)

GNAPHOSIDAE
Drassodes lapidosus (Walckenaer) (*or
    D. cupreus* (Blackwall))
Gnaphosa leporina (L. Koch)
Haplodrassus signifer (C. L. Koch).

CLUBIONIDAE
Agroeca proxima (O.P. – Cambridge)
Clubiona phragmitis C.L. Koch
C. trivialis C.L. Koch

THOMISIDAE
Oxyptila trux (Blackwall)
Xysticus cristatus (Clerck)

SALTICIDAE
Neon reticulatus (Blackwall)

LYCOSIDAE
Alopecosa pulverulenta (Clerck)
Arctosa perita (Latreille)
Pardos nigriceps (Thorell)
P. palustris (L)
P. pullata (Clerck)
Pirata piraticus (Clerck)
Trochosa terricola Thorell

GELENIDAE
Antistea elegans (Blackwall)
Cryphoeca silvicola (C.L. Koch)
Hahnia montana (Blackwall)
Tegenaria domestica (Clerck)
Textrix denticulata (Olivier)

THERIDIIDAE
Enoplognatha ovata (Clerck)
Robertus arundineti (O.P. – Cambridge)
R. lividus (Blackwall)

TETRAGNATHIDAE
Meta merianae (Scopoli)
M. segmentata (Clerck)
Pachygnatha clercki Sundevall
P. degeeri Sundevall
Tetragnatha extensa (L)

ARANEIDAE
Araneus diadematus Clerck
Zygiella x-notata (Clerck)

LINYPHIIDAE, subfamily
ERIGONINAE
Araeoncus crassiceps (Westring)
Caledonia evansi O.P. – Cambridge
Ceratinella brevipes (Westring)
Dicymbrium brevisetosum Locket
Diplocephalus cristatus (Blackwall)
D. permixtus O.P. – Cambridge
Entelecara errata O.P. – Cambridge
Erigone arctica (White)
E. atra (Blackwall)
E. capra Simon
E. dentipalpis (Wider)
E. promiscua (O.P. – Cambridge)
Erigonella hiemalis (Blackwall)
Gonatium rubens (Blackwall)
Hypomma bituberculatum (Wider)
Monocephalus castaneipes (Simon)
Oedothorax fuscus (Blackwall)
O. retusus (Westring)
Pelecopsis nemoralis (Blackwall)
Pocadicnemis pumila (Blackwall)
Rhaebothorax morulus (O.P. –
    Cambridge)
Savignya frontata (Blackwall)
Silemetropus ambiguus (O.P. –
    Cambridge)
Tiso vagans (Blackwall)

Typhochrestus digitatus (O.P. –
    Cambridge)
Walckanaera acuminata Blackwall
W. antica (Wider)
W. capito (Westring)
W. clavicornis (Emerton)
W. nudipalpis (Westring)

LINYPHIIDAE, subfamily
LINYPHIINAE
Agyneta decora (O.P. – Cambridge)
Allomengea scopigera (Grube)
Bathyphantes gracilis (Blackwall)
Bolyphantes alticeps (Sundevall)
B. luteolus (Blackwall)
Centromerita bicolor (Blackwall)
C. concinna (Thorell)
Centromerus prudens (O.P. – Cambridge)
Diplystyla concolor (Wider)
Drepanotylus uncatus (O.P. – Cambridge)
Halorates reprobus (O.P. – Cambridge)
Hilaira frigida (Thorell)
Lepthyphantes ericaeus (Blackwall)
L. leprosus (Ohlert)
L. mengei Kulczynski
L. minutus (Blackwall)
L. tenuis (Blackwall)
L. zimmermanni Bertkan
Leptorhoptrum robustum (Westring)
Meioneta gulosa (L. Koch)
M. nigripes (Simon)
M. saxatilis (Blackwall)
Oreonetides abnormis (Blackwall)
O. vaginatus (Thorell)
Phaulo thrix hardyi (Blackwall)
Poeciloneta globosa (Wider)
Porrhomma egeria Simon
P. montanum Jackson

LAND AND FRESHWATER MOLLUSCA (Nora F. McMillan)

Freshwater and terrestrial Mollusca so far recorded from Shetland total 61 species – a creditable number for a group of small islands lying out in the Atlantic so far north as Bergen.

As one goes north the number of species of Mollusca represented in a fauna diminishes, and the lack of lime in the islands is another inhibiting factor. The peat mosses and moors are almost empty of Mollusca, only a few slugs tolerating such conditions, and snails must be sought in the tiny glens and around old crofts. Rubbish dumps, as elsewhere, support a few molluscan camp-followers of man.

The following list has been compiled from all available sources, published and unpublished. Consideration of space precludes separate lists for each island although each island naturally forms a district in itself, no matter how small it may be in area. In the list there are 4 brackish-water species, 17 freshwater species, and the remainder are all land species. There are 15 species of slugs, 36 species of snails, and 10 species of bivalves (clams, mussels).

TABLE 28. Non-marine Mollusca
(Nomenclature that of the Conchological Society's *Atlas of the Non-marine Mollusca of the British Isles*, 1976)

Hydrobia ventrosa (Montagu) s.s.
H. ulvae (Pennant)
Potamopyrgus jenkinsi (Smith)
Carychium minimum Müller, s.l.
Ovatella myosotis (Draparnaud)
Leucophytia bidentata (Müller)
Lymnaea truncatula (Müller)
L. peregra (Müller)
Bathomphalus contortus (L.)
Gyraulus laevis (Alder)
Armiger crista (L)
Ancylus fluviatilis Müller
Oxyloma pfeifferi (Rossmässler)
Cochlicopa lubrica (Müller)
C. lubricella (Porro)
Columella edentula (Draparnaud) s.l.
Vertigo pygmaea (Draparnaud)
Pupilla muscorum (L.)
Lauria cylindracea (da Costa)
Punctum pygmaeum (Draparnaud)
Discus rotundatus (Müller)
Arion ater (L.) s.l.
A. subfuscus (Draparnaud)
A. circumscriptus Johnston s.s.
A. silvaticus Lohmander
A. fasciatus (Nilsson)
A. hortensis Férussac s.l.
A. intermedius Normand
Vitrina pellucida (Müller)
Vitrea crystallina (Müller) s.l.
V. contracta (Westerlund)

Nesovitrea hammonis (Ström)
Aegopinella pura (Alder)
A. nitidula (Draparnaud)
Oxychilus draparnaudi (Beck)
O. cellarius (Müller)
O. alliarius (Miller)
Milax gagates (Draparnaud)
M. sowerbyi (Férussac)
M. budapestensis (Hazaỳ)
Limax maximus L.
L. marginatus Müller
Deroceras laeve (Müller)
D. reticulatum (Müller)
D. caruanae (Pollonera)
Euconulus fulvus (Müller) s.l.
Clausilia bidentata (Ström)
Balea perversa (L.)
Candidula intersecta (Poiret)
Arianta arbustorum (L.)
Cepaea hortensis (Müller)
Margaritifera margaritifera (L.)
Sphaerium corneum (L.)
Pisidium casertanum (Poli)
P. personatum Malm
P. obtusale (Lamarck)
P. milium Held
P. subtruncatum Malm.
P. lilljeborgii Clessin
P. hibernicum Westerlund
P. nitidum Jenyns

BIRDS

Observations on Shetland birds have never been continuous and the scattered nature of the archipelago effectively makes is impossible for any individual to cover all the ground. This is particularly true when migrants are concerned since they may stop over on outlying islands for only a day or so.

The observations of the Saxbys and Edmonstons in the 19th century were largely confined to Unst, while those of the visiting naturalists – Harvie-Brown, Eagle Clarke, Evans and Buckley, etc, have only been of odd years, although they were supplied with much information by local naturalists, such as Tom Henderson. In the 20th century Shetlanders, such as R. Stuart Bruce, J. C. Grierson, L. McDougall, G. T. Kay, G. W. Russell and many others, have contributed detailed records of many observations.

All the records up to 1953 were collated and analysed in the *Birds and Mammals of Shetland* by L. S. V. and U. M. Venables, who lived in Shetland from 1947–53. This book has been the authoritative work on Shetland birds and nearly all the records prior to 1953 have been taken from it for this list.

Records since 1953 have come from Bobby Tulloch, Dennis Coutts, Robert Duthie, Johnny Simpson and many others. From 1969–72 Bobby Tulloch published an annual report, and then in 1973 P. K. Kinnear and I. Robertson founded the Shetland Bird Club. The effect that this last group of enthusiasts has had on Shetland bird observations can be gained from the fact that from 1953–70 an average of two new species annually were added to the list, while from 1970–77 the average had risen to five. There were over 100 contributors to the 1977 Shetland Bird Report.

Numerous species recorded only irregularly before 1969 have been seen regularly since, suggesting that they were in fact regular visitors before that date. It is necessary therefore to note for these species that they have been annual visitors since 'at least 1969'.

It should be noted also that definitive records of geographical races are not necessarily a true guide to their occurrence as many are difficult to distinguish in the field.

TABLE 29. Birds

The order of the list is taken from *Birds of the Western Palearctic*

SYMBOLS

R or r   Resident species: whole or most of the population remains through-
          out the year. R – Common; r – Scarce.

P or p   Partial Migrant: breeding species of which a substantial part of the
          population winters outside Shetland, the remainder remaining
          throughout the year. P – Common; p – Scarce.

S or s   Summer Resident: breeding species of which the whole or most of the population winters outwith Shetland. S – Common; s – Scarce.

M or m   Regular Migrant: M – Common; m – in small numbers.

A   Scarce Migrant: usually recorded, but not always annually.

V or v   Vagrant: V – more than 5 occurrences; v – less than 5 occurrences.

W or w Winter visitor: W – Common; w – Scarce.

Or   Order 1 1–10
                2 11–100
                3 101–1000
                4 1001–10,000
                5 10,001–100,000
                6 100,001–1,000,000

Unconfirmed or doubtful records are in brackets.

Symbols adapted from the Shetland Bird Club Report. Earliest records given when known; breeding number or order given if available; migratory months are noted although odd birds may fall outwith these months, all dates and numbers of vagrants (where known) included. Two years given with interposed stroke, *e.g.* 1950/51 – indicates overwintering. If no number is given after year, this indicates one record; if a number refers to breeding, it refers to the number of pairs.

Red-throated Diver *Gavia stellata* S   Bones found 9–10th century Jarlshof. Recorded breeding from at least 1800. 500 pairs, increasing. Main return March, departure late August/early September. A few overwintering in recent years.

Black-throated Diver *G. arctica* A   First recorded 1919. Singles every year for last decade at least exceptionally 1978(7). Previously 1919–1952 13 individuals. January–September.

Great Northern Diver *G. immer* W   Bones of individual found Bronze Age Jarlshof. Wintering from at least 1800, October–May, 200–400. Singles throughout the year.

White-billed Diver *G. adamsii* V   1946, 1947, 1950, 1952, 1964, 1969, 1974, 1977(3), 1978(2). Predominantly May/June; single records for October and January.

Little Grebe *Tachybaptus ruficollis* w   Regular winter visitor to 19th century at least, October–March, 10–20. Bred 1967.

Great Crested Grebe *Podiceps cristatus* A   1871–1953, 8 records. 1962(2), 1963, 1964(3). Singles annually for last decade at least.

Red-necked Grebe *P. grisegena* A   Mainly wintering individuals; 1970, 1971(4), 1972(3), 1973, 1974, 1976(3). Previously 2–4 regularly in winter, September–April.

Slavonian Grebe *P. auritus* w   100 September–April. Singles occasionally summer.

Black-necked Grebe *P. nigricollis* V   Unknown 19th century; 1945–1973 regular spring migrant; then 1970, 1976, 1977.

Black-browed Albatross *Diomedea melanophris* v   Single seen Hermaness since 1970.

Fulmar *Fulmarus glacialis* R   First bred Foula 1878. Now 150,000 pairs at least, increasing. Blue phase seen annually as individuals; 5 recorded between Fair Isle and Sumburgh October 1966, 14 in 1978, breed occasionally.

Cory's Shearwater *Calonectris diomedea* v   1971 and 1977, June and September, offshore.

Great Shearwater *Puffinus gravis* v   1965 and 1969, April and August, offshore; others, no date.

Sooty Shearwater *P. griseus* m   Seen offshore in small parties in late summer.

Manx Shearwater *P. puffinus* S   Or. 2–3.

Storm Petrel *Hydrobates pelagicus* S   Or. 4.

Leach's Petrel *Oceanodroma leucorhoa* sm   Records of occurrence to early this century, plus storm-driven birds 1952, 1977, 1978. Several found dead in Whalsay Storm Petrel colony 1951. First confirmation of breeding 1974, Foula.

Gannet *Sula bassana* P   First bred 1914. Now 10,000 pairs, increasing. Recorded every month.

Cormorant *Phalacrocorax carbo* R   Bones found Bronze Age and 9–10th century Jarlshof. Circa 500 pairs.

Shag *P. aristotelis* R   Bones found Bronze Age and 9–10th century Jarlshof. 10,000 pairs minimum.

Bittern *Botaurus stellaris* V   Bones of individual found Jarlshof 9–10th century. 1843–1953 5 records, 1965, 1970, 1976, 1978 one found dead; all February–May except 1942, November; 1978 December.

Little Bittern *Ixobrychus minutus* v   1883, 1917, 1965, August, May and June.

Little Egret *Egretta garzetta* v   1954, 1961, 1970, May/June.

Grey Heron *Ardea cinerea* Wm   Bones found Bronze Age and 9–10th century Jarlshof. Bred 19th century at least once, possibly 1900 and in 1930s. September–March, minimum 50; passage March–May and August–October.

Purple Heron *A. purpurea* v   1977 May.

Black Stork *Ciconia nigra* v   1977 May.

White Stork *C. ciconia* v   1977 May and previously prior to 1844.

Glossy Ibis *Plegadis falcinellus* v   1862, 1920, October and November respectively.

Spoonbill *Platalea leucorodia* v   1871(2), 1975(3), April and June respectively.

Mute Swan *Cygnus olor* V   Unsuccessful introductions with limited breeding 1930s, plus vagrant, 1970(3), 1971(2), 1975, 1976, 1977, 5 arrived January and 3 May/June; 1978.

Bewick Swan *C. columbianus* V   More numerous 19th century, then 1900, 1901, 1926, 1927(2), 1947, 1955, 1969(3), 1970, 1971, 1972 (7 plus); October–February.

Whooper Swan *C. cygnus* W   Wintering since at least 18th century, circa 400 in passage in most recent years, September–April, increasing. Wounded pair brought together and bred 1910–18. Recently occasional summering individuals, previously only exceptionally.

Bean Goose *Anser fabilis* V   1952, first record, then 1970, 1972, 1974, 1976, 1977(8), 1978. Individuals usually, January–March and October. Few previous records and none substantiated.

Pink-footed Goose *A. brachyrhynchus* m   Annually, except 1974, for last decade at least, previously few records, but probably under-recorded. Mainly September/October, also March/April. Usually small flocks, occasionally large flocks overhead.

White-fronted Goose *A. albifrons albifrons* A   *A. a. flavirostris* A   Individuals annually since 1973 and irregularly before that; more common January–April than October/November. Both races.

Greylag Goose *A. anser* Mw   Mainly October in small to large flocks, also small numbers March–May. A few winter and summer. Most common goose and previously of similar status.

Snow Goose *Branta caerulescens* V Oct–Jan 1953/54

Canada Goose *B. canadensis* V   Possibly 1843(7–8), first definite record 1946(2), 1962(3), then 1971, 1973, 1975, 1976(c20), 1977, 1978. Usually individuals June/July or October.

Barnacle Goose *B. leucopsis* m   In late 19th century annual migrant, possibly less regular in mid-twentieth century, now regular once more in small flocks September/October and February–April.

Brent Goose *B. bernicla bernicla* V   *B. b. hrota* V   Since 1969 annually except 1973, 1974 and 1975, previously irregular to 19th century when fairly regular autumn migrant. Both races occur in small flocks.

Shelduck *Tadorna tadorna* s   Bred since at least 18th century. Bones found 9–11 century Jarlshof. Less than 5 pairs breeding, decrease in recent years. Return January/February, depart July/August.

Wigeon *Anas penelope* Mwr   Fresh eggs recorded in 19th century, but first confirmed breeding this century in 1976, 1977, 1978, although suspected for a number of years. Passage September/October, 200–300 birds winter to April.

American Wigeon *A. americana* v   First recorded 1948(2), 1966, 1967(2), 1968(2), 1973, 2 January/February, 5 May/June and 1 October.

Gadwall *A. strepera* A   First recorded 1895, to 1951 only 4 records. 1965(4), 1966, 1968, then annually as individuals or pairs since 1969, exceptionally 10 1974. Usually May, occasionally October.

Teal *A. crecca* rw   Breeding Or 1-Low Or 2. Wintering October–March; September passage. Status unchanged, over this century, at least.

American Green-winged Teal *A. c. carolinensis* v
First recorded in Bruce & Grierson, no date; then 1970, 1972(3), October and February–April respectively; wintering 1975/76, 1978(2).

Mallard *A. platyrrhynchos* Rmw   Breeding Or 2. Wintering October–March, 2–300 at peak; September passage.

Pintail *A. acuta* mw   First confirmed breeding 1905, then 1906, (poss. 1920), 1930–35(1), 1977. Summer occurrence decreased since 1950s. Few individuals May/June and September/October and a few winter and summer.

Garganey *A. querquedula* A   Recently 1964, 1966 and as individuals or pairs since 1970; previously 1907, 1929, 1952 and 1953 as rare vagrant and similar in 19th century.

Shoveler *A. clypeata* mw   Bones found 9–10th century Jarlshof. Otherwise first recorded 1918. First bred 1953, then 1954, 1973, 1975. Individuals April–June and August–October. Recently a few pairs wintering and summering, previously irregular in those seasons.

Pochard *Aythya ferina* W   Wintering from at least 18th century, October–April, circa 200. Increase in last twenty years.

Ring-necked Duck *A. collaris* v   May 1978.

Tufted Duck *A. fuligula* Wr   Became common wintering species towards end of 19th century, large increase in last 20 years, October–March 300–500. First bred 1952, regularly since. About 25 pairs 1977.

Scaup *A. marila* mw   Little changed since 19th century, individuals April–June and September/October; a few winter and in last decade more regular as individuals in summer.

Eider *Somateria mollissima* R   Circa 15,000 birds. Possibly small migration/immigration.

King Eider *S. spectabilis* w   1846–1950 8 records, then 1959, 1963, 1964, 1966, 1968, 1969(3), 1970, 1971(4), 1972(2) and annually as 5–6 individuals October–June until 1971, 1978(2). Individuals occasionally summer.

Long-tailed Duck *Clangula hyemalis* W   Wintering from at least beginning of 19th century and occasionally bred then; October–April 1500–2000, individuals summering most years.

Common Scoter *Melanitta nigra* sm   First confirmed breeding 1911, 1–5 pairs regularly since. Very small winter population spring passage April/May.

Surf Scoter *M. perspicillata* v   1847, 1975. June and May.

Velvet Scoter *M. fusca* w   Bones of individual 9–10th century Jarlshof. Possibly bred 1945. Small numbers winter (Low Or 2). Individuals regularly summer.

Goldeneye *Bucephala clangula* W   October–April, 350 at peak. Very occasionally summer – 3 in June 1955.

Smew *M. albellus* mw   Previous to 1953 numerous irregular appearance in winter. Since, 1961, 1962, 1964, 1965 and regularly April/May, October and wintering since 1973. Redheads 1972, 1973, 1974, 1975, 1978, 1979.

Red-breasted Merganser *M. serrator* R   Breeding since at least 19th century, Or 2. Wintering population under 300.

Goosander *M. merganser* w   A few individuals winter and occasionally summer, possible increase in occurrence since 19th century.

Honey Buzzard *Pernis apivorus* A   4 singles in 19th century, then 1913, 1959, 1964, 1969, 1971 (2 plus), 1973, 1974, 1975 (2 poss. 3), 1976. Predominantly May/June, less frequently July and 1 September.

Black Kite *Milvus migrans* v   1966, 1975, May and June respectively.

White-tailed Eagle *Haliaeetus albicilla* v
Bred regularly before 20th century. Last bred 1910. Recorded 1949 June (poss. 1969 May).

Marsh Harrier *Circus aeruginosus* V
Rare in 19th century. Then, 1934, 1949, 1970, 1971, 1972, 1973, 1974, 1975. Mainly May and singles in April and September, October and November.

Hen Harrier *C. cyaneus* A   Casual but regular visitor all months except July, mainly September–November in last decade at least. Usually as a few individuals except 1976 (10+). Previously rare autumn migrant and winter visitor to 19th century when not uncommon winter visitor. Bred at least once in 19th century.

Montagu's Harrier *C. pygargus* v 1954, May (1964 August).

Goshawk *Accipiter gentilis* V   1859, 1860, 1969, 1976 (2), 1977. October–May.

Sparrowhawk *A. nisus* mw   A few pairs bred late 19th century. In small numbers wintering September–May and passage in May and September.

Buzzard *Buteo buteo* V   1858, 1900, 1904, 1936, 1959, 1964 (2), 1966, 1967/68 (6), 1969 (2), 1972 (3), 1973 (4), 1975 (2), 1976 (poss. 8), 1977 (3), 1978. Recorded every month except July/August and occasionally wintering. Both phases 1975.

Rough-legged Buzzard *B. lagopus* V   1884, 1915, 1919 (2), 1936, 1951, 1963, 1964, 1966, 1968, 1970, 1975 (3 poss. 4), 1976. December–June and October.

Golden Eagle *Aquila chrysaetos* V   1866 and very rare passing visitor in late 19th century, 1963 (dead), (poss. 1969), 1976, 1977 (poss. 1 more each 1976, 1977). April, June and November.

Osprey *Pandion haliaetus* m   Previous to 1953 an irregular spring migrant. Since 1965 individuals at least every year except 1968 and 1971. Exceptionally 6 in 1969. Predominantly May/June.

Kestrel *Falco tinnunculus* m   Bred in 19th century; last bred 1905. Passage May and September, often summering and occasionally wintering.

Red-footed Falcon *F. vespertinus* V 1964, 1969, 1970(1 poss. 2), 1972(2), 1973(2), 1976(2), 1978(3). Predominantly May–July, 1 October.

Merlin *F. columbarius* rm Breeding since 19th century at least, 25–30 pairs. More numerous in passage in autumn than spring.

Hobby *F. subbuteo* V 4 records 19th century, 1931, 1950, 1964, 1965, 1967, 1968, 1973, 1975. May/June.

Gyr Falcon *F. rusticola islandicus* V *F. r. candicans* V More frequent early 19th century, 1898–1930 4 *islandicus* and 4 *candicans*, 1950, 1952, 1965, 1967, 1970, 1972(1–3), (1973 1 imported for release). Subspecies predominating slightly is Greenland (*candicans*).

Peregrine *F. peregrinus* r Bones found 9–10th century Jarlshof. Bred in numbers in past centuries, drastic decrease to a very few pairs in recent years.

Red Grouse *Lagopus lagopus* R Last introduced 1901. Or 2 breeding.

Quail *Coturnix coturnix* A Bred from 1868 at least, to 1964 irregularly. A few individuals recorded 1967, 1969, 1970, 1971, 1972, 1973, 1976, 1978; mostly May–July.

Pheasant *Phasianus colchicus* r Introduced regularly as pairs. Breeds irregularly.

Water Rail *Rallus aquaticus* wm Individuals March/April and September–November; also few wintering. Summering 1973 and 1974, and previously 1918 and 1934.

Spotted Crake *Porzana porzana* A Previous to 1953 a few autumn records, 1966, 1968, 1969(2), 1970(2), 1973, 1974(2), 1976(4). April–November.

Little Crake *P. parva* v 1959 April.

Corncrake *Crex crex* s Previously a common breeder, last bred 1975. In 1977 only 1 recorded, 1978 (several).

Moorhen *Gallinula chloropus* mr First bred 1890. Decreased from Low Or 2 to 4 pairs 1977. Recorded most months.

Coot *Fulica atra* wmr Bred from 1890 at least, 1 pair only from about 1953, Usually October influx of a few birds, 1977 20–50. Exceptionally 1976 with 2–300.

Crane *Grus grus* V Several records 19th century, 1906, 1957, 1967(2), 1969, 1970(2–4), 1972, 1973, 1978. May/June, August/September.

Great Bustard *Otis tarda* v 1936 May.

Oystercatcher *Haemotopus ostralegus* S Bone found 9–10th century Jarlshof. Breeding from 18th century at least. Wintering from turn of this century in small flocks. Breeding Or 3–4 and increasing. Main return from mid February, departure September/October.

Black-winged Stilt *Himantopus himantopus* v 1 prior to 1843 and 1934 September.

Avocet *Recurvirostra avosetta* V 1843, 1871, 1936, 1952(2), 1964(2), 1974. March–May and September.

Stone Curlew *Burhinus oedicnemus* v 1955 June.

Collared Pratincole *Glareola praticola* v 1812, 1974, August and July respectively.

Little Ringed Plover *Charadrius dubius* v 1965, 1976, September and May respectively.

Ringed Plover *C. hiaticula* Pm Breeding from at least 19th century, circa 500+ pairs. Main return mid February, departing August/September. Passage birds in August.

Dotterel *C. morinellus* V 1870, about 1894, 1898, 1900, 1971, 1974(5), 1975(3), 1977(2). May–September.

Golden Plover *Pluvialis apricaria* Pmw Abundant breeder 19th century, now Or 3 high and not as widespread. Return from February, depart August–November. Large passage March–May, smaller passage July–September. Small numbers winter with occasional large flocks. *P. a. altifrons* m Common on passage with above.

Grey Plover *P. squatarola* m Previous to 1953, 10 records, rarely more than a few individuals. Since at least 1969 regular August–October as individuals or small flocks.

Lapwing *Vanellus vanellus* Sm Rare breeder early 19th century and summer visitor previously. Wintering only in this century. Breeding Or 3, small flocks winter. Returning from mid February, departing September/October. Passage birds September/October.

Knot *Calidris canutus* Mw Passage May and July–September; individuals and small flocks winter, from 19th century, at least.

Sanderling *C. alba* M Passage in small flocks, more July–September than May/June.

Little Stint *C. minuta* m Unchanged since 19th century. August/September as circa 30 birds except 1978, flock of circa 80; exceptionally spring 1974, May/June.

Temminck's Stint *C. temminckii* V 1914, 1948, 1950, 1952, 1953, 1967(3), 1973, 1975(3), 1976(3). May/June and September/November.

Least Sandpiper *C. minutilla* v 1955 August.

White-rumped Sandpiper *C. fuscicollis* v 1973 November.

Pectoral Sandpiper *C. melanotos* v 1961, 1966, 1971, 1973(3), 1978, August–November.

Curlew Sandpiper *C. ferruginea* A 1859–1871 'pretty constant'; 1886, 1896, 1902, 1914(2), 1920, 1950(2), 1952(2), 1957, 1963(2) 1967(5), 1970, 1971(4), 1972(3), 1973(2), 1975(12 plus), 1976(8), 1977, 1978(2 plus). Predominantly August/September; exceptionally May 1971 and 1972.

Purple Sandpiper *C. maritima* Wm Passage April/May and departure; arrival September/October, usually occasional flocks over 100; a few regularly summer; unchanged since 19th century at least.

Dunlin *C. alpina* SM Breeding Or 3 Low. Passage May and July–September.

Broad-billed Sandpiper *Limicola falcinellus* v 1976 November.

Stilt Sandpiper *Micropalama himantopus* v 1976 September.

Buff-breasted Sandpiper *Tryngytes subruficollis* v 1975 September, 1978 May.

Ruff *Philomachus pugnax* M May/June and July–September, more numerous in autumn, in small flocks, exceptionally 84 1973 and more than 100 1978; appears to have increased recently in spring.

Jack Snipe *Lymnocryptes minimus* mw Mainly September/October, but also March–May, usually only individuals winter.

Snipe *Gallinago gallinago* Rm Breeding Or 3. Passage mainly April/May, but also September/October.

Great Snipe *G. media* v 1890, 1904, 1930s(3), 1952(2), 1955(2) shot, 1973, 1974. March and September.

Dowitcher *Limnodromus* sp. v 1964 May, 1965 October.

Woodcock *Scolopax rusticola* m Bred probably twice in 19th century and once in 1952. Small passage mid-April and mid-October, individuals outwith this period, unusually summering.

Black-tailed Godwit *Limosa limosa* sm 1–2 pairs breeding since 1948 (possibly *L. l. islandica*). Passage April/May and July–September.

Bar-tailed Godwit *L. lapponica* mw April/May and August/September; occasionally a few winter.

Whimbrel *Numenius phaeopus* S 300 pairs minimum breeding, increasing. Arrival April/May, exodus August/September. Small autumn passage.

   American Whimbrel *N. p. hudsonicus* v 1974 July.

Curlew *N. arquata* Rm Breeding Or 3. Passage April/May and August/September. Bones 9–10th century Jarlshof.

Spotted Redshank *Tringa erythropus* m 1955, 1958, 1959, 1964, 1965 and regular as few individuals since at least 1969; April/May and August/September, usually more common in latter period, but spring passage increasing in recent years.

Redshank *T. totanus* Rmw Or 3 Low breeding and increasing. April/May and July–September.

Marsh Sandpiper *T. stagnatilis* v 1969 May.

Greenshank *T. nebularia* m Bred 1871. As individuals April/May and August/September, more common latter season.

Greater Yellowlegs *T. melanoleuca* v 1953 May.

Lesser Yellowlegs *T. flavipes* v 1976 August.

Green Sandpiper *T. ochropus* m Previous to 1947 only occasionally recorded. 1949–1953 7 records. 1965(2), 1966, then annually from 1969, and from 1974 in double figures. April/May and August. Not recorded 19th century.

Wood Sandpiper *T. glareola* m 1947, 1950(2), 1951(3), 1954, 1955, 1958, 1963, 1964, 1966 and annually since 1969 (except 1973). May and August, usually more common in former season.

Terek Sandpiper *Xenus cinereus* v 1975 June.

Common Sandpiper *Actitis hypoleucos* sm Breeding Low Or 2. Summering birds returning with migrants in May and departing with migrants in July/August.

Turnstone *Arenaria interpres* W Mainly September–May, small and occasionally large flocks, a few regularly summer.

Wilson's Phalarope *Phalaropus tricolor* v 1973, 1974, 1975, September/October and May.

Red-necked Phalarope *P. lobatus* s Maximum of 30 pairs breeding, decreasing. Return late May, depart late July/early August.

Grey Phalarope *P. fulicarius* V A few 19th century, 1921, 1928, 1930, 1949, 1961, 1963, 1967, 1971, 1972, 1973(2), 1976, 1977, 1978(2 plus). All single except for group of 3 19th century and 1973. Mainly May and September, singles October, December and February.

Pomarine Skua *Stercorarius pomarinus* m Previous to 1951 only late autumn and winter records very occasionally, i.e. 1860, 1862, 1890. Annually as at least singles since 1969, mainly May/June and September–November, most common in latter season, often recorded offshore.

Arctic Skua *S. parasiticus* S Breeding from 17th century at least. 1500 pairs minimum and increasing. Return April majority depart by September.

Long-tailed Skua *S. longicaudis* A Possibly several 1848, then 1900, 1906. Since 1969 annually (except 1971 and 1974) at least as singles, mainly May/June.

Great Skua *S. skua* S Earliest record 1774, probably previous to that. *Circa* 5500 pairs, increasing. Return April, majority left by October.

Little Gull *Larus minutus* V 1853–1938 9 records, then 1958, 1959(2), 1965, 1969(6), 1971, 1972(2), 1974(2), 1976(4), 1977(4), 1978(3 plus). All months except February/March.

Sabine's Gull *L. sabini* V 1861, 1909, 1947, 1973(2), 1974, 1976. Mainly September/October, singles January and July 1861 and 1909 respectively.

Black-headed Gull *L. ridibundus* P Breeding *c.* 1000 pairs. Returning March, departing August/September.

Common Gull *L. canus* Pm Breeding c. 2000 pairs. Passage March/April and August/September.

Lesser Black-backed Gull *L. fuscus* S Breeding *c.* 1000 pairs. Arrival late-March/April, majority departed September. Has decreased from 19th century but present trend confused. *L. f. fuscus* A 1945–1953 4 records. 1969(2), 1973, 1974(5), 1976(2). (Grossly under-recorded.)

Herring Gull *L. argentatus* R Bones numerous in Bronze Age and 9–10th century at Jarlshof. Breeding *c.* 10,000 pairs.

Iceland Gull *L. glaucoides* w October–May, small numbers.

Glaucous Gull *L. hyperboreus* W A few recorded in every month but mostly winter; exceptionally hundreds in 1969, October–December. 1975–1978 breeding between this species and *L. argentatus*.

Great Black-backed Gull *L. marinus* R Numerous bones 9–10th century Jarlshof. *Circa* 2500 pairs breeding, increasing.

Ross's Gull *Rhodostethia rosea* V 1936, 1969, 1972, 1975, 1977. September–April.

Kittiwake *Rissa tridactyla* P *Circa* 45,000 pairs.

Ivory Gull *Pagophila eburnea* V Several 19th century, 1890s, 1939, 1950, 1959/60, 1962, 1967, 1969(2). November–February.

Caspian Tern *Sterna caspia* v 1976 July/August.

Sandwich Tern *S. sandvicensis* V Bred first 1955 with 2 pairs – 1960 with 6 pairs. Previously only recorded 1949 but as occasional visitor 1961, 1963, 1965(2), 1968(6), 1969(3–4), 1970(7), 1972(2), 1973(8), 1974(2), 1975(5 plus), 1976(5), 1977(5), 1978(13+). Usually May–August.

Roseate Tern *S. dougallii* v 1974 June, 1978 May.

Common Tern *S. hirundo* S First confirmed breeding 1901. Breeding Or 3. Return May, depart by mid-August.

Arctic Tern *S. paradisaea* S *Circa* 10,000–12,000 pairs but fluctuates annually. Return May, depart August.

Little Tern *S. albifrons* V 1900(6), 1906, 1949(2), 1975, May to September excluding August; plus one record no date.

Black Tern *Childonias niger* v (1844), 1952, 1962, 1963, 1967(10–20), 1971. April–June and September.

White-winged Black Tern *C. leucopterus* v 1967 June.

Guillemot *Uria aalge* P *c.* 150,000 breeding birds. Numerous bones 9–10th century Jarlshof. Returning from early-October, departing through July.

Brunnich's Guillemot *U. lomvia* v (Single 19th century and 1947), 1968, 1977. Most recent records found dead March and December respectively. Bones numerous 9–10th century Jarlshof.

Razorbill *Alca torda* P Bones found Bronze Age Jarlshof. *c.*20,000 breeding birds. Returning from January, depart through early to mid-July.

Black Guillemot *Cepphus grylle* R Breeding birds *c.* 2000.

Little Auk *Alle alle* W Usually individuals to small flocks October–February, but large flocks occasionally, *e.g.* 200 1977, 500 1969, 1000s 1966 Foula.

Puffin *Fratercula arctica* P Breeding *c.* 250,000 birds. Offshore from January, ashore March/April, departed by mid-August. Occasionally seen offshore in winter.

Pallas's Sandgrouse *Syrrhaptes paradoxus* v 2 19th-century records of invasions – 1863, 1888 and 1 1969 May.

Rock Dove *Columba livia* R Breeding Or 3 high.

Stock Dove *C. oenas* V 2 19th century 1894 and unknown. Previous to 1953 uncommon and irregular migrant, then 1969, 1973(2), 1975(2), 1976(4), 1977(4). March–June and September/October.

Wood Pigeon *C. palumbus* Sm Became regular spring and autumn migrant second half 19th century. First bred 1939. Breeding low Or 2, increasing. Passage March–May and August–November. Seen most months of the year.

Collared Dove *Streptopelia decaocto* rm First recorded 1961, first bred 1965. Breeding Or 2, increasing. Passage May/June and August/September.

Turtle Dove *S. turtur* m May/June and August–October, more common in spring, mostly as 10–50.

Cuckoo *Cuculus canorus* sm Breeding Or 1. Passage May/June and August/September.

Black-billed Cuckoo *Coccyzus erythrophalmus* v 1953 October.

Yellow-billed Cuckoo *C. americanus* v 1952 November.

Barn Owl *Tyto alba alba* v 1928, 1945, 1973. November, December and June respectively. *T. a. guttara* v 1915, 1945(poss. 5), 1951, 1958 October–December and June.

Scops Owl *Otus scops* v 1900(2), 1905, 1926, 1928, 1954. April–June and August.

Eagle Owl *Bubo bubo* v 1863, 1871, autumn and March.

Snowy Owl *Nyctea scandiaca* P Possibly bred 19th century. Appeared 1963. First recent breeding 1967 and last 1975. Usually 1–2 resident in winter; summer birds appear April/May, several present in summer. No males 1976, 1977, 1978.

Hawk Owl *Surnia ulula* v 1860/61.

Long-eared Owl *Asio otus* rw First recorded 1868. First bred 1935, 1–2 pairs annually to 1975, not confirmed breeding 1976–78. 10–20 recorded in most winters. Passage April/May and September–November as few individuals.

Short-eared Owl *A. flammeus* m Bred once 19th century. Passage April–June and September–November, more common in former season, up to 10 individuals annually – exceptionally 1978 October (seven per day on Skerries).

Tengmalm's Owl *Aegolius funereus* v 1897(2), 1902, 1908, 1912, 1917/18. November–April.

Nightjar *Caprimulgus europaeus* v Previous to 1953 rare vagrant. 1964, 1969, 1971, 1976(2). May/June, August/September.

Swift *Apus apus* m   May–September, individuals to medium flocks (30–40) occasionally, and exceptionally large flocks, *e.g.* 100 1976.

Alpine Swift *A. melba* v   1962, 1976, 1977. May/June.

Kingfisher *Alcedo atthis* V   1935 or 1936, 1945, 1950, 1971, 1974(2). June–November.

Bee-Eater *Merops apiaster* V   1899, 1915, 1951, 1955, 1969(3), 1970(2), 1971(2), 1972. May–October.

Roller *Coracias garrulus* V   1869, (1927), 1930, 1957, 1958, 1959, 1971, 1977. June, July and autumn.

Hoopoe *Upupa epops* m   Previous to 1952 rare vagrant, annually since 1965 (except 1968 and 1971) from singles to 3. Predominantly May/June, also September/October.

Wryneck *Jynx torquilla* m   April/May and late August/September.

Green Woodpecker *Picus viridis* v   Late 1920s, 2–4.

Great Spotted Woodpecker *Dendrocopos major* m   Prior to 1953 irregular autumn migrant. Annually from 1969 at least (except 1970) as 1–10, except when irruptions 1861, 1869, 1949, 1974. May–November.

Short-toed Lark *Calandrella cinerea* m   1935, 1936 and annually as 1–3 since 1967 at least, March, May and September/October. *C. c. longipennis* v   1936, 1973, 1974. September, October and November respectively.

Woodlark *Lullula arborea* V   1844, 1921(2), 1936, 1955, 1969. February, October, March, May and April respectively.

Skylark *Alauda arvensis* S   Breeding Or 4. Main return February/March, depart September/October.

Shore Lark *Eremophila alpestris* A   1918, 1933(2), 1967, 1969(4) and annually since 1972 as 1–13 individuals. May and September/October.

Sand Martin *Riparia riparia* m   Possibly bred 1887. May/June and August/September, more common in spring.

Swallow *Hirundo rustica* sM   First bred 1831, 1900–1956 16 pairs, since 1975 5 pairs at least have bred annually. Passage April–mid-June and August–November, usually as individuals or small parties, exceptionally 100 May 1969.

Red-rumped Swallow *H. daurica* v   1971, 1972. September and May respectively.

House Martin *Delichon urbica* sM   Breeding infrequently from 19th century, *circa* 8 1900–1950; most recent confirmed breeding 1975. Passage May–mid-June and August/September as individuals or small flocks, more common in spring.

Richard's Pipit *Anthus novaeseelandiae* A   1928, 1961, 1966, 1970(4) and regular September/October migrant since 1973, usually as individuals, exceptional spring migrants 1975.

Tawny Pipit *A. campestris* V 1970, 1971, 1973, 1974(2), 1976. May/June and September/October.

Tree Pipit *A. trivialis* M Usually more common in May than mid-August/ September, from a few birds to exceptionally 'thousands', May 1969.

Pechora Pipit *A. gustavi* v 1972 October.

Meadow Pipit *A. pratensis* SM Breeding possibly Low Or 4. Main return and passage March–June, departure mid-August–October, a few wintering.

Red-throated Pipit *A. cervinus* V (1854), 1950, 1952, 1966(2), 1967, 1975, 1976(3). May/June and September/October.

Rock Pipit *A. spinoletta* Rm Breeding possibly Low Or 4. Passage May and September/October. *A. s. littoralis* v (Probably 1950), 1973, 1975. April/May.

Yellow Wagtail *Montacilla flava flavissima* m Previous to 1953 occasional autumn migrant, annually since 1969 at least. Generally mainly Yellow recorded in last decade at least, in autumn nearly all identified as this race; all races more common May/June than September.

   Blue-headed Wagtail *M. f. flava* A Occasional autumn migrant in 19th century. 1936, 1949, 1969(2), 1970(3), 1972, 1973(4–5), 1974(3), 1975(2), 1976(3), 1978. Mainly April–June and occasionally September.

   Grey-headed Wagtail *M. f. thunbergi* A 1914, 1955, 1969(4), 1970(4), 1972, 1974(3), 1976(5), 1977(3)1978. All May.

   Black-headed Wagtail *M. f. feldegg* A 1936, 1960, 1969. All May.

Citrine Wagtail *M. citreola* v 1973, 1975, 1978. September.

Grey Wagtail *M. cinerea* m Regular 19th century, 1900–1950 rare, 1950(8–10), 1951 and annually (except 1971) since 1969 at least as 1–11 birds. March–May and September–November, very occasionally wintering.

Pied Wagtail *M. alba yarelli* sm Bred sporadically between 1900–1910. Recorded only occasionally to 1953 and annually on passage March–May and September since 1969 at least; less common than White. Bred 1972(2), 1973(2), 1975(4), 1976(7), 1977(2), 1978(1+).

   White Wagtail *M. a. alba* sM Passage as Pied but regular through 20th century. Bred 1900, (1920s), 1930s, 1946, 1951, 1969(2 plus), 1970(1–2), 1972(1 plus), 1973(3), 1974(2), 1975(2), 1976(1 plus), 1977(2 plus), 1978.

Waxwing *Bombycilla garrulus* m Previous to 1953 occasional visitor. 1961 and regular migrant since 1970, predominantly October/November, occasionally winter and April–June. 1–100 birds depending if irruption, *e.g.* 1970 and 1974 most recently.

Dipper *Cinclus cinclus* V 1936, 1951, 1966(2), 1971, 1976(2), 1977, 1978, mainly January–April, also October/November.

Shetland Wren *Troglodytes troglodytes zetlandicus* R Breeding Or 3–4.

   Wren *T. t. t.* m Small passage March–May and September/October.

Dunnock *Prunella modularis* Mw 1965 eggs layed but failed to hatch. More common on passage March–May than September/October, exceptional autumn passage 1976.

Robin *Erithacus rubecula* Mw Passage March–May and September/October, from few individuals to occasionally large numbers, a few overwinter.

Thrush Nightingale *Luscinia luscinia* V 1970, 1974(2), 1976(2). May–October.

Nightingale *L. megarhynchos* V 1929, 1970, 1973(2), 1976, 1977, 1978(1 plus). May except 1929 September.

Red-spotted Bluethroat *L. svecica svecica* m More common May/June than September/October.

    White-spotted Bluethroat *L. s. cyarecula* v 1930, 1969, 1975, September, May and April respectively.

Red-flanked Bluetail *Tarsiger cyanurus* v 1947, 1971, October and May/June respectively.

Black Redstart *Phoenicurus ochruros* m April/May and September/October as individuals.

Redstart *P. phoenicurus* M Became regular migrant mid to late 19th century. (Built nest but did not breed 1907) May and September/October, more common in autumn, individuals and small parties.

Whinchat *Saxicola rubetra* M First recorded 1887. April/May and mid-August/September, individuals to small parties.

Stonechat *S. torquata* m Bred first 1961, 1962, 1975, 1976(3), 1977(2). Since 1974 regular March–May and September/October migrant. Individuals summer and occasionally winter. Dramatic increase in occurrence since 1974. Few records 1978, but no confirmed breeding. *S. t. maura/stegnegeri* v 1974 October, 1978(3) September/October.

Wheatear *Oenanthe oenanthe* SM Probably breeding Or 3/ Or 4. Returning late-March/April, departing August/September. Passage April/May and September/October. *O. o. leucorrhoa* m Seen annually on passage with above as a few individuals.

White's Thrush *Zoothera dauma* v 1975 October.

Ring Ouzel *Turdus torquatus* M Bred 1972. April/May and September/October, individuals and small flocks, occasional summering.

Blackbird *T. merula* RM First bred 1870s. Breeding Or 3, increasing. Passage January–May and September/November. Flocks over 100 regularly and occasionally over 1000.

Dusky Thrush *T. naumanni* v 1968, 1975, September/November.

Black-throated Thrush *T. ruficollis* v 1974, 1977, October/November.

Fieldfare *T. pilaris* M First bred 1968, 1969(2), 1970(2–3), 1971(1 plus), (1972),

1973(2). Passage January–May and September/November. More common in autumn and can vary from protracted passage to 'thousands', October 1977. A few winter.

Song Thrush *T. philomelos* M   First bred 1906, well established in 1945, decreased to extinction 1954, breeding once again 1976, 1977, 1978 (2 +). Passage January–May and September/October. More common in autumn, flocks over 1000 occasional, October 1977. Previously very rare 19th century.

Redwing *T. iliacus* M   Bred first 1953, 1954, 1974, 1975. January–May and September–November. More numerous in autumn from protracted passage to 'tens of thousands', October 1976, 1977. A few winter.

Mistle Thrush *T. viscivorus* m   Rare migrant 19th century, 1918, 1920, 1946, 1949, 1951 and annually since 1969 at least as circa 1–15 birds. January–May and less commonly September/October.

American Robin *T. migratorius* v   1967 November.

Lanceolated Warbler *Locustella lanceolata* v   1973, 1978, September.

Grasshopper Warbler *L. naevia* m   Annually since 1969 at least (except 1975). Most common May and occasionally September.

Aquatic Warbler *Acrocephalus paludicola* v   1969 August.

Sedge Warbler *A. schoenobaenus* m   First record 1913, then 1915, 1919, 1949, 1950, 1951, 1952 and annually from 1969 at least, except 1975, as individuals. May/June and occasionally September, also summer occasional.

Marsh Warbler *A. palustris* A   First record 1969, then 1970, 1972, 1973(2), 1976, 1977(2). May/June and September.

Reed Warbler *A. scirpaceus* A   1919(2), 1936, 1949, 1951, 1961 (several), 1967 and annually (except 1970) since 1969. More common September/October than May. Bred 1973.

Great Reed Warbler *A. arundinaceus* v   1958, 1974, 1976. May/June.

Thick-billed Warbler *A. aedon* v   1971 September.

Booted Warbler *Hippolais caligata* v   1977 September/October.

Icterine Warbler *H. icterina* m   1910, 1934, 1945, 1958, 1965(2), 1967 and annually since 1969, more common August/September than May/June.

Melodious Warbler *H. polyglotta* v   1976(3), May, July and August.

Subalpine Warbler *Sylvia cantillans* v   1966, 1968(2), 1971, 1977. April/May and August.

Ruppell's Warbler *S. rueppelli* v   1977 August.

Barred Warbler *S. nisoria* m   Almost exclusively August/September, from individuals to 50, spring records, June 1914 and 1967.

Lesser Whitethroat *S. curruca* m
Slightly more common May/June than September, occasionally summer.

Whitethroat *S. communis* m   Bred 1974. More common May/June than mid-August–early October, in small numbers.

Garden Warbler *S. borin* M   May/early June and August–early October, more common in autumn.

Blackcap *S. atricapilla* M   Bred first 1948, 1974. Became migrant only in late 19th century. Mainly September/October, also May/June and occasionally in summer and winter.

Greenish Warbler *Phylloscopus trochiloides* v   1945, 1974, September.

Arctic Warbler *P. borealis* V   1967(2), 1969, 1970, 1972(4), 1973(2), 1974, 1976(4), 1978. Exclusively August–October.

Pallas's Warbler *P. preregulus* v   1975, 1976(2), 1977, 1978. September/October.

Yellow-browed Warbler *P. inornatus* m   Previous to 1953 'possibly fairly regular'. 1955, 1964(5), 1965(2), 1967(c. 10) and annually in last decade; September/October, 1/October, 1–10 birds.

Radde's Warbler *P. schwarzi* v   1976 October.

Bonelli's Warbler *P. bonelli* v   1974 September.

Wood Warbler *P. sibilatrix* m   1913, 1914, 1920, 1951, 1969 and annually since. Slightly more common August/September than May, as a few individuals.

Chiffchaff *P. collybita* M   Common April/May and August–October. In last decade at least a few regularly summer and since 1973 occasionally individuals winter. *P. c. tristris* A   1910, 1913(2), 1914, 1977. October–December.

Willow Warbler *P. trochilus* M   Bred 1901, 1949, (1975). Small flocks late April–early June, August–early October. A few summer regularly.

Goldcrest *Regulus regulus* Mw   Rare before 1840. Bred 1972, 1976. March–early April but more common September/October, with occasional large numbers. A few winter occasionally and regularly probably in last decade at least.

Firecrest *R. ignicapillus* V   1965, 1972, 1976(2), 1977(2). October and 1 June.

Spotted Flycatcher *Muscicapa striata* M   Main passage May, also late August/September.

Red-breasted Flycatcher *Ficedula parva* m   Annually for last decade at least, with 1–8 birds. Predominantly September, but 3 spring records, 1971, 1975, 1976(3–4), May/June. Previously not recorded in spring.

Collared Flycatcher *F. albicollis* v   1947, 1975, 1976, May.

Pied Flycatcher *F. hypoleuca* m   May and mid-August/September, in small numbers. First record 1898.

Long-tailed Tit *Aegithalos caudatus* v   1860(4) April.

Coal Tit *Parus ater* v   1965(2), 1977(2). October/November.

Blue Tit *P. caeruleus caeruleus* v   1926/27, 1930, 1932, 1965/66, 1976/77. Mainly October with overwintering after irruption, small numbers, *e.g.* 1965/66 10, 1976/77 17, 1977/78/10 plus).

Great Tit *P.* [*major*] *major* V Previous to 1953 'not infrequent in October', 1959/60, 1965/66, 1966/67(2) and overwintering annually from 1974 as few to 17 birds.

Treecreeper *Certhia familiaris* V 1859, 1882, 1961, 1966(2), 1968, 1975(2), 1976. Mostly October/November. One August and September. 1972/73 birds overwintered. *C. f. familiaris* Birds of this race identified 1937, 1972/73, 1976, October/November, but Treecreeper in Shetland probably mainly this race.

Golden Oriole *Oriolus oriolus* V 1882, 1944, 1945, 1949, 1954, 1955(2), 1958, 1962, 1964(4), 1965, 1969, 1970, 1971(6), 1972(4 plus), 1973(4), 1976(7), 1977, 1978. Mainly May/June and very occasionally September/October.

Red-backed Shrike *Lanius collurio* m Bred 1870. Previous to 1953 erratic migrant. More common May/June than September/October, annually from 1969 at least.

Lesser Grey Strike *L. minor* V 1929, 1956, 1965, 1966, 1967, 1970(3), 1974(2), 1977. May–July and September–November.

Great Grey Shrike *L. excubitor* m Previous to 1953 'rare and irregular migrant', since 1966 at least become a regular April/May and September/October migrant, 1–20 birds. Wintering occasionally.

Woodchat Shrike *L. senator* V (1 19th century), 1955, 1965, 1967, 1968(3), 1969, 1970, 1972, 1973, 1974, 1976. May/June and September/October.

Jay *Garrulus glandarius* v 1861, 1890s(3–4). Autumn and August respectively.

Nutcracker *Nucifraga caryocatactes* v 1968 August.

Chough *Pyrrhocorax pyrrhocorax* v 1952 March.

Jackdaw *Corvus monedula spermologous* rm First bred 1952. Or 1–2. *C. m. mondeula* m February–May and September/November, more common in the former. (Race rarely noted.)

Rook *C. frugilegus* Rm First bred 1952. 100–200 pairs. January–April and October/November, as individuals and occasional small flocks, e.g. 1976, 1977.

Carrion Crow *Corvus corone corone* m Previous to 1953 regular but uncommon autumn migrant and rare in spring to 19th century. Annually for last decade (except 1970) at least as several individuals, more common October/November than March–June.

Hooded Crow *C. c. corvix* R Breeding Or 3.

Raven *C. corax* R Breeding Or 3.

Starling *Sturnus vulgaris zetlandicus* R Breeding Or 4. *S. v. v.* M April migration obscure. September/October in large flocks.

Rose-coloured Starling *S. roseus* V Before 1940 occasionally, 1940s(2), 1958, 1960, 1966, 1971, 1972, 1973, 1977. March–November.

House Sparrow *Passer domesticus* R Breeding Or 4.

Tree Sparrow *P. montanus* rm   Bred 1898–1905 and sometime prior to 1937, 1961 (10 pairs), 1964(8–10), 1967 and since 1970 as perhaps 2 pairs. A few migrants May and September.

Chaffinch *Fringilla coelebs* Mw   First bred 1901, 1930–1933, and 1973. Main passage September/October and a few April–May. Perhaps *circa* 100 wintering in recent years. A few summer.

Brambling *F. montifringilla* Mw   Considerably more common September/October, with up to 500, than April/May, occasionally summering; *circa* 20 minimum winter.

Serin *Serinus serinus* v   1968 November.

Greenfinch *Carduelis chloris* m   First record 1858, then became regular migrant and wintering species, subsequently in late 19th century to latest records only occasional. From 1967 at least regular migrant April–June and occasionally September–November, a few winter.

Goldfinch *C. carduelis* A   First record 1962(3) and regular since 1968(6) at least (except 1969), particularly September–November and occasionally May/June and winter visitor, as very few individuals.

Siskin *C. spinus* M   More common September/October than April/May and spring passage not every year, 8–60, exceptionally 1974, 120.

Linnet *C. cannabina* m   Prior to 1950 rare to 19th century at least, 1950 and regularly since 1969 at least, predominantly March–mid June, occasionally August/September.

Twite *C. flavirostris* R   Breeding Or 3–4.

Mealy Redpoll *C. flammea flammea* M   Most common Redpoll. March–June and large flocks when irruptions September/October, e.g. 1975; occasionally overwinter.

    Lesser Redpoll *C. f. cabaret* A   Perhaps more frequent 19th century then uncommon to recently, 1936, 1937, 1971(8), 1975, 1976(2), 1977(3). Passage as Mealy.

    Greenland Redpoll *C. f. rostrata* V   1907, 1936, 1939, (1948 and 1949), 1974, 1976(6), 1978(2). Passage as Mealy.

Arctic Redpoll *C. hornemanni* V   1905, 1968, 1965(2), 1977. October–February.

Two-barred Crossbill *Loxia leucoptera* v   1859, 1959, 1972(2). July–September.

Crossbill *L. curvirostra* A   Previous to 1953 uncommon to 19th century when quite common spring and autumn. 1959 (small flock), 1966 (invasion), 1972 (irruption ('hundreds')), 1974(3), 1976(4), 1977(2), 1978. June–November.

Parrot Crossbill *L. pytyopsittacus* v   1962(4), 1963, 1975. October–November.

Scarlet Rosefinch *Carpodacus erythrinus* m   1936(5), 1940, 1951, 1955, 1959, 1966(2), and regularly since 1969, August–October in small numbers and occasionally May/June.

Bullfinch *Pyrrhula pyrrhula* wm   Rare in 19th century. In small numbers April/May and October/November, more common in the latter season, and winter visitor.

Hawfinch *Coccothraustes coccothraustes* A   1904, 1916, 1927, 1951, 1952, 1963, 1965, 1966, 1967, 1970(2), 1971, 1972(2), 1974, 1975(2), 1976, 1977, 1978. April/May and 2 July 1916 and 1927.

Black-and-white Warbler *Mniotilta varia* v   1936 October.

Ovenbird *Seiurus aurocapillus* v   1973 October.

White-throated Sparrow *Zonotrichia albicollis* v   1971, 1973, November and May respectively.

Slate-coloured Junco *Junco hyemalis* v   1966, 1967, 1969. May.

Lapland Bunting *Calcarius lapponicus* m   1892, 1945–53(4). Annual since 1965 at least, more common September/October as 1–30 birds than May.

Snow Bunting *Plectrophenax nivalis* MW   (Bred 1861, 1881, 1907). Passage April and October, wintering as a few hundreds from September/October to April.

Yellowhammer *Emberiza citrinella* m   Slightly more common as 1–14 birds, March–May than October, previously (1945–53) thought more common in autumn. A few winter, occasionally.

Ortolan Bunting *E. hortulana* m   1945–53 'rare but regular migrant'. 1965, 1966, 1967(2), 1969 (30 plus), 1970(circa 20) and annually since 1972 at least as up to 30 birds in May, also occurring in September most years.

Rustic Bunting *E. rustica* A   1920, 1936, 1949, 1950(2), 1951(3), 1966, 1970, 1971, 1972, 1974(3), 1975(2), 1976(5), 1978. May and October/November.

Little Bunting *E. pusilla* A   1948(2), 1955, 1967, 1969(3), 1970(2), 1971, 1973(3), 1976(7), 1977, 1978(2). Mainly September/October also May.

Yellow-breasted Bunting *E. aurepla* A   1966, 1969(2), 1972(2), 1973, 1974(2), 1976, 1977(2), 1978(2 plus). September/October.

Reed Bunting *E. schoeniclus* pM   First bred 1949 at least and regularly since, increasing *e.g.* 1977 5–10 pairs. Passage April/May and September/October with a few wintering.

Black-headed Bunting *E. melanocephala* v   (1934), 1965, 1973(2), 1975, 1977, 1978. June and August–October.

Corn Bunting *E. calandra* rm   Decreased from common breeding species in 19th century to perhaps 2–3 pairs 1977. Few migrants April/May and October.

Bobolink *Dolichonyx cryzivorus* v   1975 September.

EXTINCT

Black Grouse *Tetrao tetrix*   Single bone 9–10th century at Jarlshof.

Grey Partridge *Perdix perdix*   Unsuccessful introductions 1930s.

Great Auk *Pinguinus impennis*   Bones of 3 adults found below Viking level at Jarlshof.

CATEGORY C

Mandarin Duck *Aix galericulata* v 1942 June.

Ruddy Duck *Oxyura jamaicensis* v 1974 May.

CATEGORY D

Wood Duck *Aix sponsa* v 1976 October.

Chestnut Bunting *Emberiza rutila* v 1974 July.

Red-headed Bunting *E. bruniceps* V 1950, 1952, 1961, 1965, 1967(2), 1969, 1970(3), 1972(4), 1973(4), 1975(3), 1976(7). April–September.

Blue Grosbeak *Guiraca caerulea* v 1970 August.

Painted Bunting (Eastern) *Passerina ciris* v 1972 May (appeared wild and unfamiliar with a cage), 1978 July.

NOT YET ACCEPTED

Saker Falcon *Falco cherrug* 1976 October, 1977 June, and 1978 May.

PLACES TO VISIT

WE have listed approximately 100 sites and walks, aiming at the best examples of as many of the Shetland features, ecosystems and habitats as possible. They are arranged roughly from north to south, although the smaller islands are left out of this regular sequence. It is advisable, particularly on the longer and more rugged walks, to wear proper clothing and footwear; to take a map and compass; and to inform someone at the place of residence of one's intended route and time of returning. Be extra cautious on the cliffs, especially on windy days. Walkers should follow the normal countryside code with respect to gates, fences and dykes and should familiarise themselves with the laws concerning the disturbance of nesting birds including those regulating the photographing of certain protected species. The local officers of the Nature Conservancy Council or the Royal Society for the Protection of Birds will be able to help here. They can be contacted through the Information Centre in Lerwick (see below). Because so much grazing is unfenced and because many birds nest on open moorland, pets must be kept under particularly strict control.

There is a wonderful tradition of freedom of access in Shetland, almost unique in the British Isles, but it is both good manners and good practice to seek advice and permission before entering agricultural land. It would be wise to consult the wildlife bodies (Nature Conservancy Council and/or Royal Society for the Protection of Birds) before entering a Reserve.

Shetlanders are proud of their environment and many are very knowledgeable about their wildlife; a great deal can be learned from a few minutes conversation.

Maps

Shetland is covered by Sheets 1–4 of the Ordnance Survey 1:50,000 series: Yell & Unst; Whalsay; North Mainland; South Mainland (including Foula and Fair Isle). It is contained within a single sheet (no. 62) of Batholomew's 1:100,000 series.

Getting about in Shetland

Bus services in Shetland are infrequent, with the exception of those running between the two main towns of Lerwick and Scalloway. An 'overland' bus runs on most days from Lerwick *via* the inter-island ferries to Yell and Unst.

335

Regular vehicle ferries run between the larger islands of Mainland, Bressay, Yell, Whalsay, Unst and Fetlar. Other boat services run from the Mainland to Fair Isle, Foula, Papa Stour, Vaila, Mousa, and Out Skerries. It is hazardous to navigate oneself in Shetland waters due to dangers from rapid changes of weather and strong tides.

Scheduled air services operate between the main airport of Sumburgh and Tingwall, Whalsay, Unst and Fair Isle; it is possible to charter a plane to Foula, Papa Stour or Out Skerries.

Information about travel and accommodation within the islands can be obtained from the Shetland Tourist Organization Information Centre, Lerwick, Shetland ZE1 O11 ('phone Lerwick 3434).

UNST

1. Hermaness (NNR) HP600160

A peninsula approximately 3 miles by 1 mile, with cliffs rising from 200–500 feet with stacks and skerries, overlooking Muckle Flugga and the North Stack. The latter is the most northerly part of the British Isles. With the cliffs of Saxavord it has one of the largest seabird colonies in Britain, including Gannet, Guillemot, Razorbill, Kittiwake, an immense number of Puffins, and both Great and Arctic Skuas. Grey and Common Seals breed around the coast in small numbers. Spectacular cliff scenery of gneiss and a rugged walk.

2. Burrafirth HP615140

Beach and machair system of muscovite sands, physiographically unique to Shetland. Gradation from beach to machair grassland without the presence of dunes, controlled by a complex interrelationship of past and present fluvial, marine and aeolian processes.

3. Loch of Cliff HP600120

Mesotrophic loch and minor wintering wildfowl site. Washing area for Hermaness seabirds. At the southern end, the effect of a crystalline limestone band on the vegetation can be recognized.

4. Saxavord HP630165

Fourth highest hill in Shetland. The coastline of this large block of chloritoid schist is heavily eroded and has a continuation of the Puffin, Guillemot and Kittiwake colonies of Hermaness, with Great and Arctic Skuas on the moorland. Fine view on a good day.

5. Norwick HP650148

Excellent exposure of the fault between the Saxavord schists and the Clibberswick serpentines at the Taing of Norwick. Sand dunes support the only Shetland site for the Sea Pea. To the south of the dunes and road there is an

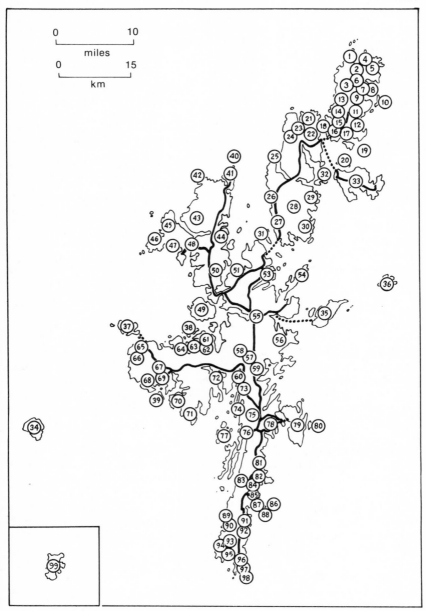

FIG 45. Places to visit – see Appendix II. Only major roads are shown.

excellent example of a diverse and productive freshwater marsh, extending almost as far as Haroldswick. The one kilometre square at Norwick has one of the greatest variety of breeding birds in the County.

6. *Quoys HP615123*
Talc quarry. From this site over the hill to Baltasound is a good example of the herb-rich sedge-grassland of serpentine.

7. *Nikkavord HP627104 & Hagdale HP640103*
Disused chromite mines. Best sites for studying these ore deposits in Britain.

8. *Keen of Hamar (NNR) HP643099* (Consult NCC before entering Reserve)
A unique area of serpentine supporting a number of arctic alpine plants and exhibiting active periglacial features at the lowest altitude they are found in the British Isles. Nearly all the features can be seen between the site and the main road (A968).

9. *Baltasound HP630085*
Minor seaduck, diver and grebe site. Good saltmarsh at the head of the sound. Halligarth plantation adjacent at HP625093.

10. *Balta Island HP660080*
Best example of a dune and machair system in Shetland.

11. *Hill of Colvadale HP620060 & Sobul HP605040*
Mettagabbro rocks supporting a herb-rich dwarf-shrub heath of predominantly heathers, giving way on the higher slopes to a Rhacomitrium moss heath. Supports a diverse bird fauna of over 20 species including the larger gulls, Common Gull, both Skuas and several wader species, including Whimbrel.

12. *Sandwick (Eastings) HP620020*
Severely deflated dune and machair area representing a late stage in the evolution of this type of system. Muness Castle nearby at HP630010.

13. *Vallafield HP585050*
High and rugged walk from the Westing to Hermaness over acidic dwarf shrub heaths. Excellent view of the effects of the various Unst bed rocks on the vegetation.

14. *The Westing HP575060*
Example of effect of limestone band, compare flora with that of the acid gneisses to the west and on Vallafield, and of the serpentines towards the main road (A968) to the east. Adjacent to site of archaeological interest at Underhoull (HP576041).

15. *Lunda Wick HP570040*
Limited sandblow site. Coastal cliffs with exposures through metasomatically zoned ultrabasic bodies, classical locality for their study.

16. *Snarravoe HP570015*
Wintering wildfowl site for Tufted and Goldeneye Duck among others.

17. *Easter Loch HP598013*
Brackish loch cut off from the sea by a shingle barrier bar. Important wintering wildfowl site for Whooper Swan, Tufted and Goldeneye Duck.

18. *Bluemull Sound HP555000*
Very large passage of seabirds from Hermaness through to the east and back, particularly in winter and early spring. Both Eider and Black Guillemot flocks can be seen in the winter months, occasionally very large.

19. *HAAF GRUNEY (NNR) HU635983*
A small uninhabited but fertile grassy holm with a flora resembling that of other areas of serpentine rock on Unst. Breeding ground of Eider, Black Guillemot, Storm Petrel and larger gulls. Favourite haul-out site for Grey and Common Seals in summer months.

20. *ISLANDS BETWEEN UNST AND FETLAR*
Small attractive grassy holms similar to Haaf Gruney.

21. *Breckin HP529052*
The largest area of blown shell sand in the islands, important for the unusual assemblage of accreting dunes and severely deflated hill machair. Includes the tiny eutrophic Kirk Loch.

22. *Cullivoe HP540030*
Beautiful example of traditional crofting area with herb-rich meadows.

23. *Gloup HP505050*
Isolated and attractive deep Shetland voe, with several mid bay bars.

24. *Gloup HP505050 to Whalefirth HU480930*
8–10 mile walk along attractive cliff; from Bratta (HU475990) to Ramna Geo (HU470967) is a 2 mile stretch of cliffs where the coarse gneiss is cut by spectacular pegmatite veins with mica crystals. Few seabirds other than Fulmar. Inland at the Lochs of Lumbister (HU490970) mica sands shine from the loch floors.

25. *Nev of Stuis HU460970*
Rugged walk to the site of the last Sea Eagle eyrie in Shetland at Erne Stack.

26. *West Sandwick HU446890*
Small and attractive dune and machair complex, although, unfortunately, the machair area is worked for sand. To landward is a fine example of hay meadows.

27. *Ness of Sound HU450825*
Excellent example of large undisturbed shingle double tombolo.

28. *Alin Knowes HU509813*
Deep, eroded blanket peat with innumerable lochs and lochans. Divers, Skuas and waders, including Whimbrel.

29. *White Hill HU547890*
Two small and easily accessible Kittiwake colonies.

30. *Horse of Burravoe HU535813*
Kittiwake, Guillemot and Puffin colonies.

31. *YELL SOUND ISLANDS*
Puffin and possibly Storm Petrel colonies, Common Seals and roosting for wintering wildfowl. The area is important for wintering Eider, Long-tailed Duck, and divers. Local Black Guillemot also gather in flocks.

32. *HASCOSAY HU555925*
Attractive little island with cross-section of Shetland breeding birds and very large Common Seal haul-out.

33. *FETLAR HU600900*
Part RSPB Reserve, consult before entering the Reserve. An extremely diverse island. The greater part of the geology is serpentine over schists and deformed conglomerates, supporting many breeding waders on herb-rich grassland and heath. Within the RSPB Reserve is the Snowy Owl nesting site. A band of gneiss runs over Lamb Hoga on the south-east headland on which are Kittiwake, Guillemot, Puffin and Shearwater colonies and also the largest Shetland colony of Storm Petrels. At the foot of the north-eastern cliffs is one of the largest Grey Seal colonies in the islands. At Funzie (HU663893) is a striking section of sheared conglomerate. Papil Water (impounded by a barrier bar of black magnetite sand) is a minor wintering wildfowl site.

34. *FOULA HT960400*

The most spectacular island in Shetland both for its topography and immense number of seabirds, including the largest colony of the Great Skua. Another notable seabird is Leach's Petrel, whose breeding was confirmed only a few years ago. The Old Red Sandstone cliffs on the western coast rise to 1200 feet at the Kame of Foula, and dip to the south with an unconformity at Smallie. The Kame cliffs are more precipitous than those of St Kilda, and can justly be regarded as the highest in the British Isles.

35. *WHALSAY HU560640*

Important island for migrant birds with many lochs, marshes and a wader houb at Kirk Ness (HU553655) formed from 3 tombolos. Small Kittiwake and Puffin colony at the southern extremity. Common Seals breed on the surrounding holms.

36. *OUT SKERRIES HU680720*

Extremely attractive group of little islands of mainly crystalline limestone, probably has as many migrants as Fair Isle. Small colonies of Eider, Black Guillemot, Gulls and Terns.

37. *PAPA STOUR HU167609*

An island of basaltic lavas and tuffs of Old Red Sandstone, the disparity in hardness of which has been eroded by the sea to produce the most impressive series of caves, stacks and arches in Britain. The caves are in volcanic rocks of rhyolite and basalt. Also small seabird colonies and breeding Common Seals. The flat nature of the island makes for easy walking.

38. *VEMENTRY HU300600*

Rugged and extremely attractive little island of deep heather; few seabirds except Fulmars, Black Guillemots and Gulls. Several lochs with divers and on the coast, Common Seals.

39. *VAILA HU230460*

A compact island with a good cross-section of Shetland seabirds including a Cormorant colony last occupied in 1970. Granite and Old Red Sandstone contact in cliffs; thermal metamorphism.

40. *RAMNA STACKS HU380970*

Forbidding collection of stacks with Guillemots and Kittiwakes. The associated island of Gruney is the only Shetland site where Grey Seals haul out well above the sea to breed on the grass.

342

41. *Fethaland HU375945*
A beautiful peninsula of gneiss and schists with a band of serpentine giving rise to a herb-rich grassland, partly maritime. Seabirds passing from the south-west to and from the colonies of Unst can be seen from here. Made more interesting by presence of ruins of picturesque haaf fishing station. Easy walking.

42. *Uyea Isle HU310930*
A small undisturbed sand tombolo, under water at high tide, connects the island to the mainland. Small colonies of Guillemots, Puffins and Kittiwakes among others. Grey Seals breed here in late autumn. A long walk.

43. *Ronas Hill and North Roe HU315845*
This is a remote mountain area of red granite-diorite of great interest on account of its virtually undisturbed periglacial features, including active and relict wind and frost patterned ground, turf-banked terraces, wind stripes, hill dunes and blockfields. Fifteen of the 25 arctic-alpine plants which occur in Shetland can be found on the Ronas Hill fellfield. On the south coast, which drops dramatically to Ronas Voe and on some of the loch holms to the north of the hill, are some of the best examples of relict scrub. At Heylor (HU290810) and on the opposite northern shore of Ronas Voe are fine examples of looped bars, and the voe itself is well known for its April population of Great Northern Divers and occasional King Eider. The voe is an extremely scenic fjord in red granite.

On the west coast, steeply eroding cliffs, backed by crevasses parallel to the coast, and the slumping of the coastline from Stonga Banks to Valla Kames have given rise to two remote and utterly unspoilt granite shingle beaches, each almost a mile long. It has also produced an impressive series of arches and stacks. At Hevdadale (HU310890) is a very large Grey Seal colony, but both seal species may be seen on this coast. The topography just to the north of Ronas Hill consists of incipient corries with ice-moulded, oligotrophic lochs (*e.g.* Roer Water: HU340860) and then gives way to a plateau dominated by Rhacomitrium moss, with interesting features, such as peat cones. The northern coast is composed of the very ancient (3000 million year old) Lewisian gneiss. This is the largest wilderness area in Shetland with extremely rugged walking and offers one the best possibilities outwith Fetlar of catching sight of a Snowy Owl.

44. *Ollaberry HU370810*
An attractive crofting area. At the Back of Ollaberry is the best example of a major tear fault in the British Isles, showing the Walls boundary fault, which itself is a continuation of the Great Glen Fault in Scotland. At Gluss (HU370775) is a fine shingle tombolo.

45. *Villians of Hamnavoe HU240824*
A contemporaneous storm beach which has been formed along the junction between andesite tuffs and lavas of Middle Old Red Sandstone; at one point the beach is over 60 feet above sea level. The rocks are well-jointed so that sections are removed in blocks and cubes giving deep rectangular shafts. At the northern end there is a stairway inlet and an immature blow-hole.

46. *Eshaness HU209790*
Cliffs of Old Red Sandstones with fine exposures of volcanic rocks including basaltic and andesite tuffs, lavas and ignumbrites. At the Villians of Ure (HU213800) is the spectacular stairway inlet and storm beach of the Grind of Navir and just to the south the Holes of Scraada, a collapsed blow-hole. At Eshaness, Stenness (HU214772) and Dore Holm (HU220762) there are Guillemot and Kittiwake colonies. At the Loch of Houlland (HU215790) there is the remains of a Broch and Tern colonies. At Stenness there are the ruins of the haaf fishing station and a shingle beach. Overall low cliff with beautiful maritime grassland and easy walking.

47. *Heads of Grocken HU265775 & the Neap HU255775*
Eroded red granite cliffs with series of stacks and arches, and a cliff foot sand beach. Cormorant colony at The Rumk. The spectacular stacks called The Drongs (HU260755) at Hillswick can be seen from here.

48. *Urafirth HU300788*
Fine example of a shingle barrier, with the beautiful Oyster Plant *(Mertensia maritima)*.

49. *Muckle Roe HU320650*
Extremely rugged cliffed coast of granite, with isolated and abandoned settlement at South Ham and Cormorant colonies at Grusterwick (HU296648) and Erne Stack (HU304672). Inland on the heather moorland makes for tough walking, with occasional Juniper, Bearberry and Honeysuckle.

50. *Sullom HU350728*
One of the best examples of the 1950s forestry plots. At Haggrister (HU349701) fine salt-marsh and looped bar. Magnetite scarn deposit.

51. *Sullom Voe HU380740*
Good wintering populations of Eider, Long-tailed Duck, Great Northern Diver, Velvet Scoters and Grebes. At the Houb of Scatsta (HU395730) opposite the oil terminal, fine wader feeding area.

52. *Burn of Valayre HU369693*
Accessible ravine with ungrazed relict scrub vegetation high on the sides, Rowan, Honeysuckle, Dog-rose and Willows.

53. *The Houb HU449723*
Composite sand and shingle tombolo and bars which connect the island of Foraness to the mainland. Represents a mature stage in the tombolo/bar development and provides an interesting comparison to the sand tombolos and shingle bars in the rest of Shetland. Fine example of drowned peat on the shores, while the tombolo usually has a Tern colony.

54. *Lunna Ness HU500700*
Fine example of ice-moulded topography with tombolos and bay-mouth bar at West Lunna Voe (HU480690), plus tombolo at Hamnavoe (HU495714). The former was the site of the Shetland Bus in the Second World War (Howarth 1951). Common Seal colony at Lunna Holm (HU528750). Fine walking on the Ness with many lochs and lochans supporting Red-throated Divers. Further interest in the old chapel at Lunna (HU485691). Stanes of Stofast erratic.

55. *Voe HU410630*
Scenically attractive with limestone band and associated flora on the south approach from Aith.

56. *Dury Voe HU455630 to Dales Voe HU450450*
Large coastal strip with wide variety of depositional features typical of Shetland, including tombolos at Skellister, Eswick Holm, Little Holm (HU475548, 483530, 448530); a double tombolo at Railsborough (HU456523); barrier bars at Lingness, Aswick and Wadbister (HU490550, 474529, 430500); mid bay bars at Dury (HU460605); bay head bars at Laxo, Dury, Wadbister and Dales Voe (HU450634, 460605, 430500, 438438); looped bar at Stavaness (HU510600), etc. The last site has a fine large and rounded boulder beach. Lingness may be the only pure shell sand beach in Shetland. The South Nesting area is a particularly attractive example of crofting townships on a crystalline limestone band. The Loch of Benston (HU460535) is a wintering wildfowl site. At Catfirth (HU439538) is a good example of an ungrazed limestone flora in the ravine. The bay of Catfirth is a wintering seaduck, diver and grebe site. At Gletness is a Shetland Pony stud (HU465515).

57. *Sandwater HU415547*
Relatively shallow loch, surrounded by acidic dwarf-shrub heath, strongly influenced by underlying band of crystalline limestone; breeding and wintering wildfowl. Also noted for large bed of Common Bulrush, unusual in Shetland.

58. *Kergord HU395540*
Series of mixed coniferous and broadleaved shelterbelts, first established early in the century and added to since; makes up the largest and most long established woodland in Shetland and provides a habitat for woodland flora and breeding birds including Rook, Jackdaw and Woodpigeon and occasionally Tree Sparrow, Goldcrest and Fieldfare. Excellent site for migrant and wintering woodland and shrub birds. The Burn of Weisdale is one of the few Shetland salmon rivers. Fluvio-glacial mounds and large landslip scar.

59. *Girlsta HU433522*
Deepest Shetland loch lying on a band of crystalline limestone and the only Shetland site for the Arctic Char. Also noted for its large Brown Trout.

60. *Weisdale Voe HU380490*
Wintering site for Goldeneye, Tufted Duck, divers and grebes and also local Mergansers. Last site of a Pilot Whale caa.

61. *Loch of Clousta HU315582*
Islands in the loch provide an interesting comparison of grazed and ungrazed vegetation, several islands support relict scrub.

62. *Clousta HU310575 – Vementry HU310600*
Attractive and relatively easy area for walking on the coast and inland. Compare vegetation of Vementry gneiss and schists with that of the sandstones of the Walls peninsula.

63. *Brindister HU287570 & Unifirth HU288560*
Saltwater wintering wildfowl site, with tombolos at the Vadills.

64. *West Burrafirth HU260575 – Brindister HU287570*
Attractive and relatively easy walk from the limestone band at Burrafirth, past the deserted crofts at Whalwick (HU258584), to the Neeans (HU273596). Varied coastal scenery with maritime and acid grasslands.

65. *Sandness HU200570*
The crofting area of Sandness lies on schists and gneiss (compare with surrounding hills of sandstone). At Melby (HU195576) and Norby (HU200577), barrier bars of sand block off the wintering wildfowl lochs. To the east are other wintering wildfowl sites at the Loch of Collaster (HU210574) and the Ness Lochs (HU217578). The latter lie on gneiss and crystalline limestone whose rugged topography is quite distinct from the rest of Sandness and the surrounding hills. The last group of lochs have breeding Tufted Duck. On the road above Collaster and further east are excellent examples of unimproved herb-rich dwarf shrub heaths.

66. Sandness HU200570 – Dale HU180530
Rugged coastal walk with high cliffs and deep valleys. Sandness Hill (817 feet) and Sel Ayre have relict periglacial features.

67. Walls Peninsula
Almost 20 square miles of relatively easy hill walking on the sandstone hills. Innumerable lochs with Red-throated Divers and occasional Common Scoter, and very occasionally with exotic Water-lilies.

68. Watsness HU170510 – Walls HU240490
Undemanding walk along an extremely varied and attractive coast.

69. Kirkiegarth HU238497 and Bardister HU238502
Two mesotrophic lochs with a wide range of aquatic flora; important wintering wildfowl sites.

70. Culswick HU274448
A mesotrophic marsh site evolved from a partially drained loch in a deep valley bottom and cut off from the sea by a barrier bar. An uncommon habitat in Shetland.

71. Culswick HU274448 – Reawick HU330450
Spectacular and relatively easy cliff walk on red granite. Cormorants at Clett Stack (HU293414) and small Kittiwake colonies at Westerwick (HU280420) and Skelda Ness (HU303405). Beaches at Westerwick, Skeld and Reawick of red granite shingle and sand.

72. Bixter Voe HU330520 & Tresta Voe HU350510
Good wintering and migrant site for seaduck, divers and grebes.

73. Loch of Strom HU400490
Largest brackish loch in the County, grading into freshwater at Stromfirth. Wintering wildfowl.

74. South Whiteness HU385445
The largest continuous area of crystalline limestone outcrop in Shetland, supporting a fine limestone flora and containing the only marl loch in the County. There is a fine saltmarsh at the Hoove (HU393461) with breeding Common and Black-headed Gulls. The vegetation of the peninsula makes a striking comparison with that of the adjacent Strom Ness which is composed mainly of acidic metamorphic rocks.

75. Lochs of Tingwall HU415425 & Asta HU413415
Two easily accessible mesotrophic lochs lying in one of the main crystalline

limestone valleys which are noted for their diverse aquatic flora, wintering wildfowl including Pochard, and breeding Tufted Duck.

76. *East Voe of Scalloway HU395385*
Seaduck site where occasional King Eider recorded.

77. *SCALLOWAY ISLANDS HU360400*
Extremely attractive, varied and peaceful little islands with a good variety of breeding birds and Common Seals.

78. *Clickhimin HU465410*
Most accessible wintering wildfowl site. The barrier bar blocking this loch from the sea is now disguised by the road. Added interest provided by the Broch of Clickhimin.

79. *BRESSAY HU500400*
Relatively easy walking on heather moorland with waders and Skuas. Old Red Sandstone cliffs rising to 500 feet on the southern coast.

80. *NOSS (NNR) HU542405*
The most accessible spectacular seabird cliffs in Shetland with the ledges formed from almost horizontally bedded Sandstones. Colonies include Gannets, both Skuas and, on the Holm of Noss, one of the largest Greater Black-backed Gull colonies in Shetland.

81. *Fladdabister HU435325*
One of the most attractive old crofting townships in Shetland, near a limestone band with herb-rich meadows. On the coast is the ruins of a lime kiln.

82. *East Voe of Quarff HU435353*
Exposure of coarse breccia conglomerates. Fine example of U-shaped glaciated valley through to Wester Quarff (HU410350).

83. *Royl Field HU396285*
Second highest hill on the Shetland Mainland, interesting in comparison with Ronas Hill and Sandness Hill. At 962 feet shows no periglacial features and is peat covered to the summit. Fairly rugged walk over blanket peat and acid moor and grassland.

84. *Cunningsburgh HU430300*
Fine example of the complex crofting township habitats with attractive hay meadows.

85. *Hoo Field HU425271*
Ultra-basic site with steatite. The marks made in carving steatite bowls from the burn can easily be seen. A bowl is in the museum at Lerwick. These steatite quarries are of Viking age. This is an area of volcanic rocks (Spilites). Attractive flora.

86. *MOUSA HU461242*
One of the most attractive and interesting of the small Shetland islands with a good cross-section of Shetland's flora and fauna, including Eiders, Skuas and Storm Petrels breeding within the walls of the Broch of Mousa. Large colony of Common Seals and herd of Shetland ponies.

87. *Sandwick HU435237*
The most accessible site to see Common Seals, often hauled out on the pier. Old peat deposits can still be seen on the beach. Site of copper mines worked in the past.

88. *Noness HU442220*
Extremely accessible small colonies of Guillemot and Kittiwake; easy walking on dwarf shrub heath and maritime grassland.

89. *St Ninian's Isle HU365210*
The largest example of a shell sand tombolo (HU372208) in the British Isles, over 1000 yards of sandy causeway connecting the island with the Mainland. Small Cormorant colony on the island. Fascinating also for its chapel ruins where a Celtic silver hoard was discovered in 1958.

90. *Bigton HU380210 – Scousburgh HU377177*
The road takes one past the tiny and attractive township of Rerwick (HU375196) with its traditional rig (field) system. Also as one approaches Scousburgh on the coast, the roadside vegetation provides a fine example of ungrazed meadow flowers and grasses. At Scousburgh there is a section through a remarkable aureole of thermally metamorphised Dunrossness phyllites, believed to be unique to Shetland.

91. *Levenwick HU414214 – Boddam HU400153*
Undemanding walk along low cliffed and varied coastline with small Kittiwake and Guillemot colonies. At Levenwick small beach backed by dunes and blown sand. At Boddam wintering seaduck, divers and grebes.

92. *Clumlie HU405175*
An acidic and dystrophic minor wintering wildfowl site. Interesting also for the abandoned township and water mill. Nearby at Dalsetter (HU403160) is

an erratic boulder from Norway, said to have been deposited in Shetland during the last Ice Age.

93. *Spiggie HU370170 & Brow HU385157*

The Loch of Spiggie is the only large eutrophic loch in the County; it is blocked off from Scousburgh Bay by a sandy bay mouth bar with a dune and machair system supporting a diverse flora. The sand extends on the loch floor for about half a mile providing rich feeding for wildfowl. This is the most important site for Whooper Swans in Shetland and usually contains a great variety of wildfowl in the winter months, including all the wintering duck and occasionally grebes. The southern extremity of the loch is more acidic but has been the breeding site for Red-necked Phalarope. The loch is noted for its silver Trout which come in from the sea at Spiggie Voe. Between Spiggie and Brow is an interesting mesotrophic marsh. Brow is a more minor wintering wildfowl site but has a special attraction for Pochard, as does the Loch of Tingwall.

94. *Noss HU360165 – Fitful HU345130 – Quendale HU370130*

Commences as a pleasant walk over maritime grassland but rapidly becomes rugged towards the top of Fitful Head. The cliffs at Fitful are formed from acidic metamorphic rocks and are the highest cliffs (900 feet) on the Shetland Mainland. There are associated stacks and skerries. There are several seabird colonies but most are not easily observed, except at Noss. At Noss, Common Seals breed, as do Grey Seals under the Fitful cliffs. At Garthsness (HU365112) is a pyrrhotite ore body on the shore.

95. *Quendale HU380134*

The largest area of sand in Shetland, containing the best examples of dune, dune slack and machair vegetation; has had considerable sand blow in the historical past. Towards the northern limit of the sand is the only machair loch in Shetland, the Loch of Hillwell (HU376140), which for its size is the most productive loch in the County with a remarkable flora. This loch attracts a great variety of wintering wildfowl and is the only breeding site for several aquatic bird species. The machair area is also the only Shetland breeding site for butterflies (except the Cabbage White). To the north of the site in Quendale is some of the best farming land in the County. Quendale Bay is one of the most important sites for wintering seaduck and divers.

96. *Pool of Virkie HU398112*

This sheltered intertidal sand and mud flat, with its rich population of *Arenicola*, is one of the most important wader feeding sites in Shetland, where a variety of interesting and rare wintering and migrant waders can be seen. It has been the site for breeding Shelduck but recent extensions to the airport runways has disturbed their breeding ground and Shelduck have not bred, although present, for several years.

97. *Grutness HU408102 & Sumburgh HU400100*
The north-south airport runway crosses a large sand tombolo with dune and machair on either side. At Grutness is a fine, though rather disturbed, boulder beach with breeding Terns. The shrub gardens of Sumburgh Hotel and the borrow-pit on the road to the lighthouse are excellent sites for migrants. Interest is added by the presence of the remarkable archaeological site at Jarlshof, named by Sir Walter Scott in his Shetland novel, *The Pirate*.

98. *Sumburgh Head HU410080*
Fine and easily observable seabird colony. In the autumn large (2000–3000) flocks of moulting Eider can be seen and in summer there is a spectacular traffic of seabirds between Noss and the Sumburgh roost, just to the south of the head. Grey Seals can also be seen around the coast and on the holms and skerries. On a fine day Fair Isle can be seen.

99. *FAIR ISLE HZ210720*
Famous island for migrants, but also has seabird colonies including a large Arctic Skua colony and a very new Gannet colony.

Most of the places in the above list can only be reached on foot, but most people will travel to the starting points by car. A little ingenuity in route planning can combine some of the more exciting sites in a single outing – and this may be necessary for those on whom time presses. Possible half day excursions from Lerwick are:

To the south: Gulberwick Beach, Quarff, Fladdabister (with a spectacular view of Noss to the north), Aithsetter, Boddam, Quendale, Spiggie, Bigton and St Ninian's Isle, and back.

To the west: Scalloway, Hamnavoe and the Burra Isles (with walks to Kettla Ness or Houss Ness) and back via Tingwall.

To the north: Out on the Walls Road to Whiteness and Weisdale (with a diversion to Kergord), Bixter, Aith, Voe, and then either straight back or *via* Nesting through Laxo and Brettabister to Girlsta and thence Lerwick.

Any of these may easily take a whole day, or can be extended, *e.g.* to the Walls Peninsula and Sandness to the west; to Lunna in the north-east; to Firth and Sullom Voe in the north, going on to Ronas Voe and Hillswick or to North Roe. It is possible to drive from one end of Shetland to the other in a day, but anyone venturing to Yell and Unst would be much better advised to stay for a night or two in the north if they are to appreciate the flavour at all.

Most people who come to Shetland have a purpose – to watch birds, botanize, study geology, pump oil, or perhaps to get 'away from it all'. All such are likely to discover that Shetland really is the group of 'friendly isles' as the tourist authorities claim, and they will almost certainly find what they are looking for. We hope that this guide will help those who want to know more about natural history. Those whose interests are more antiquarian or archaeological will find more help in books such as F. T. Wainwright's *The Northern Isles* (1962) or Lloyd Laing's *Orkney and Shetland: an Archaeological Guide* (1974) than in this work. But we recommend even the most dedicated naturalist to take time to visit at least the County Museum in Lerwick and the multi-layered archaeological site at Jarlshof, near Sumburgh Airport. And after that it is well worth going to Clickhimin Broch on the south edge of Lerwick, to the virtually complete broch on Mousa, to the croft house museum at Boddam, to Weisdale Mill, Lunna Kirk, Stanydale Neolithic 'Temple' and much else. But all that is beyond our scope . . .

BIBLIOGRAPHY

ACHESON, E. D. (1965). Epidemiology. In *Multiple Sclerosis. A Reappraisal*, 1–58. MCALPINE, D., LUMSDEN, C. E. & ACHESON, E. D. (Eds.). Edinburgh & London: Livingstone.

ALLISON, R. S. (1963). Some neurological aspects of medical geography. *Proc. R. Soc. Med.* **56**, 71–76.

ALLOT, G. (1971). A report on the lowland vegetation of Foula. *Brathay Exploration Group Field Studies Report no. 11*, 48–57.

ANDERSON, S. S. (1974). Seals in Shetland. In *Natural Environment of Shetland*, 114–118. GOODIER, R. (Ed.). Edinburgh: Nature Conservancy Council.

ANGUS, J. T. (1910). *An Etymological Glossary of some Place-names in Shetland*. Lerwick: Manson.

ARMSTRONG, E. A. (1952). The behaviour and breeding biology of the Shetland wren. *Ibis*, **94**, 220–242.

ARMSTRONG, E. A. (1953). Island wrens: conditions influencing subspeciation and survival. *Brit. Birds.* **46**, 418–420.

ASHMOLE, N. P. (1980). The spider fauna of Shetland and its zoogeographic context. *Proc. R. Soc. Edin.* **78B**.

ASTON UNIVERSITY SUB-AQUA CLUB (1974). *The Wreck of the Kennemerland*. Birmingham: Aston University.

BAILEY, P. (1971). *Orkney*. Newton Abbot: David & Charles.

BAKER, J. (1971). The ecological effects of successive oil spillages. In *The Ecological Effects of Pollution on Littoral Communities*, 21–32 COWELL, E. B. (Ed.). London: Elsevier.

BALDWIN, J. A., INNES, G., MILLAR, W. M., SHARP, G. A. & DORRICOTT, N. (1965). A psychiatric case register in north-east Scotland. *Brit. J. prev. soc. Med.* **19**, 38–42.

BALDWIN, J. R. (Ed.). (1978). *Scandinavian Shetland*. Edinburgh: Scottish Society for Northern Studies.

BALDWIN, J. R. (1978). Norse influences in sheep husbandry on Foula, Shetland. In *Scandinavian Shetland*, 97–127. BALDWIN, J. R. (Ed.). Edinburgh: Scottish Society for Northern Studies.

BALFOUR, E. (1968). Breeding birds of Orkney. *Scot. Birds*, **5**, 89–104.

BALFOUR, E. (1972). *Orkney Birds. Status and Guide*. Stromness: Senior.

BALL, D. F. & GOODIER, R. (1974). Ronas Hill, Shetland: a preliminary account of its ground pattern features resulting from the action of wind and frost. In *The Natural Environment of Shetland*, 89–106. GOODIER, R. (Ed.). Edinburgh: Nature Conservancy Council.

BALNEAVES, E. (1977). *The Windswept Isles. Shetland and its people*. London: Gifford.

BARCLAY, R. S. (1965). *The Population of Orkney 1755–1961*. Kirkwall: Kirkwall Press.

BARKHAM, J. P. (1971). A report on the upland vegetation of Foula. *Brathay Exploration Group Field Studies Report no. 11*, 25–47.

BARRETT-HAMILTON, G. E. H. (1900). On geographical and individual variation in *Mus sylvaticus* and its allies. *Proc. zool. Soc. Lond.*, 397–428.

BARRETT-HAMILTON, G. E. H. & HINTON, M. A. C. (1910–21). *A History of British Mammals*. London: Gurney & Jackson.

BAXTER, E. V. & RINTOUL, L. J. (1928). *The Geographical Distribution and Status of Birds in Scotland*. Edinburgh: Oliver & Boyd.

BEDFORD, MARY DUCHESS OF (1937). *A Bird-watcher's Diary*. London (privately printed).

BEENHAKKER, A. J. (1973). *Hollanders in Shetland*. Lerwick: J. F. Clausen.

BEIRNE, B. P. (1943). The relationships and origins of the Lepidoptera of the Outer Hebrides, Shetland, Faroes, and Iceland. *Proc. R. Irish Acad.* **49B**, 91–101.

BEIRNE, B. P. (1947). The origin and history of the British Macro-Lepidoptera. *Trans. R. ent. Soc. Lond.* **98**, 273–372.

BEIRNE, B. P. (1952). *The Origin and History of the British Fauna*. London: Methuen.

BENEDIKTSSON, G. & BJARNASON, O. (1959). Lepra i Island. *Nord. Med.* **62**, 1225–1227.

BERRY, A. C. (1974). The use of non-metrical variations of the cranium in the study of Scandinavian population movements. *Am. J. phys. Anthrop.* **40**, 345–358.

BERRY, R. J. (1967). Genetical changes in mice and men. *Eug. Rev.* **59**, 78–96.

BERRY, R. J. (1968). The biology of non-metrical variation in mice and men. In *The Skeletal Biology of Earlier Human Populations*, 103–133 BROTHWELL, D. R. (Ed.). London: Pergamon.

BERRY, R. J. (1969a). History in the evolution of *Apodemus sylvaticus* (Mammalia) at one edge of its range. *J. Zool., Lond.* **59**, 311–328.

BERRY, R. J. (1969b). Genetical factors in the aetiology of multiple sclerosis. *Acta neurol. Scand.* **45**, 459–483.

BERRY, R. J. (1969c). Non-metrical variation in two Scottish colonies of the Grey Seal. *J. Zool., Lond.* **157**, 11–18.

BERRY, R. J. (1970). Viking mice. *Listener*, **84**, 147–148.

BERRY, R. J. (1972a). Genetical approaches to taxonomy. *Proc. R. Soc. Med.* **65**, 853–854.

BERRY, R. J. (1972b). *Ecology and Ethics*. London: Inter-Varsity.

BERRY, R. J. (1973). Chance and change in British Long-tailed field mice. *J. Zool., Lond.* **170**, 351–366.

BERRY, R. J. (1974). The Shetland fauna, its significance or lack thereof. In *The Natural Environment of Shetland*, 151–163. GOODIER, R. (Ed.). Edinburgh: Nature Conservancy Council.

BERRY, R. J. (1975). On the nature of genetical distance and island races of *Apodemus sylvaticus*. *J. Zool., Lond.* **176**, 293–296.

BERRY, R. J. (1977). *Inheritance and Natural History*. London: Collins New Naturalist.

BERRY, R. J. (1979). The Outer Hebrides: where genes and geography meet. *Proc. R. Soc. Edin.* **77B**, 21–43.

BERRY, R. J. & CROTHERS, J. H. (1974). Visible variation in the Dog-whelk, *Nucella lapillus*. *J. Zool., Lond.* **174**, 123–148.

BERRY, R. J. & DAVIS, P. E. (1970). Polymorphism and behaviour in the Arctic Skua (*Stercorarius parasiticus* (L.)). *Proc. R. Soc. B*, **175**, 255–267.

BERRY, R. J. EVANS, I. M. & SENNITT, B. F. C. (1967). The relationships and ecology of *Apodemus sylvaticus* from the Small Isles of the Inner Hebrides, Scotland. *J. Zool., Lond.* **152**, 333–346.

BERRY, R. J., JAKOBSON, M. E. & PETERS, J. (1978). The house mice of the Faroe Islands: a study in microdifferentiation. *J. Zool., Lond.* **185**, 73–92.

BERRY, R. J. & MUIR, V. M. L. (1975). The natural history of man in Shetland. *J. biosoc. Sci.* **7**, 319–344.

BERRY, R. J. & ROSE, F. E. N. (1975). Islands and the evolution of *Microtus arvalis* (Microtinae). *J. Zool., Lond.* **177**, 359–409.

BERRY, R. J. & TRICKER, B. J. K. (1969). Competition and extinction: the mice of Foula, with notes on those of Fair Isle and St. Kilda. *J. Zool., Lond.* **158**, 247–265.

BIRKS, H. J. B. (1973). *Past and Present Vegetation of the Island of Skye*. Cambridge: University Press.

BIRKS, H. J. B. & RANSOM, M. E. (1969). An interglacial peat at Fugla Ness, Shetland. *New Phytol.* **68**, 777–796.

BIRSE, E. L. (1971). *Assessment of climatic conditions in Scotland. 3. The bioclimatic sub-regions.* Aberdeen: Macaulay Institute for Soil Research.

BIRSE, E. L. (1974). Bioclimatic characteristics of Shetland. In *Natural Environment of Shetland*, 24–32. GOODIER, R. (Ed.). Edinburgh: Nature Conservancy Council.

BJARNASON, O., BJARNASON, V., EDWARDS, J. H., FRIDRIKSSON, S., MAGNUSSON, M., MOURANT, A. E. & TILLS, D. (1973). The blood groups of Icelanders. *Ann. hum. Genet.* **36**, 425–458.

BLACK, G. P. (1976). *Shetland. Localities of Geological and Geomorphological Importance.* Newbury: Nature Conservancy Council.

BLACKBURN, T. (1874). Notes on beetles occurring in the Shetland Isles. *Ent. monthly Mag.* **11**, 112.

BLACKBURN, T. (1874). Description of a new species of *Apion* from the Shetland Isles. *Entomologist's mon. Mag.* **11**, 128.

BLACKBURN, T. & LILLEY, C. E. (1874). Notes on the entomology of Shetland. *Scot. Nat.* **2**, 346–349.

BLOOMFIELD, E. N. (1904). Diptera from the Shetlands and Orkneys. *Entom. monthly Mag.* **15**, 88.

BOGAN, J. A. & BOURNE, W. R. P. (1972). Polychlorinated biphenyls in North Atlantic seabirds. *Marine Pollution Bull.* **3**, 171–175.

BONNER, W. N. (1971). An aged Grey seal (*Halichoerus grypus*). *J. Zool., Lond.* **164**, 261–262.

BONNER, W. N. (1972). The Grey Seal and Common Seal in European waters. *Oceanogr. Mar. Biol. Ann. Rev.* **10**, 461–507.

BONNER, W. N. (1976). *Stocks of Grey Seals and Common Seals in Great Britain. N.E.R.C. Publications. Ser. C, no. 16.* London: N.E.R.C.

BONNER, W. N. (1978). Man's impact on seals. *Mamm. Rev.* **8**, 3–13.

BONNER, W. N., VAUGHAN, R. W. & JOHNSTON, J. L. (1973). The status of common seals in Shetland. *Biol. Conservation,* **5**, 185–190.

BORGESEN, F. (1903). The marine algae of the Shetland. *J. Bot., Lond.* **41**, 300–306.

BOTT, M. H. P. & BROWITT, C. W. A. (1975). Interpretation of geophysical observations between the Orkney and Shetland Islands. *J. geol. Soc. Lond.* **131**, 353–371.

BOTT, M. H. P. & WATTS, A. B. (1970). Deep sedimentary basins proved in the Shetland–Hebridean continental shelf and margin. *Nature, Lond.* **225**, 265–268.

BOUÉ, A. (1820). *Essai Geologique sur l'Écosse*. Paris.

BOURNE, W. R. P. (1974). Geographical variation in Shetland birds. In *The Natural Environment of Shetland*, 145–146. GOODIER, R. (Ed.). Edinburgh: Nature Conservancy Council.

BOURNE, W. R. P. & JOHNSTON, J. L. (1971). The threat of oil pollution to north Scottish seabird colonies. *Marine Pollution Bull.*, **2**, 117–120.

BOYCE, A. J., HOLDSWORTH, V. M. L. & BROTHWELL, D. R. (1973). Demographic and genetic studies in the Orkney Islands. In *Genetic Variation in Britain*, 109–128. SUNDERLAND, E. & ROBERTS, D. F. (Eds.). London: Taylor & Frances.

BOYCOTT, A. E. (1936). The habitats of freshwater Mollusca in Britain. *J. Anim. Ecol.* **5**, 116–186.

BOYD, J. M. (1963). The grey seal (*Halichoerus grypus* Fab.) in the Outer Hebrides in October 1961. *Proc. zool. Soc. Lond.*, **141**, 635–662.

BRAND, J. (1701). *A Brief Description of Orkney, Zetland, Pightland Firth and Caithness*. Edinburgh: Brown.

BRATHAY EXPLORATION GROUP (1969–1976). *Field Studies on Foula*. Ambleside: Brathay.

BRISTOWE, W. S. (1931). The spiders of the Orkney and Shetland Islands. *Proc. Zool. Soc. Lond. for 1931*, 931–956.

BRITTON, R. H. (1974). The freshwater ecology of Shetland. In *Natural Environment of Shetland*, 119–129. GOODIER, R. (Ed.). Edinburgh: Nature Conservancy Council.

BRØGGER, A. W. (1929). *Ancient Immigrants*. Oxford: University Press.

BROWN, E. S. (1965). Distribution of the *ABO* and Rhesus (*D*) blood groups in the north of Scotland. *Heredity, Lond.* **20**, 289–303.

BROWN, S. G. (1976). Modern whaling in Britain and the north-east Atlantic Ocean. *Mamm. Rev.* **6**, 25–36.

BROWN, S. G. (1978). Twenty-ninth annual meeting of the International Whaling Commission, 1977. Polar Record, **19**, 59–61.

BULLARD, E. R. (1972). *Orkney. A checklist of vascular plants, flowering plants and ferns*. Stromness: Rendall.

BURROWS, E. M. (1963). A list of the marine algae in Fair Isle. *Br. phycol. Bull.* **2**, 245–246.

BURROWS, E. M., CONWAY, E., LODGE, S. M. & POWELL, H. T. (1954). The raising of intertidal zones on Fair Isle. *J. Ecol.* **42**, 283–288.

BUTTON, J. (Ed.). (1976). *The Shetland Way of Oil*. Lerwick: Thuleprint.

CADBURY, J. (1975). A note on ancient melanism in the Lepidoptera of North Scotland. In *Natural Environment of Orkney*, 80. GOODIER, R. (Ed.). Edinburgh: Nature Conservancy Council.

CALDER, C. S. T. (1956). Report on the discovery of numerous Stone Age house-sites in Shetland. *Proc. soc. Antiquaries Scot.* **89**, 340–397.

CARLQUIST, S. (1974). *Island Biology*. New York and London: Columbia U.P.

CARPENTER, R. M. (1962). On the invertebrate fauna of Fair Isle. *Scot. Nat.* **70**, 91–95.

CENTRAL UNIT ON ENVIRONMENTAL POLLUTION (1976). Pollution of the sea. Pollution Paper no. 8. London: H.M.S.O.

CHALONER, W. G. (1972). Devonian plants from Fair Isle, Scotland. *Rev. Palaeobot. Palynol.* **14**, 49–61.

CHAPELHOW, R. (1965). On glaciation in North Roe, Shetland. *Geogrl J.* **131**, 60–70.

CHERRETT, J. M. (1964). The distribution of spiders on the Moor House National Nature Reserve, Westmorland. *J. Anim. Ecol.* **33**, 27–48.

CHILDE, V. G. (1946). *Scotland Before the Scots.* London: Methuen.

CHRISTENSEN, I. (1977). Observations of whales in the North Atlantic. *Rep. int. Whaling Comm.* **27**, 388–399.

CLAPHAM, A. R., TUTIN, T. G. & WARBURG, E. G. (1962). *Flora of the British Isles.* London: Cambridge.

CLARKE, W. E. (1912). *Studies in Bird Migration,* 2 vols. Edinburgh: Oliver & Boyd.

CLOUDSLEY-THOMPSON, J. L. (1956). On the arachnid fauna of Fair Isle. *Ann. Mag. nat. Hist.* (12) **9**, 830–832.

CLUNESS, A. T. (1951). *The Shetland Isles.* London: Hale.

CLUNESS, A. T. (Ed.). (1967). *The Shetland Book.* Lerwick: Zetland Education Committee.

CONCHOLOGICAL SOCIETY (1976). *Atlas of the Non-marine Molluscs of the British Isles.* Cambridge: Institute for Terrestrial Ecology.

CONSULTATIVE COMMITTEE (1963). *Grey Seals and Fisheries.* London: H.M.S.O.

COOPE, G. R. (1969). The contribution that the Coleoptera of glacial Britain could have made to the subsequent colonization of Scandinavia. *Opusc. Ent. Lund.* **34**, 95–108.

CORBET, G. B. (1961). Origin of the British insular races of small mammals and of the 'Lusitanian' fauna. *Nature, Lond.* **191**, 1037–1040.

CORBET, G. B. (1970). Vagrant bats in Shetland and the North Sea. *J. Zool. Lond.* **161**, 281–282.

CORBET, G. B. & SOUTHERN, H. (1977). *The Handbook of British Mammals,* 2nd edn. Oxford: Blackwell.

COSTIN, A. B. & MOORE, D. M. (1960). The effects of rabbit grazing on the grassland of Macquarie Island. *J. Ecol.* **48**, 729–732.

COULL, J. R. (1967). A comparison of demographic trends in the Faroe and Shetland Islands. *Trans. Inst. Br. Geog.* **41**, 159–166.

COWIE, J. R. (1871). *Shetland and Its Inhabitants.* Aberdeen: Lewis, Smith.

COX, M. (1976). *The Ponies of Shetland.* Lerwick: Shetland Times.

CRAMP, S., BOURNE, W. R. P. & SAUNDERS, D. (1974). *The Seabirds of Britain and Ireland.* London: Collins.

CRAMPTON, C. B. (1911). The vegetation of Caithness considered in relation to the geology. Cambridge: *Committee for the Survey and Study of British Vegetation.*

CUMMING, R. P. (1968). Organization of a surgical unit in a remote area. *Brit. med. J.* **iv**, 506–509.

CUMMINS, H. & MIDLO, C. (1943). *Finger-prints, Palms and Soles.* Philadelphia: Blakiston.

CURTIS, C. D. & BROWN, P. E. (1969). The metasomatic development of zoned ultrabasic bodies in Unst, Shetland. *Contr. Min. Petr.* **24**, 275–292.

DALBY, D. H., COWELL, E. B., SYRATT, W. J. & CROTHERS, J. H. (1978). An exposure scale for marine shores in western Norway. *J. mar. biol. Ass. U.K.* **58**, 975–996.

DANIEL, G. E. (1941). The dual nature of the megalithic colonization of prehistoric Europe. *Proc. prehist. Soc.* **7**, 1–49.

DARLING, F. F. & BOYD, J. M. (1964). *The Highlands and Islands*. London: Collins.

DAVIS, J. E. & ANDERSON, S. S. (1976). Effects of oil pollution on breeding grey seals. *Mar. Pollution Bull.* **7**, 115–118.

DAVIS, P. (1965). A list of the birds of Fair Isle. In *Fair Isle and Its Birds*, 251–296. WILLIAMSON, K. Edinburgh & London: Oliver & Boyd.

DAVIS, P. E. & DENNIS, R. H. (1959). Song-sparrow at Fair Isle: a bird new to Europe. *Brit. Birds.* **52**, 419–421.

DEGERBØL, M. (1939). The field mouse of Iceland, its systematic position (*Apodemus sylvaticus grandiculus* sub sp. nov.) and biology. *Zoology Iceland Pt. 76*, appendix.

DEGERBØL, M. (1942). Mammalia. *Zoology Faroes Pt. 65*, 1–133.

DELANY, M. J. (1963). A collection of *Apodemus* from the Island of Foula, Shetland. *Proc. zool. Soc. Lond.* **140**, 319–320.

DELANY, M. J. (1964). Variation in the Long-tailed field mouse (*Apodemus sylvaticus* (L.)) in north-west Scotland. I. Comparison of individual characters. *Proc. R. Soc. Lond. B.* **161**, 191–199.

DELANY, M. J. & DAVIS, P. E. (1961). Observations on the ecology and life history of the Fair Isle field mouse *Apodemus sylvaticus fridariensis* (Kinnear). *Proc. Zool. Soc. Lond.* **136**, 439–452.

DENNIS, R. W. G. (1972). Fungi of the Northern Isles. *Kew Bull.*, **26**, 427–432.

DENNIS, R. W. G. & GRAY, E. G. (1954). A first list of the fungi of Zetland (Shetland). *Trans. bot. Soc., Edin.* **36**, 215–223.

DENNY, P. (1963). *Vegetation of Ronas Hill, analysed by a new technique*. Unpublished B.Sc. Thesis, University of St. Andrews.

DEYELL, A. (1975). *My Shetland*. Lerwick: Thuleprint.

DIXON, P. S. (1963). Marine algae of Shetland collected during the meeting of the British Phycological Society, August 1962. *Br. phycol. Bull.* **2**, 236–243.

DONALDSON, G. (1958). *Shetland Life under Earl Patrick*. Edinburgh & London: Oliver & Boyd.

DONALDSON, G. (1966). *Northwards by Sea*. Edinburgh: Grant.

DONALDSON, G. (1969). The Scottish settlement. Inaugural address at Quincentenary Historical Congress, Lerwick. *Shetland Times* for 22 August, 1969.

DONEGANI, J., DUNGAL, N., IKIN, E. & MOURANT, A. (1950). The blood groups of the Icelanders. *Ann. Eug.* **15**, 147–152.

DOTT, H. E. M. (1967). Numbers of Great Skuas and other seabirds of Hermaness, Unst. *Scot. Birds.* **4**, 340–350.

DROSIER, R. (1830–31). Account of an ornithological visit to the island of Shetland and Orkney in the summer of 1828. *Mag. nat. Hist.* for 1830, 321–326; 1831, 193–199.

DRUCE, G. C. (1922). Flora Zetlandica. *Rep. Bot. Soc. Exch. Club* for 1921, 457–546.

DRUCE, G. C. (1925). Additions to Flora Zetlandica (1924). *Rep. Bot. Soc. Exch. Club*, **7**, 628–657.

DUNCAN, U. K. (1961). A visit to the Shetland Isles. *Lichenologist*, **1**, 267–268.

DUNCAN, U. K. (1963). A list of Fair Isle lichens. *Lichenologist*, **2**, 171–178.

DUNGAL, N. (1961). The special problem of stomach cancer in Iceland. *J. Am. med. Assoc.* **178**, 789–798.

DUNN, R. (1837). *The Ornithologist's Guide to the Islands of Orkney and Shetland.* Hull.

DUNN, R. (1848). Some notes on the birds of Shetland. *Zoologist*, 2187–2188.

DUNNET, G. M. (1974). Impact of the oil industry on Scotland's coasts and birds. *Scott. Birds*, **8**, 3–16.

DYCK, J. & MELTOFTE, H. (1975). The guillemot *Uria aalge* population of the Faeroes 1972. *Dansk orn. Foren. Tidsskr.* **69**, 55–64.

EARLL, R. (1975). An extensive survey of the shallow sublittoral fauna of Shetland. *Proc. 4th World Congr. of Underwater Activities. Vol. I. Archaeology and Biology*, 193–200. ADOLSON, J. (Ed.). Stockholm: Vorderwater.

EDMONSTON, A. (1809). *A View of the Ancient and Present State of the Zetland Islands.* Edinburgh: Ballantyne.

EDMONSTON, B. & SAXBY, J. M. E. (1889). *The Home of a Naturalist.* London: Nisbet.

EDMONSTON, T. (1845). *A Flora of Shetland.* Aberdeen.

EGGELING, W. J. (1964). A nature reserve management plan for the Island of Rhum, Inner Hebrides. *J. appl. Ecol.* **1**, 405–419.

ERDTMAN, G. (1924). Studies in micropalaeontology of post-glacial deposits in North Scotland and the Scotch Isles with especial reference to the history of the woodlands. *J. Linn. Soc. Bot.* **46**, 449–504.

EUNSON, J. (n.d.). *The Shipwrecks of Fair Isle.* Fair Isle: W. S. Wilson.

EVANS, A. H. & BUCKLEY, T. E. (1899). *A Vertebrate Fauna of the Shetland Islands.* Edinburgh: Douglas.

EVANS, F. C. & VEVERS, H. G. (1938). Notes on the biology of the Faeroes mouse (*Mus musculus faeroensis*). *J. Anim. Ecol.* **7**, 290–297.

EVANS, P. G. H. (1976*a*). An analysis of sightings of Cetacea in British waters. *Mammal Rev.* **6**, 5–14.

EVANS, P. G. H. (1976*b*). *Guide to Identification of Cetaceans in British Waters.* Reading: Mammal Society.

FENTON, A. (1973). *The Various Names of Shetland.* Privately printed.

FENTON, E. W. (1978). *The Northern Isles: Orkney and Shetland.* Edinburgh: Donald.

FENTON, E. W. (1937). The influence of sheep on the vegetation of hill-grazings in Scotland. *J. Ecol.* **25**, 424–430.

FERGUSON, T. (1960). Mortality in Shetland a hundred years ago. *Scot. med. J.* **5**, 107–112.

FERREIRA, R. E. C. (1959). Scottish mountain vegetation in relation to the geology. *Trans. bot. Soc. Edinb.* **37**, 229–250.

FIELD, E. J. (1973). A rational prophylactic therapy for multiple sclerosis? *Lancet*, **ii**, 1080.

FINLAY, T. M. (1926*a*). A tongsbergite boulder from the boulder-clay of Shetland. *Trans. Edinb. geol. Soc.* **12**, 180.

FINLAY, T. M. (1926*b*). The Old Red Sandstone of Shetland. Part I: South-eastern area. *Trans. R. Soc. Edinb.* **53**, 553–572.

FINLAY, T. M. (1930). The Old Red Sandstone of Shetland. Part II: North-western area. *Trans. R. Soc. Edinb.* **56**, 671–694.

FISHER, J. (1952) *The Fulmar*. London: Collins.
FISHER, J. & LOCKLEY, R. M. (1954). *Sea Birds*. London: Collins New Naturalist.
FISHER, J. & VENABLES, L. S. V. (1938). Gannets (*Sula bassana*) on Noss Shetland, with an analysis of the rate of increase in this species. *J. Anim. Ecol.* **7**, 305–313.
FISHER, J., STEWART, T. M. & VENABLES, L. S. V. (1938). Gannet colonies of Shetland. *Brit. Birds.* **32**, 162–169.
FISHER, R. A. & TAYLOR, G. L. (1940). Scandinavian influence in Scottish ethnology. *Nature, Lond.* **145**, 590.
FLINN, D. (1958). On the nappe structure of North-east Shetland. *Quart J. geol. Soc. Lond.* **114**, 107–136.
FLINN, D. (1959). Extension of the Great Glen Fault beyond the Moray Firth. *Nature, Lond.* **191**, 589–591.
FLINN, D. (1964). Coastal and submarine features around the Shetland Islands. *Proc. Geol. Ass.* **75**, 321–339.
FLINN, D. (1967). The metamorphic rocks of the southern part of the mainland of Shetland. *Geol. J.* **5**, 251–290.
FLINN, D. (1969*a*). On the development of coastal profiles in the north of Scotland, Orkney and Shetland. *Scot. J. Geol.* **5**, 393–399.
FLINN, D. (1969*b*). A geological interpretation of the aeromagnetic maps of the continental shelf around Orkney and Shetland. *Geol. J.* **6**, 279–292.
FLINN, D. (1970*a*). The glacial till of Fair Isle, Shetland. *Geol. Mag.* **107**, 273–276.
FLINN, D. (1970*b*). Some aspects of the geochemistry of the metamorphic rocks of Unst and Fetlar, Shetland. *Proc. geol. Ass.* **81**, 509–527.
FLINN, D. (1973). The topography of the sea floor around Orkney and Shetland and in the northern North Sea. *Quart. J. geol. Soc. Lond.* **129**, 39–59.
FLINN, D. (1974). The coastline of Shetland. In *Natural Environment of Shetland*, 13–23. GOODIER, R. (ed.). Edinburgh: Nature Conservancy Council.
FLINN, D. (1977). The erosion history of Shetland: a review. *Proc. Geol. Ass.* **88**, 129–146.
FLINN, D. (1978). The most recent glaciation of the Orkney–Shetland Channel and adjacent areas. *Scot. J. Geol.* **14**, 109–123.
FLINN, D., MAY, F., ROBERTS, J. L. V. & TREAGUS, J. E. (1972). A revision of the stratigraphic succession of the east mainland of Shetland. *Scot. J. Geol.* **8**, 335–343.
FLINN, D., FRANK, P. L., BROOK, M. & PRINGLE, I. R. (1979). Basement-cover relations in Shetland. In *The Caledonides of the British Isles*, HARRIS, A., HOLLAND, C. H. & LEAKE, B. E. (Eds.). London: Geological Society.
FOG, M. & HYLLESTED, K. (1966). Prevalence of disseminated sclerosis in the Faeroes, the Orkneys and Shetland. *Acta neurol. Scand.* **42**, suppl. 19, 9–11.
FORD, E. B. (1945). *Butterflies*. London: Collins New Naturalist.
FORD, E. B. (1955*a*). *Moths*. London: Collins New Naturalist.
FORD, E. B. (1955*b*). Polymorphism and taxonomy. *Heredity*, **9**, 255–264.
FOWLER, J. A. (1977). Preliminary studies on the fauna and flora of Yell, Shetland. Leicester Polytechnic, School of Life Sciences.
FRASER, F. C. (1934 etc.). *Reports on Cetacea Stranded on the British Coasts*. London: British Museum (Natural History).
FRASER, F. C. (1966). *Guide for the Identification and Reporting of Stranded Whales, Dolphins and Porpoises on the British Coasts*. London: British Museum (Natural History).

FRESSON, E. E. (1967). *Air Road to the Isles*. London: Rendel.

FRIEND, G. F. (1959). Subspeciation in British char. *Syst. Assoc. Publ.* **3**, 121–129.

FURNESS, R. W. (1977). The effect of Great Skuas on Arctic Skuas in Shetland. *Brit. Birds,* **70**, 96–107.

FURNESS, R. W. (1978). Energy requirements of seabird communities: a bio-energetics model. *J. Anim. Ecol.* **47**, 39–53.

GEORGE, R. S. (1970). Fleas, and a few other animals, from the island of Foula in the Shetlands. *Ent. Gaz.* **21**, 30–32.

GIBSON, G. A. (1877). *The Old Red Sandstone of Shetland*. Edinburgh & London: Williams & Norgate.

GIFFORD, T. (1786). *An Historical Description of the Zetland Islands*. London: J. Nichols.

GILLHAM, M. E. (1967). *Sub-antarctic Sanctuary*. London: Gollancz.

GIMINGHAM, C. H. (1964a). Dwarf shrub heaths. In *The Vegetation of Scotland,* 232–287. BURNETT, J. H. (Ed.). Edinburgh: Oliver & Boyd.

GIMINGHAM, C. H. (1964b). Maritime and sub-maritime communities. In *The Vegetation of Scotland*, 67–129. BURNETT, J. H. (Ed.). Edinburgh: Oliver & Boyd.

GIMINGHAM, C. H. (1972). *Ecology of Heathlands*. London: Chapman & Hall.

GOATER, B. (1969). Entomological excursions to the Shetlands, 1966 and 1968. *Entomol. Gaz.* **20**, 73–82.

GOATER, B. (1973). Some further observations on Shetland Lepidoptera, 1972. *Entomol. Gaz.* **24**, 7–12.

GOLDSMITH, F. B. (1975). The sea-cliff vegetation of Shetland. *J. Biogeog.* **2**, 297–308.

GOODE, D. A. (1974). The flora and vegetation of Shetland. In *The Natural Environment of Shetland*, 50–72. GOODIER, R. (Ed.). Edinburgh: Nature Conservancy Council.

GOODIER, R. (Ed.). (1974). *The Natural Environment of Shetland*. Edinburgh: Nature Conservancy Council.

GOODIER, R. (Ed.). (1975). *The Natural Environment of Orkney*. Edinburgh: Nature Conservancy Council.

GOODLAD, C. A. (1971). *Shetland Fishing Saga*. Lerwick: Shetland Times.

GORE, A. J. P. (1975). An experimental modification of upland peat vegetation. *J. appl. Ecol.* **12**, 349–366.

GORHAM, E. (1958). The physical limnology of northern Britain: an epitome of the Bathymetrical Survey of the Scottish Freshwater Lochs, 1897–1909. *Limnol. Oceanogr.* **3**, 40–50.

GOUDIE, G. (1904). *The Celtic and Scandinavian Antiquities of Shetland*. Edinburgh & London: Blackwood.

GREWAL, M. S. (1962). The rate of genetic divergence of sublines in the C57BL strain of mice. *Genet. Res., Camb.* **3**, 375–391.

GRIME, J. P. & HUNT, R. (1975). Relative growth rate: its range and adaptive significance in a local flora. *J. Ecol.* **63**, 393–422.

GRIMSHAW, P. H. (1905). Diptera Scotica. IV. Orkney and Shetland. *Ann. Scot. nat. Hist. for 1905*, 22–35.

GROUNDWATER, W. (1974). *Birds and Mammals of Orkney*. Kirkwall: Kirkwall Press.

HALDANE, J. B. S. (1948). The theory of a cline. *J. Genet* **48**, 277–284.

HALDANE, R. C. (1904). Whaling in Shetland. *Ann. Scot. nat. Hist. for 1904*, 74–77.

HALDANE, R. C. (1905). Notes on whaling in Shetland in 1904. *Ann Scot. nat. Hist. for 1905*, 65–72.

HALE, M. E. (1974). *The Biology of Lichens*, 2nd edn. London: Arnold.

HALL, R. E. (1954). Some Chironomidae from the Shetland Isles. *J. Soc. Br. Entomol.* **4**, 66–69.

HALL, D. J., ROBERTSON, N. C., DORRICOTT, N., OLLEY, P. C. & MILLAR, W. M. (1973). The North-East Scottish psychiatric case register – the second phase. *J. Chron. Dis.* **26**, 375–382.

HAMILTON, F. (1974). The importance of Shetland birds in a United Kingdom context. In *The Natural Environment of Shetland*, 147–150. GOODIER, R. (Ed.). Edinburgh: Nature Conservancy Council.

HAMILTON, J. R. C. (1956). *Excavations at Jarlshof, Shetland*. Edinburgh: H.M.S.O.

HAMILTON, J. R. C. (1962). Brochs and broch-builders. In *The Northern Isles*, 53–90. WAINWRIGHT, F. T. (Ed.). Edinburgh & London: Nelson.

HAMILTON, J. R. C. (1968). *Excavations at Clickhimin, Shetland*. Edinburgh, H.M.S.O.

HANSEN, H. M. (1930). Studies on the vegetation of Iceland. *Botany Iceland*, vol. 3.

HARDY, A. C. (1956). *The Open Sea: its Natural History. Part I: The World of Plankton*. London: Collins New Naturalist.

HARDY, A. C. (1959). *The Open Sea: its Natural History. Part II: Fish and Fisheries*. London: Collins New Naturalist.

HARE, E. J. (1963). Shetland macro-Lepidoptera. *Ent. Rec.* **75**, 238.

HARMER, S. F. (1914, etc.). *Reports on Cetacea Stranded on the British Coasts*. London: British Museum (Natural History).

HARRIS, M. P. (1976). The seabirds of Shetland in 1974. *Scot. Birds.* **9**, 37–68.

HARTMAN, O. & LUNDEVALL, J. (1944). Blood group distribution in Norway. *Skr. Norske Vidensk. Akad.* **2**, 1–68.

HARVIE-BROWN, J. A. (1892). Hedgehog (*Erinaceus europaeus* L.) in Shetland. *Ann. Scot. nat. Hist. for 1892*, 132.

HARVIE-BROWN, J. A. (1893). Contributions to a fauna of the Shetland Islands. *Ann. Scot. nat. Hist. for 1893*, 9–25.

HARVIE-BROWN, J. A. (1895). The starling in Scotland, its increase and distribution. *Ann. Scot. nat. Hist. for 1895*, 2–22.

HARWOOD, J. (1978). The effect of management policies on the stability and resilience of British grey seal populations. *J. appl. Ecol.* **15**, 413–421.

HARWOOD, J. & PRIME, J. H. (1978). Some factors affecting the size of British grey seal populations. *J. appl. Ecol.* **15**, 401–411.

HAWKSWORTH, D. L. (1966). The lichen flora of Foula (Shetland). *Lichenologist,* **3**, 218–223.

HAWKSWORTH, D. L. (1969a). Notes on the flora and vegetation of Foula, Shetland (V.C. 112). *Proc. bot. Soc. B.I.* **7**, 537–547.

HAWKSWORTH, D. L. (1969b). The bryophyte flora of Foula (Shetland). *Rev. Bryol. Lichenol.* **36**, 213–218.

HAWKSWORTH, D. L. (1970). Studies on the peat deposits of the Island of Foula, Shetland. *Trans. bot. Soc. Edinb.* **40**, 576–591.

HAWKSWORTH, D. L. & ROSE, F. (1976). *Lichens as Pollution Monitors*. London: Arnold.

HAWKSWORTH, D. L. & SEAWARD, M. R. D. (1977). *Lichenology in the British Isles 1568–1975*. Richmond: Richmond Publishing.

HEDDLE, M. F. (1878). *The County Geognosy and Mineralogy of Scotland, Orkney and Shetland*. Truro.

HEINEBERG, H. (1972). *Die Shetland-Inseln ein Agrarisches Problem gebiet Schott lands*. Bochumer Geographische Arb. vol. 5.

HENDERSON, T. (1978). Shetland boats and their origins. In *Scandinavian Shetland*, 49–55. BALDWIN, J. R. (Ed.). Edinburgh: Scottish Society for Northern Studies.

HEWER, H. R. (1964). The determination of age, sexual maturity, longevity and a life-table in the grey seal (*Halichoerus grypus*). *Proc. zool. Soc. Lond.* **142**, 593–624.

HEWER, H. R. (1974). *British Seals*. London: Collins New Naturalist.

HIBBERT, S. (1822). *Description of the Shetland Islands*. Edinburgh: Constable.

HILLIAM, J. (1977). *Phytosociological Studies in the Southern Isles of Shetland*. Unpublished Ph.D. Thesis, University of Durham.

HINTON, M. A. C. (1914). Notes on the British forms of *Apodemus*. *Ann. Mag. nat. Hist.* (9) **14**, 117–134.

HINTON, M. A. C. (1919). The field mouse of Foula, Shetland. *Scot. Nat. for 1919*, 177–181.

HOLBOURN, I. B. S. (1938). *The Isle of Foula*. Lerwick: Manson.

HOLDGATE, M. W. (1960). The fauna of the mid-Atlantic islands. *Proc. R. Soc. Lond. B*, **152**, 550–567.

HOLDGATE, M. W. & WACE, N. M. (1961). The influence of man on the floras and faunas of southern islands. *Polar Rec.*, **10**, 475–493.

HOPPE, G. (1965). Submarine peat in the Shetland islands. *Geogr. Annlr.* **47A**, 195–203.

HOPPE, G. (1974). The glacial history of the Shetland Islands. *Trans. Inst. Br. Geog.* Special Publication no 7, 197–210.

HOWE, G. M. (1963). *National Atlas of Disease Mortality in the United Kingdom*. London & Edinburgh: Nelson.

HOWARTH, D. (1951). *The Shetland Bus*. London & Edinburgh: Nelson.

HUXLEY, T. (1974). Wilderness. In *Conservation in Practice*, 361–374. WARREN, A. & GOLDSMITH, F. B. (Eds.). New York & Chichester: Wiley.

INNES, G., KIDD, C. & ROSS, H. S. (1968). Mental subnormality in north-east Scotland. *Brit. J. Psychiat.* **114**, 35–41.

IRVINE, D. E. G. (1962). The marine algae of Shetland: a phyto-geographical account. *Br. Phycol. Bull.* **2**, 181–182.

IRVINE, D. (1974). The marine vegetation of the Shetland Isles. In *The Natural Environment of Shetland*, 107–113. GOODIER, R. (Ed.). Edinburgh: Nature Conservancy Council.

IRVINE, S. G. (1968). An outline of the climate of Shetland. *Weather*, **23**, 392–403.

JACKSON, E. E. (1966). The birds of Foula. *Scot. Birds.* **4**, supplement.

JAKOBSEN, J. (1928). *An Etymological Dictionary of the Norn Language in Shetland*. London: Nutt, and Copenhagen: Vilhelm Prior.

JAKOBSEN, J. (1936). *The Place-names of Shetland*. London: Nutt, and Copenhagen: Vilhelm Prior.

JAMESON, R. (1798). *Outline of Mineralogy of the Shetland Islands and of Arran*. Edinburgh.

JEFFERIES, D. J. & PARSLOW, J. L. F. (1976). The genetics of bridling in guillemots from a study of hand-reared birds. *J. Zool. Lond.* **179**, 411–420.

JEFFREYS, J. G. (1869). Last Report on dredging among the Shetland Isles. *Rep. 38th Meeting Brit. Assoc.* 232–247.

JENSEN, A. D. (Editor) (1928–72). *The Zoology of the Faroes.* Copenhagen: Høst.

JEWELL, P. A., MILNER, C. & BOYD, J. M. (1974). *Island Survivors: the Ecology of the Soay Sheep of St. Kilda.* London: Athlone.

JOENSEN, A. H. (1966). *The Birds of Faroe.* Copenhagen: Rhodos.

JOHANSEN, J. (1975). Pollen diagrams from the Shetland and Faroe Islands. *New Phytol.* **75**, 369–387.

JOHANSEN, J. (1978). The age of the introduction of *Plantago lanceolata* to the Shetland Islands. *Geol. Survey of Denmark Yearbook for 1976*, 45–78.

JOHNSTON, J. L. (1974). Shetland habitats, an outline ecological framework. In *The Natural Environment of Shetland*, 33–49. GOODIER, R. (Ed.). Edinburgh: Nature Conservancy Council.

JOHNSTON. J. L. (1976). The environmental impact. In *The Shetland Way of Oil*, 58–71. BUTTON, J. (Ed.). Lerwick: Thuleprint.

JOHNSTON, R. (1977). What North Sea oil might cost fisheries. *Rapp. P.-v. Reun. Cons. int. Explor. Mer.* **171**, 212–223.

JONES, A. M. (1975). The marine environment of Orkney. In *The Natural Environment of Orkney*, 85–94. GOODIER, R. (Ed.). Edinburgh: Nature Conservancy Council.

JONES, A. M., JONES, Y. M. & JAMES, J. L. (1979). The incidence of the nemertine *Malacobdella grossa* in the bivalve *Cerastoderma edule* in Shetland. *J. mar. Biol. Ass. U.K.* **59**, 373–375.

JONES, N. V. & MORTIMER, M. A. E. (1974). Stream invertebrates on Foula. *Glasgow Nat.* **19**, 91–100.

JONSSON, J. (1965). Whales and whaling in Icelandic waters. *Norwegian Whaling Gaz.* **54**, 245–253.

KAY, G. T. (1947). The young Guillemot's flight to the sea. *Brit. Birds*, **40**, 156–157.

KAY, G. T. (1948). The gannet in Shetland in winter. *Brit. Birds*, **41**, 268–270.

KETTLEWELL, H. B. D. (1961a). Geographical melanism in the Lepidoptera of Shetland. *Heredity, Lond.* **16**, 393–402.

KETTLEWELL, H. B. D. (1961b). Selection experiments on melanism in *Amathes glareosa* Esp. (Lepidoptera). *Heredity, Lond.* **16**, 415–434.

KETTLEWELL, H. B. D. (1965). Insect survival and selection for pattern. *Science, N.Y.* **148**, 1290–1296.

KETTLEWELL, H. B. D. (1973). *The Evolution of Melanism.* Oxford: Clarendon.

KETTLEWELL, H. B. D. & BERRY, R. J. (1961). The study of a cline. *Heredity, Lond.* **16**, 403–414.

KETTLEWELL, H. B. D. & BERRY, R. J. (1969). Gene flow in a cline. *Heredity, Lond,* **24**, 1–14.

KETTLEWELL, H. B. D., BERRY, R. J., CADBURY, C. J. & PHILLIPS, G. C. (1969). Differences in behaviour, dominance and survival within a cline. *Heredity, Lond.* **24**, 15–25.

KETTLEWELL, H. B. D. & CADBURY, C. J. (1963). Investigations on the origins of non-industrial melanism. *Ent. Rec.* **75**, 149–160.

KIKKAWA, J. (1959). Habitats of the field mouse on Fair Isle in spring, 1956. *Glasg. Nat.* **18**, 65–77.

KING, H. G. R. (1969). *The Antarctic.* London: Blandford.

KING, J. J. F. X. (1890). Tipulidae from the Island of Unst. *Entomol. monthly Mag.* **26**, 176–180.

KING, J. J. F. X. (1896). Notes on Trichoptera (including *Agrypnia picta* Kol.) taken in Unst, Shetland. *Entomol. monthly Mag.* **32**, 151–152.

KINNEAR, N. B. (1906). On the mammals of Fair Isle with a description of a new subspecies of *Mus sylvaticus. Ann. Scot. nat. Hist. for 1906*, 65–68.

KINNEAR, P. (1976). Birds and oil. In *The Shetland Way of Oil*, 92–99. BUTTON, J. (Ed.). Lerwick: Thuleprint.

KLOET, G. S. & HINCKS, W. D. (1972). *A Check List of British Insects. Part 2: Lepidoptera.* 2nd edn, revised. London: Royal Entomological Society.

KRUUK, H. & HEWSON, R. (1978). Spacing and foraging of otters (*Lutra lutra* L.) in a marine habitat. *J. Zool. Lond.* **185**, 205–212.

KURTÉN, B. (1959). Rates of evolution in fossil mammals. *Cold Spr. Harbor Symp. quant. Biol.* **24**, 205–215.

KURTZKE, J. F. (1966). An evaluation of the geographic distribution of multiple sclerosis. *Acta neurol. Scand.* **42**, suppl. 19, 91–117.

LACAILLE, A. C. (1954). *The Stone Age in Scotland.* London: Oxford University Press.

LACK, D. (1942). Ecological features of the bird faunas of British small islands. *J. Anim. Ecol.* **11**, 9–36.

LACK, D. (1959). British pioneers in ornithological research 1859–1939. *Ibis*, **101**, 71–81.

LACK, D. (1960). A comparison of 'drift migration' at Fair Isle, the Isle of May, and Spurn Point. *Scot. Birds*, **1**, 295–327.

LACK, D. (1969). The numbers of bird species on islands. *Bird Study*, **16**, 193–209.

LACK, D. (1976). *Island Biology.* Oxford: Blackwell.

LAING, L. (1974). *Orkney and Shetland. An archaeological guide.* Newton Abbot: David & Charles.

LAWS, R. M. (1977). Seals and whales of the Southern Ocean. *Proc. R. Soc. Lond. B*, **279**, 81–96.

LEA, D. & BOURNE, W. R. P. (1975). Birds of Orkney. In *The Natural Environment of Orkney*, 98–128. GOODIER, R. (Ed.). Edinburgh: Nature Conservancy Council.

LEWIS, A. (1977). *Phytosociological Studies in the Northern Isle of Shetland.* Unpublished Ph.D. Thesis, University of Durham.

LEWIS, F. J. (1907). The plant remains in the Scottish peat mosses. III. The Scottish Highlands and the Shetland Islands. *Trans. R. Soc. Edinb.* **46**, 33–70.

LEWIS, F. J. (1911). The plant remains of the Scottish peat mosses. IV. The Scottish Highlands and Shetland. *Trans. R. Soc. Edinb.* **47**, 793–833.

LINDROTH, C. H. (1955). Insects and spiders from Fair Isle. *Ent. monthly Mag.* **91**, 216.

LINDROTH, C. H. (1970). Survival of animals and plants on ice-free refugia during the Pleistocene glaciations. *Endeavour*, **29**, 129–134.

LINKLATER, E. (1965). *Orkney and Shetland. A historical, geographical, social and scenic survey.* London: Hale.

LIVESEY & HENDERSON (1973). Sullom Voe and Swarbacks Minn area. Master

Development Plan related to oil industry requirements: report to Zetland County Council.

LIVINGSTONE, W. P. (1947). *Shetland and the Shetlanders*. Edinburgh: Nelson.

LLOYD, C. (1975). Timing and frequency of census counts of cliff-nesting auks. *Brit. Birds*, **68**, 507–513.

LOCKIE, J. D. (1952). The food of the Great Skua on Hermaness, Unst. *Scot. Nat.* **64**, 158–162.

LOCKLEY, R. M. (1966). *Grey Seal, Common Seal*. London: Deutsch.

LORIMER, R. I. (1975). Lepidoptera in Orkney. In *The Natural Environment of Orkney*, 57–79. GOODIER, R. (Ed.). Edinburgh: Nature Conservancy Council.

LOW, G. (1774). *A Tour through the Islands of Orkney and Shetland* (1978 reprint). Inverness: Melven.

MACARTHUR, R. H. & WILSON, E. O. (1967). *The Theory of Island Biogeography*. Princeton: University Press.

McGILLIVRAY, J. W. (1920). Agriculture in Shetland. *Scot. J. Agric.* **3**, 414–429.

McINTYRE, A. D. (1961). Quantitative differences in the fauna of boreal mud associations. *J. mar. biol. Ass. U.K.* **41**, 599–616.

McINTYRE, A. D. (1970). The range of biomass in intertidal sand, with special reference to the bivalve *Tellina tenuis*. *J. mar. Biol. Ass. U.K.* **50**, 561–575.

McKAY, A. G. (1974). A sub-bottom profiling survey of the St. Magnus Bay deep, Shetland. *Scot. J. Geol.* **10**, 31–34.

McLACHLAN, R. (1884). Trichoptera from Unst, North Shetland. *Entomol. monthly Mag.* **21**, 91; 153–155.

McVEAN, D. N. & RATCLIFFE, D. A. (1962). *The Plant Communities of the Scottish Highlands*. London: H.M.S.O.

MACAN, T. T. & WORTHINGTON, E. B. (1951). *Life in Lakes and Rivers*. London: Collins New Naturalist.

MAITLAND, P. S. (1972). A key to the freshwater fishes of the British Isles. *Sci. Publ. Freshw. Biol. Assoc.* **27**, 1–139.

MANLY, B. F. J. (1975). A second look at some data on a cline. *Heredity, Lond.* **34**, 423–426.

MARWICK, E. (1975). *The Folklore of Orkney and Shetland*. London: Batsford.

MATHER, A. S. & SMITH, J. S. (1974). *Beaches of Shetland*. Aberdeen: University Department of Geography.

MATTHEWS, J. R. (1955). *Origin and Distribution of the British Flora*. London: Hutchinson.

MATTHEWS, L. H. (1952). *British Mammals*. London: Collins New Naturalist.

MAY, F. (1970). Movement, metamorphism amd migmatization in the Scalloway region of Shetland. *Bull. geol. Surv. Gr. Br.* no 31, 205–226.

MAYR, E. (1954). Change of genetic environment and evolution. In *Evolution as a Process*, 157–180. HUXLEY, J., HARDY, A. C. & FORD, E. B. (Eds.). London: Allen & Unwin.

MAYR, E. (1963). *Ancient Species and Evolution*. London: Oxford.

MAYR, E. (1967). The challenge of island faunas. *Aust. Natural Hist.* **15**, 369–374.

MERCADO, G. I. (1967). *Notes on Shetland Freshwater Life and Arthropods*. Lerwick: Manson.

METCALFE, G. (1950). The ecology of the Cairngorms. II. The mountain Callu-
netum. *J. Ecol.* **38**, 46–74.

MIKKOLA, K. (1967). Immigrations of Lepidoptera, recorded in Finland in the
years 1946–1966, in relation to air currents. *Ann. ent. fenn.* **33**, 65–99.

MILLER, J. A. & FLINN, D. (1966). A survey of the age relations of Shetland rocks.
Geol. J. **5**, 95–116.

MILLS, E. L. (1978). Edward Forbes, John Gwyn Jeffreys, and British dredging
before the *Challenger* expedition. *J. Soc. Biblio. Nat. Hist.* **8**, 507–536.

MILNER, C. (1978). Shetland ecology surveyed. *Geogr. Mag.* 730–753.

MOFFAT, W. (1934). *Shetland: the isles of nightless summer.* London: Cranton.

MOHR, J. (1951–52). Taste sensitivity to phenyl-thio-urea in Denmark. *Ann. Eug.* **16**,
282–286.

MØLLER, F. H. (1945). *Fungi of the Faeroes. Part I.* Copenhagen.

MØLLER, F. H. (1958). *Fungi of the Faeroes. Part II.* Copenhagen.

MOORE, D. M. (1968). The vascular flora of the Falkland Islands. *Brit. Ant. Survey Sc.
Rep.* no. 60.

MORRISON, I. (1973). *The North Sea Earls. The Shetland/Viking Archaeological Expedition.* London: Gentry.

MORRISON, I. A. (1978). Aspects of Viking small craft in the light of Shetland
practice. In *Scandinavian Shetland*, 57–75. BALDWIN, J. R. (Ed.). Edinburgh:
Scottish Society for Northern Studies.

MURRAY, J. & PULLAR, L. (1910) *Bathymetric Survey of the Scottish Freshwater Lochs.*
Edinburgh: Challenger.

MYKURA, W. (1972a). Tuffisitic breccias, tuffisites and associated carbonate-
sulphide mineralization in south-east Shetland. *Bull. geol. Survey Gt. Br.* no 40,
51–82.

MYKURA, W. (1972b). The Old Red Sandstone sediments of Fair Isle, Shetland
Islands. *Bull. geol. Survey Gt. Br.* no 41, 1–31.

MYKURA, W. (1972c). Igneous intrusions and mineralization in Fair Isle, Shetland
Islands. *Bull. geol. Surv. Gt. Br.* no 41, 33–53.

MYKURA, W. (1974). The geological basis of the Shetland environment. In *The
Natural Environment of Shetland*, 1–12. GOODIER, R. (Ed.). Edinburgh: Nature
Conservancy Council.

MYKURA, W. (1975). The geological basis of the Orkney environment. In *The
Natural Environment of Orkney*, 1–9. GOODIER, R. (Ed.). Edinburgh: Nature Conservancy Council.

MYKURA, W. (1976). *Orkney and Shetland (British Regional Geology).* Edinburgh:
H.M.S.O. for Institute of Geological Sciences.

MYKURA, W. & PHEMISTER, J. (1976). The geology of western Shetland. *Mem.
geol. Surv. Gt. Br.* no. 125.

NELSON, G. (1977). *Reminiscences of the Shetland Fireside.* Lerwick: Thuleprint.

NEUSTEIN, S. A. (1964). A review of pilot and trial plantations established by the
Forestry Commission in Shetland. *Scot. Forestry*, **18**, 199–211.

NICOLSON, J. R. (1972). *Shetland.* Newton Abbot: David & Charles.

NICOLSON, J. R. (1975). *Shetland and Oil.* London: Luscombe.

NICOLSON, J. R. (1978). *Traditional Life in Shetland.* London: Hale.

NICOLSON, J. R. (1978). The slaughter of the herring. *Shetland Times*, 21 July.
NORMAN, A. M. (1869). Shetland final dredging report. II. On the Crustacea, Tunicata, Polyzoa, Echinodermata, Actinozoa, Hydrozoa, and Porifera. *Rep. 38th Meeting Brit. Assoc.* 247–340.

ODDIE, B. C. V. (1959). The composition of precipitation at Lerwick, Shetland. *Quart. J. R. met. Soc.* **85**, 163–165.
O'DELL, A. C. (1939). *The Historical Geography of the Shetland Isles*. Lerwick: Manson.
O'DELL, A. C. (1940). *Zetland. Report of the Land Utilisation Survey of Britain*. London: Geographical.
OLDHAM, C. (1930). Notes on the land and freshwater Mollusca of Foula. *Scot. Nat. for 1930*, 37–38.
OLDHAM, C. (1932). Notes on some Scottish and Shetland Pisidia. *J. Conch.* **19**, 271–278.
OSTENFELD, C. H. (1908). The land vegetation of the Faeroes. *Botany of the Faeroes*, **3**, 867–1026.
OSTENFELD, C. H. & GRONTVED, J. (1934). *The Flora of Iceland and the Faeroes*. London: Williams & Norgate.

PALMER, R. C. & SCOTT, W. (1969). *A Check-list of the Flowering Plants and Ferns of the Shetland Isles*. Arbroath: Buncle.
PARKE, M. & DIXON, P. S. (1976). Check-list of British marine algae – third revision. *J. mar. Biol. Ass. U.K.* **56**, 527–594.
PARSLOW, J. L. (1973). *Breeding Birds of Britain and Ireland*. Berkhamstead: Poyser.
PATON, J. A. (1965). *Census Catalogue of British Hepatics*, 4th edn. British Bryological Society.
PATON, J. A. (1973). Hepatic flora of the Shetland Islands. *Trans. bot. Soc. Edin.* **42**, 17–29.
PEACH, B. N. & HORNE, J. (1879). The glaciation of the Shetland Isles. *Quart. J. geol. Soc. Lond.* **35**, 778–811.
PEACH, B. N. & HORNE, J. (1884). The old red volcanic rocks of Shetland. *Trans. R. Soc. Edinb.* **32**, 359–388.
PEACH, C. W. (1865). On traces of glacial drift in the Shetland Islands. *Rep. Br. Ass. Adv. Sci., Bath* in 1864, 59–61.
PEARSON, T. H. & STANLEY, S. O. (1977). The benthic ecology of some Shetland voes. In *Biology of Benthic Organisms*, 503–512. KEEGAN, B. F., CREIDIGH, P. O. & BOADEN, P. J. S. (Eds.). Oxford & New York: Pergamon.
PENNANT, J. (1784–85). *Arctic Zoology*. London.
PERRING, F. H. & WALTERS. S. M. (1962). *Atlas of the British Flora*. London: Nelson.
PERRY, R. (1948). *Shetland Sanctuary*. London: Faber.
PERSSON, I. (1969). The fate of the Icelandic Vikings in Greenland. *Man*, **4**, 620–628.
PITT, F. (1923). *Shetland Pirates*. London: Allen & Unwin.
PHEMISTER, J. (1978). The Old Red Sandstone intrusive complex of northern Northmaven, Shetland. *Rep. Inst. geol. Sci.* no 78/2.
PLOYEN, C. (1840, English translation 1896). *Reminiscences of a Voyage to Shetland, Orkney & Scotland*. Lerwick: Manson.

POORE, M. E. D. & McVEAN, D. N. (1957). A new approach to Scottish mountain vegetation. *J. Ecol.* **45**, 401–439.

POPPIUS, B. (1904–05). Contributions to the knowledge of the Coleopterous fauna of the Shetland and Orkney Islands. *Ofvers. finska vetensk. Soc. Forh.* **47** (17), 1–19.

POWELL, H. T. (1957). Studies in the genus *Fucus* L. II. Distribution and ecology of forms of *Fucus distichus* L. emend. Powell in Britain and Ireland. *J. mar. biol. Ass. U.K.*, **36**, 663–693.

POWELL, H. T. (1963). New records of *Fucus distichus* subspecies for the Shetland and Orkney Islands. *Br. phycol. Bull.* **2**, 247–254.

POWELL, M. (1938). *200,000 Feet on Foula*. London: Faber.

PRICE, W. R. (1929). Notes on the vegetation of Zetland. *Rep. Bot. Soc. exch. Club.* **8**, 770–781.

PRINGLE, J. R. (1970). The structural geology of the North Roe area of Shetland. *Geol. J.* **7**, 147–170.

PROCTOR, J. (1971). The plant ecology of serpentine. II. Plant responses to serpentine soils. *J. Ecol.* **59**, 397–410; 827–842.

PROCTOR, J. & WOODELL, S. R. J. (1975). The ecology of serpentine soils. *Adv. ecol. Res.* **9**, 255–366.

RAEBURN, H. (1888). The summer birds of Shetland. *Proc. R. phys. Soc. Edinb.* **9**, 542–562.

RAEBURN, H. (1891). The birds of Papa Stour, with an account of the Lyra Skerry. *Zoologist*, 3rd ser., **15**, 126–135.

RANKIN, N. (1947). *Haunts of British Divers*. London: Collins.

RASMUSSEN, R. (1952). *Føroya Flora*. Torshavn: Thomsen.

RATCLIFFE, D. A. (1968). An ecological account of the Atlantic bryophytes in the British Isles. *New Phytol.* **67**, 365–439.

READ. H. H. (1934). The metamorphic geology of Unst in the Shetland Islands. *Quart. J. geol. Soc. Lond.* **90**, 637–688.

READ, H. H. (1937). Metamorphic correlation in the polymetamorphic rocks of the Valla Field Block, Unst, Shetland Islands. *Trans. R. Soc. Edinb.* **59**, 195–221.

REINERT, A. (1971). Højere dyr på land. *Danmarks Natur*, **10**, 537–538.

REINIKAINEN, A. (1937). The irregular migration of the crossbills and their relation to the cone-crop of the conifers. *Ornis Fennica*, **14**, 55–64.

RENDALL, R. (1946). *Country Sonnets and other poems*. Kirkwall: The Orcadian.

RENDALL, R. (1960). *Orkney Shore*. Kirkwall: Kirkwall Press.

ROMANUS, T. (1965). Ability to taste P.T.C. among Swedish men and women. *Acta genet.* **14**, 417–420.

ROSS, H. S., INNES, G. & KIDD, C. (1967). Some observations on the prevalence of Down's syndrome. *Scot. med. J.* **12**, 260–263.

ROTHSCHILD, M. (1958). The bird-fleas of Fair Isle. *Parasitology*, **48**, 382–412.

ROYAL COMMISSION ON ENVIRONMENTAL POLLUTION (1974). Fourth Report. *Pollution control: progress and problems*. Cmnd. 5780. London: H.M.S.O.

RYDER, M. L. (1968). The evolution of Scottish breeds of sheep. *Scott. Stud.* **12**, 127–167.

RYDER, M. L. (1971). Cycles of wool follicle activity in some Shetland sheep. *Anim. Prod.* **13**, 511–520.

RYDER, M. L., LAND, R. B. & DITCHBURN, R. (1974). Coat colour inheritance in Soay, Orkney and Shetland sheep. *J. Zool., Lond.* **173**, 477–485.

SALOMONSEN, F. (1935). Aves. *Zoology Faeroes*, 3(2), part 64, 1–269.
SANDISON, S. (1968). *Unst. My Island Home and its Story*. Lerwick: Shetland Times.
SAXBY, C. F. A. (1903). *Edmonston's Flora of Shetland*. Edinburgh & London: Oliphant, Anderson & Ferrier.
SAXBY, H. L. (1874). *The Birds of Shetland*. Edinburgh: Maclaren & Stewart.
SCOTT, D. & DUTHIE, R. (1894). The inland waters of the Shetland islands. *Thirteenth Rep. Fish Board Scot.* **3**, 174–191.
SEAWARD, M. R. D. (Ed.). (1977). *Lichen Ecology*. London: Academic.
SELECT COMMITTEE ON SCIENCE AND TECHNOLOGY (1978). Fourth Report. *House of Commons* no. 684.
SELOUS, S. (1905). *The Bird Watcher in the Shetlands*. London: Dent.
SHELDRICK, M. C. (1976). Trends in the strandings of Cetacea on the British coasts. *Mammal Rev.* **6**, 15–23.
SHEPHERD, S. (1971). *Like a Mantle, the Sea*. London: Bell.
SHETELIG, H. (1940). *Viking Antiquities in Great Britain and Ireland*. Oslo: Aschehoug.
SHETLAND BIRD REPORTS, various editors from 1969 on. Lerwick: Shetland Bird Club.
SHETLAND ISLANDS COUNCIL (1977). *Shetland's Oil Era*. Lerwick: S.I.C. Research and Development Department.
SHEWRY, P. R. & PETERSON, P. J. (1976). Distribution of chromium and nickel in plants from serpentine and other sites. *J. Ecol.* **64**, 195–212.
SIBBALD, R. (1711). *Description of the Islands of Orkney and Zetland*. Edinburgh: Stevenson.
SHIRREFF, J. (1814). *General View of the Agriculture of the Orkney and Shetland Isles, with report on minerology by Rev. John Fleming*. Edinburgh: Board of Agriculture.
SINCLAIR, C. (1840). *Shetland and the Shetlanders or The Northern Circuit*. Edinburgh: Whyte.
SINCLAIR, J. (1795). *General View of the Agriculture of the Northern Counties and Islands of Scotland*. London: Board of Agriculture.
SISSONS, J. B. (1974). The Quaternary in Scotland: a review. *Scot. J. Geol.* **10**, 311–337.
SLATKIN, M. (1973). Gene flow and selection in a cline. *Genetics*, **75**, 733–756.
SMALL, A. (1967–8). Distribution of settlement in Shetland and Faroes in Viking times. *Saga-Book of the Viking Club*, **17**, 145–155.
SMALL, A. (1968). The historical geography of the Norse Viking colonization of the Scottish Highlands. *Norsk geogr. Tidsskr.* **22**, 1–16.
SMALL, A. (1969). Shetland: location the key to historical geography. *Scot. Geogr. Mag.* **85**, 155–161.
SMALL, A., THOMAS, C. & WILSON, D. M. (1973). *St. Ninian's Isle and its Treasure*. Oxford: University Press.
SMIT, F. G. A. M. (1955). The recorded distribution and hosts of Siphonaptera in Britain. *Ent. Gaz.* **8**, 45–75.
SMIT, F. G. A. M. (1957). *Handbook for the Identification of British Insects: Siphonaptera*. London: Royal Entomological Society.

SMITH, E. A. (1966). A review of the world's grey seal population. *J. Zool., Lond.* **150**, 463–489.

SMITH, H. D. (1977). *The Making of Modern Shetland.* Lerwick: Shetland Times.

SMITH, J. (1661). *The Trade and Fishing of Great Britain Displayed, with a description of Orkney and Shetland.* (Reprinted 1971 Edinburgh: Toucan).

SOUTH, R. (1888). Distribution of Lepidoptera in the Outer Hebrides, Orkney, and Shetland. *Entomologist,* **21**, 28–30; 98–99.

SOUTHERN, H. N. (1939). The status and problem of the bridled Guillemot. *Proc. zool. Soc. Lond.* 31–41.

SOUTHERN, H. N. (1943). The two phases of *Stercorarius parasiticus* (Linnaeus). *Ibis,* **85**, 443–485.

SOUTHERN, H. N. (1962). Survey of bridled guillemots, 1959–60. *Proc. zool. Soc. Lond.* **138**, 455–472.

SPEED, J. G. & SPEED, M. G. (1977). *The Exmoor Pony.* Chippenham: Country-wide Livestock.

SPENCE, D. H. N. (1957). Studies on the vegetation of Shetland. I. The serpentine debris vegetation in Unst. *J. Ecol.* **45**, 917–945.

SPENCE, D. H. N. (1958). The flora of Unst, Shetland, in relation to the geology. *Trans. bot. Soc. Edinb.* **37**, 163–173.

SPENCE, D. H. N. (1959). Studies on the vegetation of Shetland. II. Reasons for the restriction of the exclusive pioneers to serpentine debris. *J. Ecol.* **47**, 641–649.

SPENCE, D. H. N. (1960). Studies on the vegetation of Shetland. III. Scrub in Shetland and in South Uist, Outer Hebrides. *J. Ecol.* **48**, 73–95.

SPENCE, D. H. N. (1964). The macrophytic vegetation of lochs, swamps and associated fens. In *The Vegetation of Scotland,* 306–425. BURNETT, J. H. (Ed.). Edinburgh: Oliver & Boyd.

SPENCE, D. H. N. (1970). Scottish serpentine vegetation. *Oikos,* **21**, 22–31.

SPENCE, D. H. N. (1974). Subarctic debris and scrub vegetation of Shetland. In *The Natural Environment of Shetland,* 73–88. GOODIER, R. (Ed.). Edinburgh: Nature Conservancy Council.

SPENCE, D. H. N. (1979). *Shetland's Living Landscape: a Study in Island Plant Ecology.* Lerwick: Thuleprint.

SPENCE, D. H. N. & MILLAR, E. A. (1963). An experimental study of the infertility of a Shetland serpentine soil. *J. Ecol.* **51**, 333–343.

STEPHEN, A. C. (1929–30). Studies on the Scottish marine fauna: the fauna of the sandy and muddy areas of the tidal zone. *Trans. R. Soc. Edin.* **56**, 219–306; 521–535.

STEPHEN, A. C. (1935). Notes on the intertidal fauna of North Uist. *Scot. Nat. for 1935,* 137–142.

STEWART, G. C. (1962). Kergord Plantations, Shetland. *Forestry,* **35**, 35–36.

STEWART, I. (1965). Shetland farm names. In *Fourth Viking Congress,* 247–266. SMALL, A. (Ed.). Edinburgh: Oliver & Boyd.

STEWART, J. (1954). Udal law and government in Shetland. In *Viking Congress, Lerwick July 1950,* 83–111. SIMPSON, W. D. (Ed.). Edinburgh & London: Oliver & Boyd.

STRANGE, I. (1972). *Falkland Islands.* Newton Abbot: David & Charles.

SULLOM VOE ENVIRONMENTAL ADVISORY GROUP (1976). *Oil Terminal at Sullom Voe: Environmental Impact Assessment.* Lerwick: Thuleprint.

SUMMERS, C. F. (1978). Trends in the size of British grey seal populations. *J. appl. Ecol.* **15**, 395–400.

SUMMERS, C. F., BONNER, W. N. & VAN HAAFTEN, J. (1978). Changes in the seal populations of the North Sea. *Rapp. P.-v. Reun. Couns. int. Explor. Mer.* **172**, 278–285.

SUTHERLAND, J. M. (1956). Observations on the prevalence of multiple sclerosis in northern Scotland. *Brain*, **79**, 635–654.

SVARDSON, G. (1957). The 'invasion' type of bird migration. *Brit. Birds*, **50**, 314–343.

SVENSSON, R. (1954). *Lonely Isles*. London: Faber.

SWAN, M. A. (1957). Specimens of char from Shetland and the Faeroes. *Scot. Nat.* **69**, 67–70.

SWAN, W. B. & SENIOR, W. H. (1972). *Survey of Agriculture in Caithness, Orkney and Shetland*. H.I.B.D. Special Report no. 8. Inverness: Highlands & Islands Development Board.

TAIT, E. S. R. (Ed.). (1925). *The Statistical Account of Shetland 1791–1799*. Lerwick: Manson.

TAYLOR, A. B. (1955). British and Irish place-names in Old Norse Literature. In *Annen Viking Kongress*, 113–122. FALK, K. (Ed.). Bergen: University Press.

TAYLOR, B. W. (1954). The flora, vegetation and soils of Macquarie Island. *Aust. Nat. Antarct. Res. Exped. Rep. B.* **2**.

THOMSON, W. P. L. (1970). Funzie, Fetlar: a Shetland run-rig township in the nineteenth century. *Scot. geogr. Mag.* **86**, 170–185.

THORNE, R. (1977). *Fetlar: some facts and stories*. Cambridge: Bluebell.

TICKELL, W. L. N. (1970). The exploitation and conservation of the Common Seal (*Phoca vitulina*) in Shetland. *Biol. Conservation*, **2**, 179–184.

TOYNE, S. M. (1948). *The Scandinavians in History*. London: Arnold.

TRAILL, J. W. H. (1888). The Lepidoptera of the Outer Hebrides, Orkney and Shetland. *Scot. Nat.* **8**, 298–304.

TRAILL, J. W. H. (1889–90). Revision of the Scotch Discomycetes. *Scot. Nat.* **10**, 125–142; 171–190; 220–223.

TRAILL, T. S. (1806). Observations chiefly mineralogical on the Shetland Islands made in the course of a tour through these islands in 1803. *Nicholson's J.* **15**, 353–367.

TUDOR, J. R. (1883). *The Orkneys and Shetland: their past and present state*. London: Stanford.

TULINUS, S. (1965). Personal communication cited by A. E. Mourant, A. C. Kopec, & K. Domaniewska- Sobozak (1974). *The Distribution of the Human Blood Groups*, 2nd edn. Oxford: University Press.

TULLOCH, R. J. (1967). Birds on Out Skerries, Shetland 1966. *Scot. Birds.* **4**, 467–480.

TULLOCH, R. J. (1968). Snowy owls breeding in Shetland in 1967. *Brit. Birds.* **61**, 119–132.

TULLOCH, R. J. (1978). *A Guide to Shetland Mammals*. Lerwick: Shetland Times.

TULLOCH, R. & HUNTER, F. (1972). *A Guide to Shetland Birds*. Lerwick: Shetland Times.

TYLDESLEY, J. B. (1973). Long-range transmission of tree pollen to Shetland. *New Phytol.* **72**, 175–181; 183–190; 691–698.

VAUGHAN, H. (1880). The micro-lepidoptera of the Shetland Isles. *Entomologist.* **12**, 291–292.

VAUGHAN, R. W. (1975). Seals in Orkneys. In *The Natural Environment of Orkney*, 95–97. GOODIER, R. (Ed.). Edinburgh: Nature Conservancy Council.

VAUGHAN, R. W. (1977). A review of the status of the Common Seal, *Phoca vitulina*, in Scotland. *I.C.E.S. Marine Mammals Committee.* **18**, 1–5.

VENABLES, L. S. V. & VENABLES, U. M. (1948). A Shetland bird population: Kergord Plantations. *J. Anim. Ecol.* **17**, 66–74.

VENABLES, L. S. V. & VENABLES, U. M. (1950a). The corncrake on Shetland. *Brit. Birds.* **43**, 137–141.

VENABLES, L. S. V. & VENABLES, U. M. (1950b). The whooper swans of Loch Spiggie, Shetland. *Scot. Nat.* **62**, 142–152.

VENABLES, L. S. V. & VENABLES, U. M. (1952). The Blackbird in Shetland. *Ibis.* **94**, 636–653.

VENABLES, L. S. V. & VENABLES, U. M. (1955). *Birds and Mammals of Shetland.* Edinburgh & London: Oliver & Boyd.

VENABLES, U. M. (1952). *Tempestuous Eden.* London: Museum.

VENABLES, U. M. (1956). *Life in Shetland. A World Apart.* Edinburgh & London: Oliver & Boyd.

VENABLES, U. M. & VENABLES, L. S. V. (1955). Observations on a breeding colony of the seal *Phoca vitulina* in Shetland. *Proc. zool. Soc. Lond.* **125**, 521–532.

VENABLES, U. M. & VENABLES, L. S. V. (1957). Mating behaviour of the seal *Phoca vitulina* in Shetland. *Proc. zool. Soc. Lond.* **128**, 387–396.

VENABLES, U. M. & VENABLES, L. S. V. (1959). Vernal coition of the seal *Phoca vitulina* in Shetland. *Proc. zool. Soc. Lond.* **132**, 665–669.

WACE, N. (1960). The botany of the southern oceanic islands. *Proc. R. Soc. B.* **152**, 575–590.

WAINWRIGHT, F. T. (1962a). Picts and Scots. In *The Northern Isles*, 91–116. WAINWRIGHT, F. T. (Ed.). Edinburgh & London: Nelson.

WAINWRIGHT, F. T. (1962b). The Scandinavian Settlement. In *The Northern Isles*, 117–162. WAINWRIGHT, F. T. (Ed.). Edinburgh & London: Nelson.

WARREN, A. & HARRISON, C. M. (1974). A proposed nature conservation plan for Shetland. *Discussion Paper in Conservation, no. 7.* London: University College.

WATERSTON, G. (1946). Fair Isle. *Scot. geogrl Mag.* **62**, 111–116.

WATSON, H. (1978). *Coastal Otters in Shetland.* Privately printed.

WATT, A. S. & JONES, E. W. (1948). The ecology of the Cairngorms. I. The environment and the altitudinal zonation of the vegetation. *J. Ecol.* **36**, 283–304.

WEIR, J. J. (1880). The macrolepidoptera of the Shetland Isles. *Entomologist*, **13**, 249–291.

WELCH, S. G., BARRY, J. V., DODD, B. E., GRIFFITHS, P. D., HUNTSMAN, R. G., JENKINS, C. G., LINCOLN, P. J., McCATHIE, M., MEARS, G. W. & PARR, C. W. (1973). A survey of blood group, serum protein and red cell enzyme polymorphisms in the Orkney Islands. *Hum. Hered.* **23**, 230–240.

WELCH, S. G. & MEARS, G. W. (1972). Genetic variants of human indophenol oxidase in the Westray Island of the Orkneys. *Hum. Hered.* **22**, 38–41.

WEST, J. F. (1972). *Faroe, the Emergence of a Nation.* London: Hurst.

WEST, W. (1912). Notes on the flora of Shetland with some ecological observations. *J. Bot., Lond.* **1**, 265–275; 297–306.

WEST, W. & WEST, T. G. S. (1904). Freshwater algae from the Orkneys and Shetlands. *Trans. Proc. Bot. Soc. Edin.* **23**, 3–41.

WESTOLL, T. S. (1937). Old red sandstone fishes of the north of Scotland, particularly Orkney and Shetland. *Proc. Geol. Ass.* **48**, 13–45.

WHITE, F. B. (1882). The Lepidoptera of Orkney, Shetland, and the Outer Hebrides. *Scot. Nat.* **6**, 289–291; 337–344.

WILLIAMSON, K. (1948). *Atlantic Islands.* London: Collins.

WILLIAMSON, K. (1951a). The wrens of Fair Isle, *Ibis.* **93**, 599–601.

WILLIAMSON, K. (1951b). The moorland birds of Unst, Shetland. *Scot. Nat.* **63**, 37–43.

WILLIAMSON, K. (1958). Population and breeding environment of the St. Kilda and Fair Isle wrens. *Brit. Birds*, **51**, 369–393.

WILLIAMSON, K. (1958). Bergmann's rule and obligatory overseas migration. *Brit. Birds*, **51**, 209–232.

WILLIAMSON, K. (1965). *Fair Isle and its Birds.* Edinburgh & London: Oliver & Boyd.

WILLIAMSON, K. & SPENCER, R. (1960). Ringing recoveries and the interpretation of bird movements. *Bird migration*, **1**, 176–181.

WILLS, J. (1978). *The Lands of Garth. A short history of Calbeck Ness.* Lerwick: Shetland Times.

WILSON, G. V. & KNOX, J. (1936) The geology of the Orkney and Shetland Isles. *Proc. Geol. Ass.* **47**, 270–282.

WOLFF, N. L. (1971). Lepidoptera. *Zoology Iceland*, **3**(45), 1–193.

YEATS, G. K. (1948). *Bird Haunts in Northern Britain.* London: Faber.

ZETLAND COUNTY COUNCIL (1974). *Sullom Voe District Plan.* Lerwick: Z.C.C. Planning Department.

ZIEGLER, P. A. (1978). North-western Europe: tectonics and basin development. *Geologie en Mejnbouw*, **57**, 589–626.

INDEX

Species which receive only a brief mention in the text are not indexed